CHEMISTRY
for
IGCSE

chemistry

Andrew Clegg

Heinemann

Heinemann Educational Publishers
Halley Court, Jordan Hill, Oxford OX2 8EJ
A Division of Reed Educational & Professional Publishing Ltd

OXFORD MELBOURNE AUCKLAND
JOHANNESBURG BLANTYRE GABORONE
IBADAN PORTSMOUTH (NH) USA CHICAGO

British Library Cataloging in Publication Data: A catalogue record for this book is available from the British Library.

ISBN 0435 96675 8

Cover design by Stafford & Stafford

Cover photograph by Science Photo Library/Manfred Kage

Phototypeset and illustrated by Photographics, Honiton, Devon
Printed and bound in Great Britain

00 01 02 10 9 8 7 6 5 4

The author and publishers would like to thank the following for supplying photographs:

Air Products (Figure 7.6); Ann Ronan at Image Select (Figures 2.6, 2.8, 2.9); BASF (Figures 7.7a & b, 11.11); British Museum (Figure 2.5); Bruno Nebe (Figure 3.7); Andrew Clegg (Figure 4.11); GSF Picture Library (Figures 1.7, 4.1, 5.3a & b, 7.9, 7.10b); Hulton Deutsch (Figure 1.5); Hutchison Library (Figures 2.30b, 4.10, 5.12); Image Select (Figures 7.1, 11.1 left); Ironbridge Gorge Museum (Figure 3.2); JEOL UK (Figure 2.1); Mary Evans Picture Library (Figure 9.3); Meg Sullivan Photograph (Figures 1.2, 2.29, 8.2, 11.1 right); Microscopix Photolibrary (Figures 2.2, 2.26); NASA (Figure 7.12); The Natural History Museum (Figure 6.5); Robert Harding Picture Library (Figures 1.1, 5.10, 6.10); Science Photo Library (Figures 2.10, 2.28, 3.3, 4.2, 5.4, 7.10a); Thames Water (Figure 3.12b); The Mansell Collection (Figures 1.4, 2.7, 4.6, 6.11, 6.21); The Science Museum/Science & Society Picture Library (Figure 2.12); Trip (Figures 1.3, 3.12a, 3.15, 4.16, 4.18, 5.15, 6.1, 6.2, 6.18, 6.26, 8.4); Zefa (Figures 2.30a, 6.9).

Contents

Note

This book covers both the **Core** and **Extended Curriculum** of the syllabus for IGCSE Chemistry. Students following the Extended Curriculum need to cover all the material in the book. Students following the Core Curriculum do not need to cover the tinted sections in the book which are headed 'Supplement'. Symbolic equations and questions which are in tinted boxes are also part of the Extended Curriculum and therefore do not need to be covered by Core Curriculum students.

Safety

This book contains a number of investigations. Although some instructions are given for them, you will need help from your teacher. Investigations in chemistry should always be done carefully because many substances can be harmful in one way or another. Harmful chemicals in the investigations are indicated with standard hazard symbols. These symbols are shown and explained below.

Explosive

These substances may explode if ignited in air or exposed to heat. A sudden shock or friction may also start an explosion. Particular care should be taken in warm climates.

Oxidising

These substances produce much heat as they react with other materials. They can create a fire risk. They will react with organic substances such as wood.

Highly flammable

These are solids, liquids or gases that may easily catch fire in a laboratory under normal conditions.

Poisonous

These substances are a serious risk to health. Some can cause death. These chemicals can affect you if you swallow them, inhale them, or they are asorbed through the skin. They should be stored in a locked cupboard.

Harmful

These chemicals are less of a health risk than poisonous substances, but they must still be handled with care.

Corrosive

These chemicals destroy living tissues, including eyes and skin. If they are spilt on to your skin, you should wash the exposed area with plenty of water.

Irritant

These substances are not corrosive but they can cause reddening of the skin. The effect may be immediate or it may only be observed after prolonged, or repeated, contact with the chemical.

Radioactive

The radioactive chemicals used in schools have low activity. They are normally only used by teachers, for demonstrations. They should be treated in the same way as poisonous substances.

1

Chemicals: what they are and where they come from

Chemistry is part of all of our lives. Chemists have done many things which affect the way we live. The purpose of this book is to help you understand chemistry, the benefits it brings us and the problems it can cause.

Chemists have helped us in very many ways. Figures 1.1, 1.2 and 1.3 show three of these ways.

What is chemistry?

Here are some more ways in which chemists have influenced the way we live.

• When we are ill, we use medicines developed by chemists to help us get better.

• Chemists have helped to make food safe to eat.

• Chemists have developed ways of making water clean and safe to drink and of purifying sewage so that the water can be re-used.

• Chemists have discovered and developed many different materials that are part of our daily lives. Think of paints, glues, cleaning materials, insecticides, fertilisers and many more.

• Chemists called metallurgists have developed all the different kinds of metals we use in our daily lives.

• Chemists have invented explosives. These have been used to help us get useful materials out of the ground, but they have also been used to make ammunition and bombs which have killed or injured millions.

• Chemists have even made artificial diamonds!

You can probably think of many more things that chemists have done which affect your life.

You may also be able to see around you some of the unpleasant consequences of chemistry, such as pollution and destruction of the environment.

■ **Figure 1.1** The Severn Bridge is made of materials, mainly metals, developed by chemists.

■ **Figure 1.2** Can you imagine a world without plastics? These versatile materials were invented by chemists in the last 50 years.

■ **Figure 1.3** Fuels allow us to travel further and faster than ever before. Petrol and diesel were developed by chemists from crude oil.

Matter

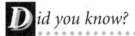

Did you know?

The chemist who invented dynamite, an explosive used for quarrying, was a Swede called Alfred Nobel. The invention earned him a large fortune. In his will, he left the money to the Swedish Academy of Sciences to be invested. He instructed them to use the money earned by the investment to give prizes each year to scientists who make major discoveries. These are called the Nobel prizes. Figures 1.4 and 1.5 show Nobel prize winners.

Chemistry is the study of matter. Chemists try to find out the answers to important questions like these.

• What are substances made of?

• Why do substances behave in the way they do?

• Can we discover any patterns in the way some substances behave which will allow us to predict how other substances might behave?

They can then go on to ask useful questions.

• How can we obtain useful materials from the earth and from living things?

• How can we make new substances that are useful to us?

This book will show you some of the answers to some of these kinds of questions.

Investigation 1.1

Cut out pictures from newspapers and magazines which you think show aspects of chemistry. Stick them in your book and write next to each what aspect of chemistry is shown in the picture.

All the substances we can see and feel around us are made up of matter. Many millions of different substances are known, and all of them are either solids, liquids or gases.

Did you know?

A Greek poet and philosopher called Democritus, who lived at the time of Pythagoras over 2500 years ago, reasoned that matter was made from particles. He imagined cutting a piece of matter in half, then cutting a half piece in half, and so on. He reasoned that it was not theoretically possible to continue dividing matter in

■ **Figures 1.4 and 1.5** Two famous chemists. Marie Curie (left) was awarded two Nobel prizes, one for chemistry and one for physics, for the work she did on radioactivity. Dorothy Hodgkin (right) received her prize for using X-rays to work out the structure of some large and complicated biochemical molecules such as vitamins.

half for ever, and that there would come a time when each of the halves was one particle of matter, which could not be cut further. He called such a particle an 'atomos' which means 'something that cannot be divided'.

Solids, liquids and gases

We now know that all matter is made up of tiny particles. All these particles have energy and this energy causes them to move.

The particles in a solid are arranged in rows in a regular way. They are unable to move around because they are held together by strong forces of attraction. They can, however, move by vibrating.

When a solid is heated, the particles vibrate faster. To do this, they need a little more space and so they have to move slightly further apart. This explains why solids expand slightly when they are heated. When enough energy is given to particles in a solid, they can move out of their fixed positions and move round each other. This happens when the solid **melts**. In the liquid that is formed, the particles are still as close to each other as in the solid. They have enough energy to move around but they do not have sufficient energy to overcome the forces that hold them next to each other.

If more energy is given to the particles, they move and vibrate faster and faster until they have enough energy to overcome the forces holding them together. The particles can then escape from the liquid and move around quickly and independently. This is what happens when liquids **boil** (see Figure 1.6).

When gas particles cool, the opposite processes happen. The gas particles move more and more slowly until they do not have enough energy to overcome the attractive forces that keep them stuck together when they hit each other. At this point, the gas **condenses** to a liquid. As the liquid particles get cooler, they move more and more slowly until they are unable to move at all. They all

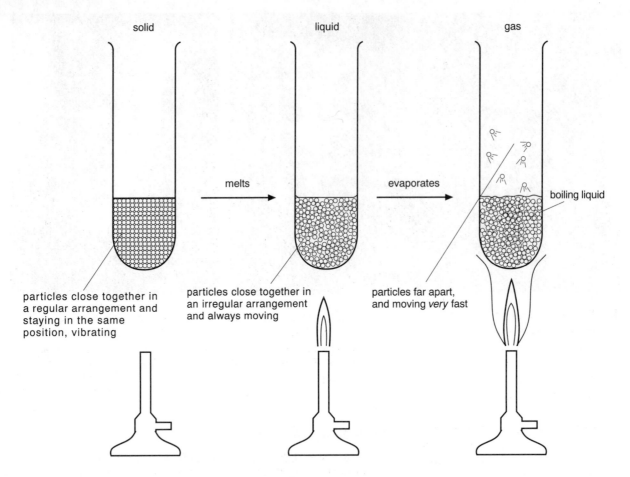

solid   liquid   gas

melts

evaporates

boiling liquid

particles close together in a regular arrangement and staying in the same position, vibrating

particles close together in an irregular arrangement and always moving

particles far apart, and moving *very* fast

■ **Figure 1.6** Diagram showing changes of state.

fall in line with each other when they stop moving. When this happens, the liquid **freezes** or **solidifies**.

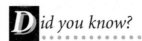

id you know?

The particles in glass are arranged randomly and not in straight lines. This means glass is a liquid and not a solid. The particles do not move around each other because they are large and do not have enough energy to move. However, if the thickness of a large glass window that has been in position for many years is measured very accurately, it is often found that the bottom is very slightly thicker than the top. The glass particles have moved down slightly causing the bottom to bulge slightly.

Some substances, such as iodine and carbon dioxide, do not form a liquid when heated. They change from a solid directly to a gas. When the gas is cooled, it condenses to a solid, not a liquid. This process is called **sublimation**.

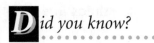

Did you know?

Substances sublime because the energy needed to change them from a solid to a liquid is more than the energy needed to change them from a liquid to a gas. This is very rare. It means that the boiling points of such substances are actually lower than their melting points!

Evidence for the existence of particles

The idea that matter is made up of particles is a scientific **theory**. Theories are ways of explaining our observations. A good theory is one that can explain many different observations. The theory of the existence of particles is an example of a good theory. The particle theory, as you have already seen, explains the differences between solids, liquids and gases, and what happens at melting points and boiling points. You will learn later in this chapter of many other observations that can be explained by the particle theory.

Try these investigations. The results you will observe in all of them can easily be explained by the particle theory. Can you think of a different theory of matter that can explain all these results better than the particle theory? If you can, you may be awarded a Nobel prize!

Investigation 1.2

potassium
permanganate

Particles in a liquid
You will need:
- a beaker
- a straw
- a potassium permanganate crystal.

1 Put a straw in a beaker of water. Drop one crystal of potassium permanganate down the straw.

2 Place your finger over the end of the straw and carefully lift it out of the water, taking the water inside it with it. You should have been able to get the crystal to the bottom of the beaker without making any of the water purple.

3 Leave the beaker for several hours. Look at it occasionally to see what happens.

Investigation 1.3

nitric acid

(**CARE** This investigation involves the use of concentrated nitric acid which can cause burns and damage to clothing. The gas produced is poisonous. The experiment **must** be done by a teacher.)

Particles in a gas

You will need:

- two gas jars or jam jars
- concentrated nitric acid
- copper turnings
- filter paper.

1 Pour a little concentrated nitric acid into the bottom of a gas jar or jam jar.

2 Add one or two copper turnings to the acid. (Optional – put a filter paper on the top of the jar.)

3 Put another similar jar upside-down over the top of the first one. You will see that the reaction between the copper and the nitric acid produces a visible brown gas (nitrogen dioxide).

4 Leave the jars for 20 minutes or so, and watch what happens.

5 At the end of the experiment, pour the liquid into plenty of water.

Both of these investigations demonstrate the same thing: that one substance can move through another. This is called **diffusion**. Diffusion can easily be explained by the particle theory. The particles of the potassium permanganate move between the particles of water. The particles of the brown gas diffuse between the air particles.

You will note that the particles moving in the air move much faster than the particles moving in water. This is because the air particles are further apart than the water particles and it is easier for the other particles to move in between them.

If you used a filter paper in the nitrogen dioxide experiment, you will have noticed that the brown gas moved easily through the filter paper. This showed that the gas particles are smaller than the tiny holes in the filter paper. In fact, they are many millions of times smaller.

Supplement

Small particles move faster than large particles with the same energy. The reason for this is easy to understand. You can throw a small stone much faster than you can throw a large rock. Your physics tells you that the energy of movement (kinetic energy) of a particle depends on its mass and its velocity. If a particle with a large mass has the same kinetic energy as a particle with a small mass, its velocity will be smaller.

The rate of diffusion of particles depends on how fast they are moving. This will depend therefore on two things: how much energy they have and their mass. The energy the particles have depends on how hot they are. Particles at the same temperature have the same energy. Some particles have a greater mass than others and, at the same temperature, will move more slowly. The rate of diffusion will therefore decrease as particle mass increases.

Questions

1.1 Explain the following processes by describing what happens to the particles of matter in each case.

a Clothes drying on a line.

b Sugar dissolving in a cup of coffee.

c Frost forming on a cold night.

1.2 A gas tap in a laboratory is turned on. Explain, in terms of particles, why everyone in the laboratory can smell the gas within a few minutes.

1.3 Explain why an inflated balloon often goes down in a few days.

Making useful materials

All substances are either pure substances or mixtures. Almost all naturally occurring substances are mixtures (see Figure 1.7). To make useful materials from them, it is necessary to separate these mixtures into their pure components. After we have separated a mixture, we need to know whether the substances we have obtained are pure. This section is about ways of separating mixtures and ways of telling whether or not the products are pure substances.

Separating mixtures

Most mixtures contain one useful substance and a number of impurities. We want to obtain the useful substance in a pure form. There are many ways in which we might be able to do this. The way we choose makes use of a difference between the pure substance and the impurities. It is useful to classify mixtures into four categories to help us think about these differences.

- Mixtures of solids and liquids (such as sea water)
- Mixtures of two or more solids (such as the ore in Figure 1.7)
- Mixtures of two or more liquids (such as crude oil)
- Mixtures of two or more gases (such as air)

Mixtures of solids and liquids

We can classify this group still further. The solid we want to get in a pure form might be soluble or it might be insoluble.

If the solid is insoluble, then **filtering** is the usual method. If the solid is soluble, then the liquid must be **evaporated**. A useful way of ensuring that a soluble solid is obtained in a pure form is to evaporate off most of the liquid and then leave the solid to form crystals. The liquid above the crystals will contain any soluble impurities and can be poured off. This process, called **crystallisation**, is the usual way of making salt from sea water, and it is also widely used in the pharmaceutical industry for making drugs which must be very pure.

If the liquid, rather than the solid, is required pure, a process called **distillation** is used (see Figure 1.8). The liquid is evaporated and the vapour is then condensed to give a pure liquid. Some countries

■ **Figure 1.7** This ore is a mixture. It contains a mineral called galena which you can see as crystals in the ore. Galena is the mineral from which lead is extracted. The mineral galena has to be purified before the lead can be extracted from it.

1 Dissolve salt

Add water to rock salt.
Salt dissolves. Sand is
insoluble.

2 Filter

Sand remains in filter paper.
Salt solution flows through.

3 Evaporate

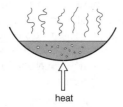

heat

Boil away most of the water.

4 Salt and sand separated

pure salt
in evaporating basin

sand on filter
paper

■ **Figure 1.9** Purification of rock
salt.

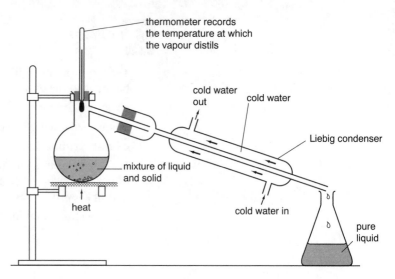

■ **Figure 1.8** Distillation. The vapour is condensed by the cold
water in the outer tube of the Liebig condenser.

in the Middle East around the Persian Gulf use this process to get
drinking water from sea water.

Mixtures of two or more solids

These mixtures can often be separated by the methods mentioned
above if one of the solids is soluble. For example, salt is a very
important raw material for the chemical industry and it is often
found in the form of rock salt. The rock salt formed millions of
years ago when a sea dried up. In rock salt, there is often a lot of
sand. The salt and the sand can easily be separated by dissolving in
water, filtering, evaporating and crystallising. Figure 1.9 shows how
this can be done on a small scale in a laboratory.

Separating mixtures is an extremely important part of the waste
recycling industry which is growing rapidly all over the world.
When metal objects are recycled, it is often difficult to separate one
metal from another. There is an easy way to separate iron from
'non-ferrous' metals and that is to use a large **electromagnet**. This
lifts all objects containing iron and leaves behind non-ferrous
objects.

*I*nvestigation 1.4

Separating two solids

Containers of salt and pepper have broken and the two
have become mixed. Use your knowledge of the two
substances to design a method for separating the
mixture to recover the pure salt and pepper.

Mixtures of two or more liquids

The usual way to separate liquids makes use of the fact that they
will almost certainly have different boiling points. **Distillation** can

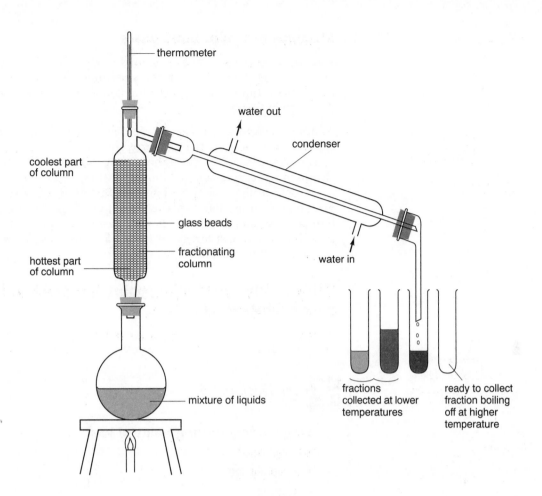

thermometer

water out

condenser

coolest part
of column

glass beads

fractionating
column

water in

hottest part
of column

mixture of liquids

fractions
collected at lower
temperatures

ready to collect
fraction boiling
off at higher
temperature

■ **Figure 1.10** Laboratory
fractionating column being
used to separate a mixture
of liquids.

then be used to separate the liquids. This is used widely in the
drinks industry to make spirits.

Distillation, however, does not separate two liquids very well. The
mixture distilled in the drinks industry contains the two liquids,
ethanol (alcohol, boiling point 78 °C) and water (boiling point
100 °C). If a mixture of ethanol and water is distilled, the liquid
that **condenses** will not be pure ethanol. It will also contain some
water. It can be distilled again and then the proportion of ethanol
will be greater. Each time the product is redistilled, purer ethanol is
obtained. There is a process that does a lot of redistillations in one
operation and it is called **fractional distillation** or **fractionation**.

Fractional distillation requires a tall column above the distillation
flask. This column has barriers inside which do not block it but
allow the vapour to rise and the liquid to flow downwards slowly.
The liquid is continuously condensed and redistilled as it rises up
the column. The hottest part of the column is at the bottom near
the heated distillation vessel. The coolest part of the column is at
the top. Figure 1.10 shows a laboratory **fractionating column** being
used to obtain ethanol from a mixture of ethanol and water. In this
column, the barrier to the flow is provided by small pieces of glass
that are packed into the column.

Fractional distillation is used in the oil industry and this will be
studied in Chapter 8.

Mixtures of two or more gases

Fractional distillation can also be used to separate a mixture of two or more gases. First, however, the gases must be cooled until they turn into a liquid. The fractional distillation of liquid air is described in Chapter 7.

Another method often used to remove a gaseous impurity from another gas is to pass the gas through a solid chemical that will react with the impurity. This is how gas masks work. This method is also used to remove sulphur dioxide from the gases produced by large coal-burning power stations. Sulphur dioxide is a serious air pollutant in some parts of the world, particularly in northern Europe. The gases in the chimney are passed though calcium oxide granules. As you will learn in Chapter 5, these granules will react with the sulphur dioxide.

Using melting and boiling point data to tell us how pure a substance is

After we have obtained a substance from a mixture, how do we know whether it is pure? Try this simple investigation.

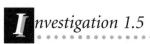nvestigation 1.5

What is the melting point of ice?
You will need:
- crushed ice
- beaker
- thermometer
- salt.

1 Take some crushed ice that is melting, put a thermometer in it and read the temperature.

2 Then take some crushed ice that has been made with salty water (or add a little salt to the crushed ice in the first part of the investigation). Take the temperature of the melting ice mixed with salt.

You will find that the melting point of pure ice water is 0 °C whereas the melting point of salty ice water is below zero. You may also have noticed that the salt water ice melted over a range of temperatures while the pure ice melted at exactly 0 °C.

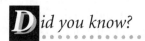id you know?

The sea freezes only in very severe climates, and, in a country which has cold winters, salting lorries sprinkle salt on icy roads to make the ice melt at temperatures below 0 °C.

There are two important observations here.

• Pure substances melt (and boil) at a temperature that is always the same for a particular substance (though you will have learnt in physics that the boiling point depends on atmospheric pressure). Pure water always boils (at 1 atmosphere pressure) at 100 °C whereas pure alcohol (ethanol) always boils at 78 °C.

• If there is an impurity in a liquid, the boiling point of the liquid is raised slightly and the freezing point is lowered and neither of the points is sharp. So salty water will freeze over a range of temperatures a little below 0 °C and it will boil over a range of temperatures just above 100 °C.

We can therefore use the melting and boiling point of a pure substance to tell us:

• whether the substance is pure

• what the substance might be.

Estimating purity using chromatography

There is another technique which will tell us whether a substance is pure or not and it is called **chromatography**.

*I*nvestigation 1.6

Do inks contain a single dye or a mixture?

You will need:

• felt pens with water-soluble inks

• filter paper

• beaker or jam jar

• spills

• paper clips.

1 Draw a pencil line near the bottom of some chromatography paper (see Figure 1.11). Put some spots of ink from water-soluble felt pens on it.

2 Put the paper in a jar of water as shown. Watch what happens as the water rises up the paper. Take the paper out when the water has almost reached the top of the paper.

You will notice that some dyes rise up the paper more easily than others. The technique will separate a mixture of dyes. It can tell us whether a dye is a pure substance or not. The technique works because of the different strengths of the forces holding the dye to the paper. When these are weak, the dye will move easily. The paper at the end of the experiment is called a **chromatogram**.

Chromatography that uses paper is called paper chromatography. There are many other kinds of chromatography. One useful one uses a column of pure sand (silica) in a glass tube instead of the paper and the liquid runs down instead of up. This is called column chromatography.

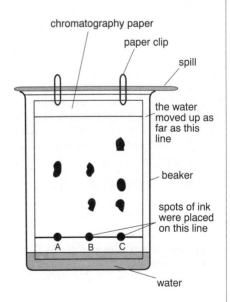

Figure 1.11 Chromatography experiment.

Labels on figure:
chromatography paper
paper clip
spill
the water moved up as far as this line
beaker
spots of ink were placed on this line
water
A   B   C

Chromatography can also be used to tell us about the purity of colourless substances. There are two common ways of doing this. The first is to use a 'locating agent'. This is a substance that is sprayed onto the paper after the experiment, and which reacts with the colourless spots to make a coloured substance.

The second way is to use paper (or silica) that has been treated with a substance that fluoresces when ultra-violet light shines on it. The spots cover up this substance, and so the spots can be seen as dark patches under an ultra-violet light.

Chromatography is a very important technique with many uses. Its main use is to tell us what substances might be present in a mixture. We call this process **analysis**. We use chromatography to **analyse** the mixture to try and find out what it contains.

The list gives some examples of the use of chromatography for analysis.

• To analyse polluted air and water.

• In hospital laboratories to analyse medical samples such as blood and urine.

• To check the purity of foods and drinks when they are manufactured.

• To find out whether drugs are pure and safe.

• To help solve crimes by analysing blood stains and other substances that might be found where a crime has been committed.

Wherever there is a chemistry laboratory, you will almost always find some chromatography being done.

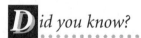

*D**id you know?*

The American spacecraft called Viking that landed on Mars in the early 1980s carried many instruments with it. One of them was a device which automatically analysed samples of the Martian soil by chromatography.

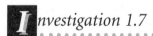

*I**nvestigation 1.7*

Design an experiment to investigate the purity of dyes used to colour sweets such as Smarties.

Questions

1.4 How would you separate the substance named in the following mixtures:

a pure ethanol (alcohol) from beer

b iron filings from a mixture of metal filings

c water from tea.

1.5 Look at the chromatogram in Figure 1.11. What does it tell you about the three dyes? Do any of the dyes contain the same colour?

Compounds and elements

In the last section you found out about the different methods chemists use to make pure useful substances out of the mixtures we find around us. These methods are called **physical** methods of purification. The pure substances produced by these methods have sharp melting and boiling points and chromatography – if it is possible – will show that they only produce one spot. A few of these substances are what we call **elements**, but the great majority will be substances that we call **compounds**.

All the physical processes for separating mixtures have one thing in common. They can easily be reversed. In order to understand the difference between elements and compounds, it is necessary to study **chemical** processes. Most chemical processes cannot easily be reversed, as the next investigation shows.

Investigation 1.8

magnesium
ribbon

Burning

You will need:

• candle

• jam jar

• some magnesium ribbon

• tongs

• a beaker of cold water.

1 Light the candle and hold the beaker of cold water briefly above the flame. Look for any changes.

2 Place the jam jar upside-down over the candle. Watch what happens.

3 Hold the magnesium ribbon in tongs and light it. Note what happens to the magnesium.

(**CARE** Do not look directly at the very bright magnesium flame.)

When the candle burns, one of the products is water. You will have seen condensation on the cold beaker. When the shiny metal magnesium burns, it produces a white powder. Both of these are examples of a chemical reaction. The oxygen in the air takes part in the reaction, and the reaction stops when the oxygen in the air is used up. This is why the candle under the jar goes out after a short time. The burning reaction is irreversible. Can you imagine the white magnesium oxide giving the oxygen back to the air and the magnesium forming again?

As well as being irreversible, these two chemical reactions involve an energy change. Chemical energy in the candle wax and the magnesium was changed into heat energy and light energy during the reaction. During chemical reactions there is always an energy change. In most chemical reactions energy is produced (given out), but in a few reactions it is taken in.

Magnesium, oxygen and magnesium oxide are all pure substances. Magnesium and oxygen are examples of elements. When they combine or join together during burning, they form magnesium oxide which is a compound. **Compounds are substances that are formed when two or more elements combine chemically**.

Water is also a compound. It is made up of the elements hydrogen and oxygen. Candle wax is mainly one compound. When the candle burns, water is formed and this means that one of the elements in candle wax must be hydrogen. The other element present in the compound candle wax is carbon and, when the wax burns, the carbon forms carbon dioxide. When the candle wax burns, the compound is breaking up and the elements in it are combining with oxygen.

So we can summarise.

- All matter is made from chemical elements.
- These elements are often joined together to form compounds.
- Most matter around us is made up of mixtures of different compounds, and sometimes some elements.
- Mixtures can be separated into pure substances which may be compounds or elements.
- Mixtures can be separated by physical techniques. These processes are easily reversed.
- Elements can be turned into compounds by chemical methods which are not easily reversed.

Chemical changes happen when substances change into other substances and:

- a change of energy is involved
- the process is usually very difficult to reverse (but more about that in Chapter 11)
- the products are different from the substances used.

So:

- melting and boiling are examples of **physical changes**, but
- burning and cooking are examples of **chemical changes**.

We can classify elements as solids, liquids and gases (at room temperature). There are many gaseous elements but there are only two liquid ones, mercury and bromine. We can also classify elements as metals and non-metals. All the metals except mercury are solids. Altogether, there are 92 natural elements and most of these are metals. The material that makes up the earth's crust and its atmosphere is made mainly from non-metals. We say that non-metals are more **abundant** in the earth's crust than metals.

Table 1.1

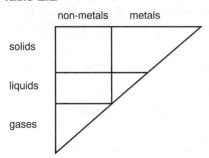

##

Questions

1.6 Using the data below, write a total of 10 elements in a copy of Table 1.1 so that there is at least one element in every space in the table.

1.7 Classify each of the following substances as metallic element, non-metallic element, mixture or compound: **sea water**, **pure water**, **air**, **nitrogen**, **gold**, **brass**, **ethanol**.

Tables 1.2 and 1.3 give some information about a number of common elements and compounds.

■ **Table 1.2 Data on common elements.** Their states at room temperature are shown by 's', 'l' or 'g'. The abbreviation 'sub' indicates that the element sublimes. The densities of gases are at 25 °C.

Element	Symbol	Atomic number	Relative atomic mass	State	Melting point (°C)	Boiling point (°C)	Density (g cm^{-3})
Aluminium	Al	13	27	s	660	2350	2.70
Argon	Ar	18	40	g	−189	−186	0.00166
Barium	Ba	56	137	s	710	1640	3.59
Beryllium	Be	4	9	s	1285	2470	1.85
Boron	B	5	11	s	2030	3700	2.47
Bromine	Br	35	80	l	−7	59	3.12
Calcium	Ca	20	40	s	840	1490	1.53
Carbon (diamond)	C	6	12	s	3550	4827	3.53
Carbon (graphite)	C	6	12	s	3720 (sub)		2.25
Chlorine	Cl	17	35.5	g	−101	−34	0.00299
Chromium	Cr	24	52	s	1860	2600	7.19
Cobalt	Co	27	59	s	1494	2900	8.80
Copper	Cu	29	64	s	1084	2580	8.93
Fluorine	F	9	19	g	−220	−188	0.00158
Gallium	Ga	31	70	s	30	2070	5.91
Germanium	Ge	32	73	s	959	2850	5.32
Gold	Au	79	197	s	1064	2850	19.28
Helium	He	2	4	g	−270	−269	0.00017
Hydrogen	H	1	1	g	−259	−253	0.00008
Iodine	I	53	127	s	114	184	4.95
Iron	Fe	26	56	s	1540	2760	7.87
Krypton	Kr	36	84	g	−157	−153	0.00346
Lead	Pb	82	207	s	327	1760	11.34
Lithium	Li	3	7	s	180	1360	0.53
Magnesium	Mg	12	24	s	650	1100	1.74
Manganese	Mn	25	55	s	1250	2120	07.47
Mercury	Hg	80	201	l	−39	357	13.55
Neon	Ne	10	20	g	−249	−246	0.00084
Nickel	Ni	28	59	s	1455	2150	8.91
Nitrogen	N	7	14	g	−210	−196	0.00117
Oxygen	O	8	16	g	−219	−183	0.00133
Phosphorus (white)	P	15	31	s	44	280	1.82
Platinum	Pt	78	195	s	1772	3720	21.45
Potassium	K	19	39	s	63	777	0.86
Silicon	Si	14	28	s	1410	2620	2.33
Silver	Ag	47	108	s	962	2160	10.50
Sodium	Na	11	23	s	98	900	0.97
Sulphur (monoclinic)	S	16	32	s	115	445	1.96
Sulphur (orthorhombic)	S	16	32	s			2.07
Tin	Sn	50	119	s	232	2720	7.28
Uranium	U	92	238	s	1135	4000	19.05
Xenon	Xe	54	131	g	−112	−108	0.0055
Zinc	Zn	30	65	s	420	913	7.14

■ Table 1.3 Data on common compounds. Their states at room temperature are shown by 's', 'l' or 'g'. The solubility of each compound in water at room temperature is broadly classified as 'i' (insoluble), 'sps' (sparingly soluble), 's' (soluble) or 'vs' (very soluble). The abbreviation 'r' indicates that the compound reacts with water. Some compounds can have hydrated forms. This is shown by 'h'. These forms will usually dehydrate before the melting point. The abbreviation 'dec' means that the compound decomposes on heating; the abbreviation 'sub' means that it sublimes. Unless stated otherwise, all the compounds are white or colourless.

Compound	Formula	State	Melting point (°C)	Boiling point (°C)	Solubility	Notes
Aluminium chloride	$AlCl_3$	s	sub		r	
Aluminium oxide	Al_2O_3	s	2015	2980	i	
Ammonium chloride	NH_4Cl	s	sub		s	
Barium chloride	$BaCl_2$	s	963	1560	s	h
Barium sulphate	$BaSO_4$	s	1580		i	
Calcium carbonate	$CaCO_3$	s	dec		i	
Calcium chloride	$CaCl_2$	s	782	2000	s	h
Calcium hydroxide	$Ca(OH)_2$	s	dec		sps	
Calcium nitrate	$Ca(NO_3)_2$	s	561	dec	vs	h
Calcium oxide	CaO	s	2600	3000	r	
Carbon monoxide	CO	g	−205	−191	i	
Carbon dioxide	CO_2	g	sub		sps	
Chromium(III) oxide	Cr_2O_3	s	2435	4000	i	green
Cobalt(II) chloride	$CoCl_2$	s	730	1050	s	h, red
Copper(II) chloride	$CuCl_2$	s	620	dec	s	h, green
Copper(II) nitrate	$Cu(NO_3)_2$	s	114	dec	vs	h, green
Copper(I) oxide	Cu_2O	s	1235		i	red
Copper(II) oxide	CuO	s	1326		i	black
Copper(II) sulphate	$CuSO_4$	s	dec		s	h, blue
Hydrogen bromide	HBr	g	−87	−67	vs	
Hydrogen chloride	HCl	g	−114	−85	vs	
Hydrogen fluoride	HF	g	−93	20	s	
Hydrogen iodide	HI	g	−51	−35	s	
Hydrogen oxide (water)	H_2O	l	0	100		
Hydrogen peroxide	H_2O_2	l	0	150	vs	
Hydrogen sulphide	H_2S	g	−85	−60	sps	
Iron(II) chloride	$FeCl_2$	s	677	sub	s	yellow–green
Iron(III) chloride	$FeCl_3$	s	307	dec	s	h, orange
Iron(III) oxide	Fe_2O_3	s	1565		i	red
Iron(II) sulphate	$FeSO_4$	s	dec		s	pale green
Iron(II) sulphide	FeS	s	1196	dec	i	black
Lead(II) bromide	$PbBr_2$	s	370	914	i	
Lead(II) chloride	$PbCl_2$	s	501	950	sps	
Lead(II) nitrate	$Pb(NO_3)_2$	s	dec		s	
Lead(II) oxide	PbO	s	886	1472	i	yellow
Lead(IV) oxide	PbO_2	s	dec		i	brown
Magnesium chloride	$MgCl_2$	s	714	1418	s	h
Magnesium nitrate	$Mg(NO_3)_2$	s	89		vs	h
Magnesium oxide	MgO	s	2800	3600	i	
Manganese(IV) oxide	MnO_2	s	dec		i	black
Mercury(II) chloride	$HgCl_2$	s	276	302	sps	
Mercury(II) oxide	HgO	s	dec		i	red
Nitric acid	HNO_3	l	−42	83	vs	
Nitrogen hydride (ammonia)	NH_3	g	−78	−34	vs	
Nitrogen oxide	NO	g	−163	−151	sps	
Nitrogen dioxide	NO_2	g	−11	21	s	brown
Phosphorus trichloride	PCl_3	l	−112	76	r	
Phosphorus pentachloride	PCl_5	s	dec		r	
Phosphorus pentoxide	P_4O_{10}	s	sub		r	
Potassium bromide	KBr	s	730	1435	s	
Potassium chloride	KCl	s	776	1500	s	

Compound	Formula	State	Melting point (°C)	Boiling point (°C)	Solubility	Notes
Potassium hydroxide	KOH	s	360	1322	vs	
Potassium iodide	KI	s	686	1330	vs	
Potassium manganate(VII)	$KMnO_4$	s	dec		s	purple
Potassium nitrate	KNO_3	s	334	dec	vs	
Silicon dioxide (quartz)	SiO_2	s	1610	2230	i	
Silver bromide	AgBr	s	432	dec	i	cream
Silver chloride	AgCl	s	455	1550	i	
Silver iodide	AgI	s	558	1506	i	yellow
Silver nitrate	$AgNO_3$	s	212	dec	vs	
Sodium bromide	NaBr	s	755	1390	s	
Sodium carbonate	Na_2CO_3	s	851	dec	s	h
Sodium chloride	NaCl	s	808	1465	s	
Sodium hydroxide	NaOH	s	318	1390	s	
Sodium nitrate	$NaNO_3$	s	307	dec	s	
Sodium oxide	Na_2O	s	sub		r	
Sodium sulphate	Na_2SO_4	s	890		s	h
Sulphur dioxide	SO_2	g	–75	–10	vs	
Sulphur trioxide	SO_3	l	–17	43	r	
Sulphuric acid	H_2SO_4	l	10	330	vs	
Zinc chloride	$ZnCl_2$	s	283	732	vs	
Zinc oxide	ZnO	s	1975		i	
Zinc sulphate	$ZnSO_4$	s	740	dec	vs	h

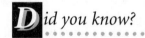

D *id you know?*

Most of the matter in the universe consists of just two elements. About 75% of the matter in the universe is the element hydrogen and 25% is helium. All the other elements together make up just a very tiny fraction of one per cent. Our planet therefore is very different from most of the rest of the universe.

Review questions on this chapter can be found on page 237.

2 | *Combining atoms*

*In the last chapter you studied how matter is made out of particles. The smallest of these particles is called an **atom**. Most particles, however, are made out of two or more atoms combined together. These are called **molecules**. All the molecules in a particular pure substance are identical and they are different from the molecules of any other substance.*

How big are atoms and molecules?

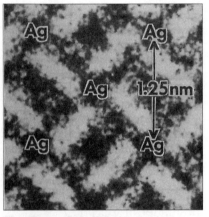

■ **Figure 2.1** This is an electron micrograph of a silver compound, showing individual silver atoms.

The experiment in Chapter 1, in which you put a potassium permanganate crystal into water, suggested that matter was made out of particles and it was clear that these particles are extremely small. Figures 2.1 and 2.2 give some idea of the small size of the particles of matter. It is possible to carry out a simple investigation which gives us a rough idea of how small the particles actually are. What we do is to try and measure the thickness of a thin layer of oil on top of water. This layer cannot be less than one molecule thick so, if we can measure it, we will know that a molecule must be smaller than this thickness.

You must have seen at some time a thin layer of oil on the top of water; it often appears to be coloured like a rainbow. In the next investigation you can try to estimate the thickness of such a layer.

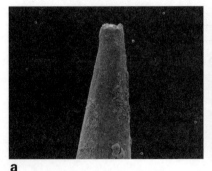

a

b

c

■ **Figure 2.2** A microscope using light allows us to see things as small as these bacteria on the point of a pin. The bacteria in (c) are magnified 10 000 times.

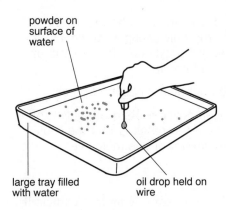

powder on surface of water

large tray filled with water

oil drop held on wire

■ **Figure 2.3** Oil drop experiment.

■ **Figure 2.4** Diagram showing how to calculate the volume of the oil drop and patch.

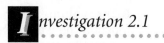

Estimating the thickness of a layer of oil on water

You will need:

- large metal tray
- piece of thin wire
- oil (any oil will do but the kind used for oiling a bicycle is best)
- fine powder such as pollen
- detergent.

1 Clean the tray thoroughly with detergent and water. Wash off all the detergent. Do not touch the inner surface with your fingers after this. Put clean water in the tray.

2 Take one small drop of oil on the end of the thin wire (see Figure 2.3). Estimate the diameter (and hence the radius) of the oil drop in millimetres. Looking at it through a magnifying glass with a ruler just behind will help.

3 Touch the water surface in the middle of the tray with the oil drop. The oil will spread over the water surface. You can see the patch of oil if you look carefully. If you spread a fine powder (such as pollen) on the water before you add the drop, the patch is easier to see.

4 Estimate the area of the oil patch in square millimetres.

5 Calculate the volume of the original drop. Remember that the formula for the volume of the drop is $4\pi r^3/3$. Work in millimetres and the volume will be in cubic millimetres. (See Figure 2.4.)

Measuring the volume of the oil drop

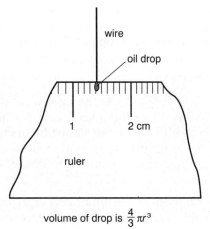

wire

oil drop

1   2 cm

ruler

volume of drop is $\frac{4}{3}\pi r^3$

Measuring the volume of the oil patch

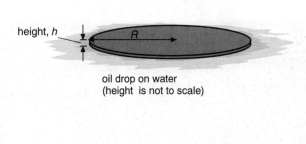

height, h

R

oil drop on water
(height is not to scale)

volume of patch $= \pi R^2 h$

$$\frac{4}{3}\pi r^3 = \pi R^2 h$$

From this, h can be calculated

6 The volume of the drop did not change when it touched the water. The drop only changed its shape. It is now the shape of a very flat cylinder. The volume of this cylinder is given by the formula:

Volume of cylinder = area of patch × height of patch.

Using this formula, you can now calculate the height of the patch (in millimetres). If the patch is one molecule thick, this height is the diameter of one molecule.

It is unlikely that the patch of oil is just one molecule thick. It is probably nearer ten or more molecules thick. Your answer was probably around 0.000001 mm. We can therefore say that the diameter of an oil molecule must be less than 0.000001 mm. How many molecules would you need to make a row of them (touching each other) that is 1 mm long?

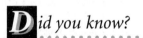
Did you know?

If you throw a bucketful of water into the Atlantic Ocean in Argentina and then travel across the Atlantic Ocean to Namibia and take out a bucketful of the Atlantic Ocean there, there will probably be some of the molecules from your Argentinian bucketful in your Namibian bucket. This is because there are many more molecules of water in a bucketful than there are bucketfuls of water in the South Atlantic Ocean!

The atomic theory

Scientists think up theories which explain all the observations they make. You have already studied the particle theory which explains why matter behaves as it does. When scientists make any observation that cannot be explained by the theory, the theory must be modified so that it does explain it. If this cannot be done, the theory has to be thrown out and a completely new one thought up.

Early atomic theories

The atomic theory is a very old one. As we saw on pages 2–3, it started with Democritus, a Greek thinker and poet who lived over 2500 years ago. He decided that matter must be made up of tiny particles because he could not imagine that it was possible to continue for ever, cutting a bit of matter into smaller and smaller pieces.

Democritus was not a scientist. He did not do experiments to find out anything about his 'atomos'. It was not until over 2000 years later, around 1800, that the chemist John Dalton did more work on the theory (see Figure 2.5). It was Dalton who suggested the name 'atom' for the particles that make up all matter. The main points of Dalton's theory are these:

Figure 2.5 John Dalton (1776–1844) is known as one of the fathers of physical science. He worked in Manchester, England and his best known work was his atomic theory (1807).

- All matter is made up of tiny particles called atoms.
- Atoms cannot be made or destroyed.
- Atoms of the same element are all the same.
- Atoms of different elements are different from each other. They have, for example, different sizes and masses.
- Atoms can join together to form larger particles.

Dalton was the first scientist to propose a set of symbols representing the elements (see Figure 2.6). He was able to use these to show how the atoms joined together to form compounds. The word 'molecule' was not proposed until later.

Dalton's idea of symbols to represent elements is very useful. It allows us to understand clearly how the atoms join together. These days we no longer use these symbols, but a form of shorthand to represent the elements. Each element is represented by one or (more usually) two letters. These letters usually come from the modern English name of the element (Ca for calcium, Mg for magnesium). However, some of the elements have been known for a long time and the shorthand comes from the ancient Latin name. (Iron is Fe from *Ferrum*, Gold is Au from *Aureum*). Table 2.1 shows the shorthand symbols for some common elements.

The symbols allow us, like Dalton, to write shorthand formulae for molecules formed when atoms combine together. The small number to the right of the symbol in a formula tells us how many atoms of that element there are in the molecule of the compound. Table 2.2 shows how this works.

Table 2.1 Symbols for common elements.

Element	Symbol	Element	Symbol	Element	Symbol
Aluminium	Al	Helium	He	Oxygen	O
Argon	Ar	Hydrogen	H	Phosphorus	P
Bromine	Br	Iodine	I	Potassium	K
Calcium	Ca	Iron	Fe	Silicon	Si
Carbon	C	Lead	Pb	Silver	Ag
Chlorine	Cl	Magnesium	Mg	Sodium	Na
Chromium	Cr	Mercury	Hg	Sulphur	S
Cobalt	Co	Neon	Ne	Tin	Sn
Copper	Cu	Nickel	Ni	Uranium	U
Gold	Au	Nitrogen	N	Zinc	Zn

Table 2.2 Atoms in compounds.

Name	Formula	Numbers of each atom in molecule
Water	H_2O	2 atoms of hydrogen, 1 atom of oxygen
Carbon dioxide	CO_2	1 atom of carbon, 2 atoms of oxygen
Glucose	$C_6H_{12}O_6$	6 atoms of carbon, 12 atoms of hydrogen, 6 atoms of oxygen
Sulphuric acid	H_2SO_4	2 atoms of hydrogen, 1 atom of sulphur, 4 atoms of oxygen

Figure 2.6 Dalton's symbols for elements and compounds.

Modern atomic theories

The first change in Dalton's theory came in 1897 when J.J. Thomson (see Figure 2.7) discovered a very tiny particle, much smaller than an atom, with a negative charge. He made these particles by heating certain metals in a vacuum. These tiny particles he called 'electrons' and he realised they must have come from inside the atoms of the metal. He suggested that atoms consisted of lumps of positively charged matter with tiny negatively charged electrons inside them, rather like currants in a currant bun.

Until early in the twentieth century, scientists thought that atoms were tiny, hard, round balls as Dalton had suggested. One experiment in 1909, however, changed all this. The experiment was carried out under the direction of Ernest Rutherford in Manchester, England (see Figure 2.8). In the experiment, a very thin sheet of gold, only a few atoms thick, was bombarded by the newly discovered alpha-particles, which are particles given out by radioactive substances. (You will study radioactivity later in this chapter.) To the great surprise of the scientists, almost all the alpha-particles went straight through the gold. It was almost as though the atoms of gold were not there! The atoms of gold were not hard balls packed together, they were almost all empty space. The atomic theory had to be re-thought.

■ **Figure 2.7** J.J. Thomson (1856–1940) is widely thought of as the father of modern atomic physics. He received a Nobel prize in 1906 and members of his research team in Cambridge University later received a total of no less than seven Nobel prizes between them.

■ **Figure 2.8** Ernest Rutherford (1871–1937) was a New Zealander who worked in England, in Manchester and later in Cambridge where he took over as Professor of Physics when Thomson retired in 1919. He won the Nobel physics prize in 1908.

■ **Figure 2.9** Niels Bohr (1885–1962) was a Danish physicist who was working with Rutherford in Manchester, England when he produced his ideas about the atom. The work gained him a Nobel prize in 1922 (Bohr came from a noted scientific family; his brother was a famous mathematician. Later his son was also to win a Nobel physics prize.)

Following Rutherford's famous experiment, the modern idea of the atom took shape. In 1911 he suggested that the atom had a tiny dense positive centre, called the nucleus. This nucleus was surrounded by empty space in which the electrons moved around. Rutherford also suggested that the positive charge in the nucleus was caused by positive particles called protons.

The next refinement to the atomic theory was made by the Danish physicist, Niels Bohr, in 1913 (see Figure 2.9). Bohr proposed that the electrons circulate around the nucleus in definite orbits just as the planets go round the sun. The electrons in orbits (the name 'shell' is used instead of 'orbit') far away from the nucleus could be removed from the atom more easily than the ones near the nucleus. This idea explained how and why atoms joined together in molecules, as you will see on pages 30–2.

One other discovery was still to be made, however. It was not until 1932 that the physicist James Chadwick (see Figure 2.10) discovered the neutron. This was a third particle in the atom. This one had the same mass as the proton but had no charge. The neutrons, like the protons, were part of the nucleus.

The story of the atomic theory continues today as scientists make more and more observations that have to be explained. Many more scientists have won Nobel prizes for their work on atoms (30 between 1930 and 1996) and, no doubt, more will do so in the future. The big unanswered question today is to describe how the different forces that hold the particles in the atom together are related to each other.

■ **Figure 2.10** James Chadwick (1891–1974) was a British scientist working in the famous Cavendish Laboratory in Cambridge like Thomson and Rutherford before him. His discovery of the neutron in 1932 gained him a Nobel prize.

■ **Table 2.3 Summary of atomic theories.**

Name of scientist	Year	Description of model	
John Dalton	1803	Matter consists of tiny particles called atoms. Atoms are solid and cannot be split	
Joseph John Thomson	1897	Atoms contain negative charges which are scattered evenly through the positively charged atom	negative particles / positive atom
Ernest Rutherford	1911	The mass of an atom is concentrated in its centre in a *very small* particle called the **nucleus**. The nucleus has a positive charge. Negatively charged particles called **electrons** move in the space around the nucleus	
Niels Bohr	1913	The electrons move around the nucleus only in certain **shells** or orbits. The size and shape of these shells depends on the amount of energy the electrons have	
James Chadwick	1932	The nucleus consists of protons with a positive charge and neutrons which have no charge	

Table 2.4 summarises our picture of the atom. It consists of three particles, the proton, the neutron and the electron.

The mass of the particles is not given in the usual mass units, kilograms. This is because one proton has a mass of approximately 0.000 000 000 000 000 000 000 000 006 kg, which is a rather inconvenient number to use! Instead, we take as our unit of mass the mass of the proton. We call the mass of the proton one **atomic mass unit** (amu). The neutron has the same mass as the proton but the electron is much lighter, almost 1/2000 amu.

Table 2.5 shows some details of the six lightest elements. The masses are in amu. If an atom has a relative mass of 12, this means that it has a mass that is 12 times the mass of the proton.

Notice that the number of protons is always equal to the number of electrons. This is because the charges on the atom must balance, as the atom itself has no overall charge. Notice also that the total relative mass of the atom is equal to the number of protons plus the number of neutrons.

We call the number of protons the **proton number**, or sometimes the atomic number. It is often represented by the capital letter Z.

We call the relative mass of the atom the **nucleon number**, or sometimes the mass number. This is often represented by the capital letter A.

■ **Table 2.4 Summary of properties of protons, neutrons and electrons.**

Particle	Where in the atom	Relative mass	Charge
Proton	Nucleus	1	+1
Neutron	Nucleus	1	None
Electron	Orbiting the nucleus	about 1/2000	−1

■ **Table 2.5 Data on the first six elements.**

Element	Symbol	Number of particles			Relative mass
		Protons	Neutrons	Electrons	
Hydrogen	H	1	0	1	1
Helium	He	2	2	2	4
Lithium	Li	3	4	3	7
Beryllium	Be	4	5	4	9
Boron	B	5	6	5	11
Carbon	C	6	6	6	12

Isotopes

Table 2.6 shows some details of two atoms. They both have the same proton number and therefore they must be atoms of the same element, chlorine.

Table 2.6 Chlorine atoms.

Protons	Neutrons	Electrons	Relative mass
17	16	17	35
17	18	17	37

Note that the two atoms of chlorine differ only in the number of neutrons. One atom has 16 and the other has 18 neutrons. Both are atoms of chlorine and they have exactly the same chemical properties. Atoms of the same element which have different numbers of neutrons are called **isotopes**.

About 75% of all chlorine atoms are the lighter isotope (called chlorine-35) and the remaining 25% are atoms of the chlorine-37 isotope. This means that the average relative mass of chlorine is 35.5.

All elements occur naturally in the form of two or more isotopes. For most elements, one isotope is much more common than the others.

We can write the element to show the nucleon number (A) and the proton number (Z) in the shorthand symbol for the element. How this is done is shown in Figure 2.11.

The two isotopes of chlorine can therefore be represented as $^{37}_{17}Cl$ and $^{35}_{17}Cl$.

■ **Figure 2.11** Diagram showing the symbol of magnesium with A and Z.

Atomic and molecular mass

It was Dalton, way back in 1807, who first realised that atoms of different elements had different masses. He realised that hydrogen was the lightest and he gave it a mass of 1. He called this the 'atomic weight'. We now call it the **relative atomic mass**. All the other atoms are heavier than hydrogen. Carbon, for example, has a relative atomic mass of 12.

These numbers for hydrogen and carbon are the same as the nucleon number for the common isotopes of these elements. But this is not so for many elements because they exist naturally in the form of several isotopes. Each isotope has a different nucleon number, and the relative atomic mass is the average of all the nucleon numbers of all the atoms in the sample of the element. Because of this, the relative atomic mass of most elements is not a whole number. Chlorine, as you found out above, has a relative atomic mass of 35.5. This is because chlorine consists of a mixture of the two isotopes, chlorine-35 and chlorine-37.

If the relative atomic mass of hydrogen is 1, and that of oxygen is 16, we can easily calculate the **relative molecular mass** of the compound water, as long as we know how many atoms of hydrogen and oxygen there are in a molecule of water.

The molecule of water (H_2O) contains two atoms of hydrogen and one of water. Water therefore has a relative molecular mass of $1 + 1 + 16 = 18$.

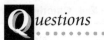

Questions

2.1 Copy and complete Table 2.7 showing the atomic structures of a number of atoms.

■ **Table 2.7** Atomic structures of four elements.

Element	Number of protons	Number of neutrons	Number of electrons	Nucleon number
Oxygen			8	16
Sodium	11	12		
Argon	18			40
Iron		30	26	

2.2 How many protons and neutrons are there in the nuclei of the following isotopes?

$^{12}_{6}C$, $^{56}_{26}Fe$, $^{64}_{29}Cu$, $^{235}_{92}U$, $^{238}_{92}U$.

2.3 Using the relative atomic masses given in Table 1.2 on page 15 calculate the relative molecular masses of the following compounds.

Ammonia (NH_3), Carbon dioxide (CO_2), Copper sulphate ($CuSO_4$), glucose($C_6H_{12}O_6$)

A pattern of elements – the Periodic Table

■ **Figure 2.12** Dimitri Mendeleev, 1834–1907, produced his well known Periodic Table of the Elements in 1869.

Before scientists can think up useful scientific theories to help us understand the universe around us, they have to make a lot of observations and collect data. This was what many scientists were busy doing 150 years ago. They then looked for patterns in the data. It was from the patterns they found that they could devise the theories that explained the observations they had made.

By around 150 years ago, scientists had discovered many elements and had also been able to calculate their atomic masses (even though they only had a very simple idea of what an atom was like). It was then that they began looking for patterns among the elements. A German chemist called Johann Döbereiner was the first. He realised that many elements could be grouped together in threes. The elements in each group were very similar. Lithium, sodium and potassium were in one group and chlorine, bromine and iodine were in another.

A little later, in 1864, an Englishman called John Newlands realised that, if he arranged the elements in a list in order of their relative atomic masses, each element was often very similar to the one eight places above it.

Then in 1869, the Russian, Dmitri Mendeleev (Figure 2.12) used all these ideas and produced his *Periodic Classification of the Elements*. This combined the ideas of Döbereiner and Newlands and it has proved to be very useful and has helped us to understand much more about the elements that make up the matter in the universe. The modern Periodic Table (Figure 2.13) on the opposite page is based on Mendeleev's original.

Group VIII elements

(sometimes called Group 0). These are all gases. They do not form compounds with other elements and are called **noble** or **inert gases.**

Group VII elements

These are all very reactive non-metals. They are poisonous elements, but some of their compounds (like table salt) are essential for us to live. They are called halogens.

Transition metals

These are all rather unreactive metals with high melting points. Many of them are very useful. Many of the compounds of these elements are coloured.

Group I elements

These are all soft, light metals such as sodium and potassium. They react very fast with water. They are very similar and are called the **alkali metals.**

B-metals

Below the stepped line are metals that also show some characteristics of non-metals.

The Lanthanides and Actinides are all metals that have very similar properties. They are rare and, apart from uranium, have few uses.

Periodic Table

I	II		Transition metals									III	IV	V	VI	VII	VIII
																	He Helium 2
H Hydrogen 1																	
Li Lithium 3	Be Beryllium 4											B Boron 5	C Carbon 6	N Nitrogen 7	O Oxygen 8	F Fluorine 9	Ne Neon 10
Na Sodium 11	Mg Magnesium 12											Al Aluminium 13	Si Silicon 14	P Phosphorus 15	S Sulphur 16	Cl Chlorine 17	Ar Argon 18
K Potassium 19	Ca Calcium 20	Sc Scandium 21	Ti Titanium 22	V Vanadium 23	Cr Chromium 24	Mn Manganese 25	Fe Iron 26	Co Cobalt 27	Ni Nickel 28	Cu Copper 29	Zn Zinc 30	Ga Gallium 31	Ge Germanium 32	As Arsenic 33	Se Selenium 34	Br Bromine 35	Kr Krypton 36
Rb Rubidium 37	Sr Strontium 38	Y Yttrium 39	Zr Zirconium 40	Nb Niobium 41	Mo Molybdenum 42	Tc Technetium 43	Ru Ruthenium 44	Rh Rhodium 45	Pd Palladium 46	Ag Silver 47	Cd Cadmium 48	In Indium 49	Sn Tin 50	Sb Antimony 51	Te Tellurium 52	I Iodine 53	Xe Xenon 54
Cs Caesium 55	Ba Barium 56	La Lanthanum 57	Hf Hafnium 72	Ta Tantalum 73	W Tungsten 74	Re Rhenium 75	Os Osmium 76	Ir Iridium 77	Pt Platinum 78	Au Gold 79	Hg Mercury 80	Tl Thallium 81	Pb Lead 82	Bi Bismuth 83	Po Polonium 84	At Astatine 85	Rn Radon 86
Fr Francium 87	Ra Radium 88	Ac Actinium 89															

Lanthanides

Ce Cerium 58	Pr Praseodymium 59	Nd Neodymium 60	Pm Promethium 61	Sm Samarium 62	Eu Europium 63	Gd Gadolinium 64	Tb Terbium 65	Dy Dysprosium 66	Ho Holmium 67	Er Erbium 68	Tm Thulium 69	Yb Ytterbium 70	Lu Lutetium 71

Actinides

Th Thorium 90	Pa Protactinium 91	U Uranium 92	Np Neptunium 93	Pu Plutonium 94	Am Americium 95	Cm Curium 96	Bk Berkelium 97	Cf Californium 98	Es Einsteinium 99	Fm Fermium 100	Md Mendelevium 101	No Nobelium 102	Lr Lawrencium 103

the zig-zag line separates the metals from the non-metals

Figure 2.13 Periodic Table.

The modern Periodic Table has eight columns of elements called **Groups**. The elements in each Group are all chemically similar. The elements are numbered horizontally in lines called **Periods**. This number is called the **atomic number** of the element. In between Groups II and III, starting in Period 4, there is a collection of metals called the transition metals. In Periods 6 and 7 there are an additional 14 transition metals. These are called the Lanthanides (or Rare Earth Elements) in Period 6, and the Actinides in Period 7.

One reason why Mendeleev's classification of the elements was so successful was that he realised that some of the elements had not been discovered in 1869 and so he left gaps for them. He was able to predict many of the properties of the ones that had not been discovered. One of the undiscovered ones was the element germanium, the third element in Group IV. Mendeleev called this 'eka-silicon' ('eka' is Greek for 'like') because he predicted that it would have properties very like silicon. This element was discovered 15 years later. Table 2.8 shows how close Mendeleev was in his predictions.

■ **Table 2.8 Comparison of eka-silicon and germanium.**

Property	Mendeleev's prediction in 1871 of the properties of eka-silicon	Properties of germanium, discovered in 1886
Appearance	Grey metal	Grey metal
Melting point	About 800 °C	958 °C
Density	About 5.5 g cm^{-3}	5.47 g cm^{-3}
Relative atomic mass	73.4	72.6
Reaction with oxygen	Reacts to form an oxide with formula MO_2 which will have a density of 4.7 g cm^{-3}	Reacts to form GeO_2 which has a density of 4.7 g cm^{-3}

The electronic structure of the elements

As you have already read, it was the Danish chemist, Niels Bohr, who was responsible for the modern atomic theory that explains how and why atoms combine together. He realised that the electrons circulating round the nucleus were not all the same. Some had more energy than others. The ones with most energy are to be found furthest from the nucleus, just as an object far from the centre of the earth has more (gravitational) potential energy than an identical object nearer to it.

The electrons in an atom are to be found in orbits (called **shells**) around the nucleus. The nearest shell to the nucleus is full when it contains two electrons. The next shell can hold up to eight electrons before it is full. This shell contains electrons with more energy than the first shell. The third shell can also contain up to eight electrons. The shell nearest the nucleus fills first. When it is full, electrons go into the next shell, and so on. The diagrams of the atoms of hydrogen, carbon and magnesium show this (see Figure 2.14).

Bohr's atomic theory, proposed in 1913, explains the shape of the Periodic Table which had been proposed by Mendeleev almost 50 years earlier. In the Periodic Table, the first Period contains only two

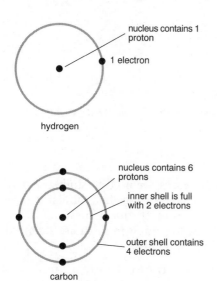

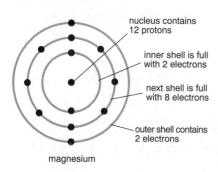

Figure 2.14 Electronic structures of H, C and Mg with explanations.

Table 2.9 Electronic structures of the first 20 elements.

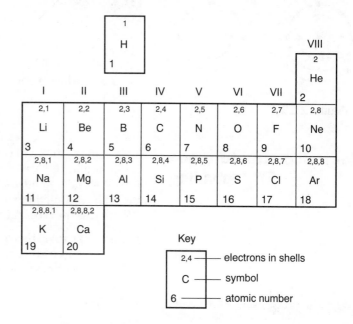

elements, hydrogen and helium. The other Periods contain elements divided into eight Groups and each Group contains elements with similar properties. Table 2.9 shows the electronic structures of the first 20 elements.

The following important points can be seen from Table 2.9.

• Each shell is gradually filled across each Period until Group 8 is reached, and the shell is full. The next shell is then filled across the Group below.

• Every element in any particular Group has the same number of electrons in the outer shell. This number is the same as the Group number.

• Elements in Group VIII, the inert gases which do not react with other elements, have full outer shells.

The fourth Period of the Periodic Table is more complicated. It contains not eight elements but 18. Between Group II and Group III there are an extra ten elements which are all metals with similar properties, called the **transition** elements. Bohr's atom is also rather more complicated. After element 20, the next 10 electrons do not go into the outer fourth shell. Instead, they go into the third shell and the number that this shell can hold goes up from 8 to 18 electrons. Because of this, the number of electrons in the outer shell of the transition elements stays the same at 2, like calcium.

These points are important because they affect the way that the elements react. This will be described in the next section.

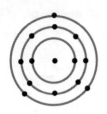

■ **Figure 2.15**

Electronic structure and bonding

Questions

2.4 Draw the electronic structures of the element in Period 2, Group V and of the element in Period 3, Group VII.

2.5 In which Period and Group are the elements in Figure 2.15?

If we want to know how a radio works, we need to study the parts inside it and the way these parts are put together. Similarly, if we want to understand the properties of chemical compounds, we must know something about how the atoms in them are arranged. We call this the **structure** of the compound.

In the next investigation you will try to classify a number of substances according to their properties. You could think of the following: hardness, electrical conductivity, solubility, whether the substance shatters when struck with a hammer (brittleness), melting and boiling points.

nvestigation 2.2

Classifying materials

Collect together a number of common substances such as these:

- some strips of some metals
- some pieces of plastic and glass
- some crystalline compounds such as table salt, copper sulphate, marble, etc.
- some liquids such as water and ethanol (methylated spirits).

1 Investigate the following physical properties of these substances:

- Appearance
- Hardness and brittleness by hitting the sample with a hammer (**CARE**, wear eye protection)
- Solubility in water
- Electrical conductivity of both the solid and the solution if the substance is soluble
- How easily the substance melts when it is heated.

2 Classify the substances according to their properties.

You can explain many of your observations if you know something about how the atoms are held together in the compounds.

Four types of bond will be studied. They have special names as follows:

- covalent bonds

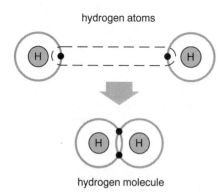

hydrogen atoms

hydrogen molecule

■ **Figure 2.16** Covalent bonds in a hydrogen molecule.

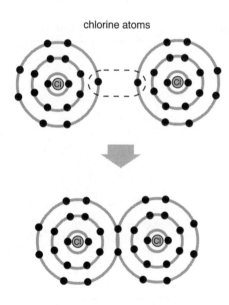

chlorine atoms

■ **Figure 2.17** Covalent bonds in a chlorine molecule.

- ionic bonds
- bonds in macromolecules
- metallic bonds.

Covalent bonds

Look again at the Periodic Table on page 27. The elements in Group VIII are the inert gases. They are called 'inert' because they do not usually take part any chemical reactions. Look carefully at helium and compare it with hydrogen. The only difference in the arrangement of electrons is that hydrogen has one electron in its shell and helium has two. It is the full shell of electrons that makes helium unreactive.

A full shell is a stable arrangement of electrons

You will see that this is a very important idea for understanding why atoms combine. By combining with other atoms they are able to achieve this stable arrangement of electrons.

Hydrogen gas does not consist of individual atoms. The atoms have joined together into hydrogen molecules and each molecule consists of two atoms of hydrogen. Pairing like this allows the atoms to share electrons so that each atom has two in its shell. The shell is full with two electrons and a full shell is a stable arrangement of electrons (see Figure 2.16).

The halogens (Group VII in the Periodic Table) are elements which need only one extra electron to fill their outer shells. Like hydrogen, they can do this by sharing electrons. Figure 2.17 shows how two chlorine atoms join together to form a chlorine molecule.

Atoms of different elements can combine in the same way. Oxygen has six electrons in its outer shell. It needs two more to fill it. Figure 2.18 shows how two atoms of hydrogen combine with one atom of oxygen by sharing electrons so that all three atoms have full outer shells.

Carbon is in Group IV of the Periodic Table. It has four electrons in the outer shell and therefore needs another four to fill the shell. Figure 2.19 shows how this can happen if it combines with four hydrogen atoms.

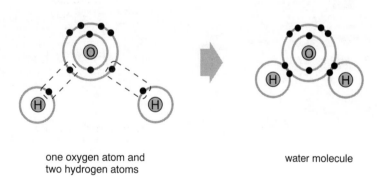

one oxygen atom and two hydrogen atoms

water molecule

■ **Figure 2.18** Covalent bonds in a water molecule.

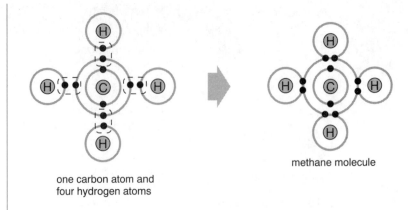

methane molecule

one carbon atom and
four hydrogen atoms

■ **Figure 2.19** Covalent bonds in a methane molecule.

Formulae for these covalent compounds are shown in Table 2.10.

■ **Table 2.10 Formulae and structures of covalent compounds.**

Compound	Formula	Structural formula
Hydrogen	H_2	H—H
Chlorine	Cl_2	Cl—Cl
Water	H_2O	O (with H and H below)
Methane	CH_4	H—C—H (with H above and below)

The formulae tell us how many atoms of each element join together to form a molecule of the compound. The formula H_2O tells us that each molecule of water contains two atoms of hydrogen joined to one of oxygen. In the **structural** formula of the compound, the bonds between the atoms are shown by lines. Each bond is made from a pair of electrons shared between the two atoms.

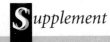
Supplement

■ **Figure 2.20** Covalent bonds in an oxygen molecule.

Like hydrogen, oxygen gas consists of molecules and not atoms. Also, like hydrogen, each molecule of oxygen contains two atoms. But oxygen needs two electrons, not one, to fill its outer shell. It can do this by sharing two electrons with another atom of oxygen. Figure 2.20 shows how this happens.

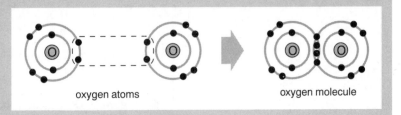

oxygen atoms

oxygen molecule

$$O=O$$

Figure 2.21 Structural formula of oxygen.

In this molecule two pairs of electrons are shared. We call this a **double** bond. We draw it with two lines as in Figure 2.21.

Another common molecule containing double bonds is carbon dioxide. In this case the carbon needs four extra electrons and can gain them by forming double bonds with two oxygen atoms as in Figure 2.22.

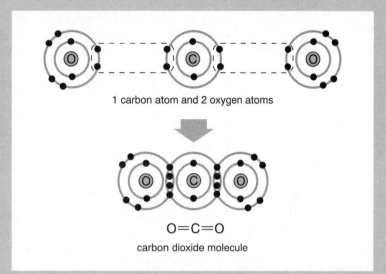

1 carbon atom and 2 oxygen atoms

$$O=C=O$$

carbon dioxide molecule

Figure 2.22 Structural and electronic formula of carbon dioxide.

There are many millions of covalent compounds in nature. Most of them are compounds containing carbon and you will meet some of them in Chapters 8 and 9. Table 2.11 shows the electronic structure and the structural formula of some of them.

Table 2.11 The structures of nitrogen, ethene, methanol and ethanol.

Name	Formula	Structural formula	Description
Nitrogen	N_2	$N \equiv N$	Colourless gas
Ethene	C_2H_4	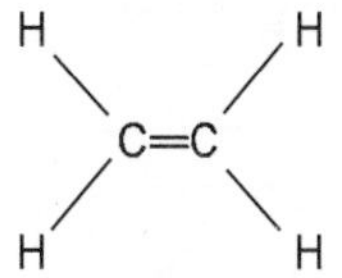	Colourless, flammable gas
Methanol	CH_3OH	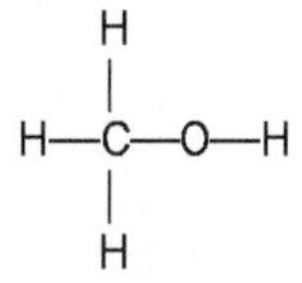	Colourless, flammable liquid
Ethanol	C_2H_5OH	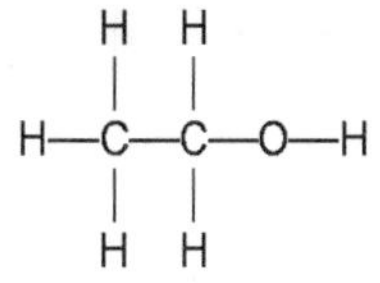	Colourless, flammable liquid

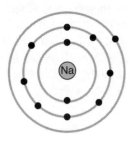

electronic structure
of a sodium atom

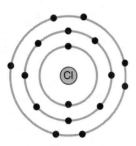

electronic structure
of a chlorine atom

■ **Figure 2.23** Structures of
sodium and chlorine atoms.

Ionic bonds

In Investigation 2.2 you will have found a group of substances that look crystalline and are easily shattered when you hit them with a hammer. They are also mostly soluble in water to give a solution which conducts electricity. These substances have what is called an **ionic** structure. A typical ionic compound is table salt, sodium chloride.

Figure 2.23 shows the electronic structures of the two atoms. Note that sodium (Group I) has one electron in its outer shell. Chlorine (Group VII) has seven electrons in its outer shell.

The sodium atom could achieve a full outer shell if it could lose one electron. The chlorine atom could fill its outer shell if it could gain an extra electron. What happens when sodium and chlorine combine is that the sodium gives up its single outer electron to the chlorine. Both atoms then have a stable full outer shell. This is shown in Figure 2.24.

The chlorine atom gains one electron. Because the electron has a negative charge, the chlorine atom will gain a negative charge. This negatively charged chlorine atom is called a chloride **ion**. The sodium atom loses an electron. This will leave the atom with one more proton than it has electrons and so it will have a positive charge. This is called a sodium **ion**. We have a shorthand way of writing ions which shows the symbol and the charge.

The sodium ion is written as **Na$^+$**

The chloride ion is written as **Cl$^-$**

Ions with more than one charge are written like these:

The magnesium ion, is written as **Mg^{++}** or **Mg^{2+}**

The oxide ion is written as **O^{--}** or **O^{2-}**

Any element that has a small number of electrons in its outer shell can lose them to form a positive ion. Elements with small numbers of atoms in their outer shell are found on the left of the Periodic Table in Groups I and II and in the transition metals.

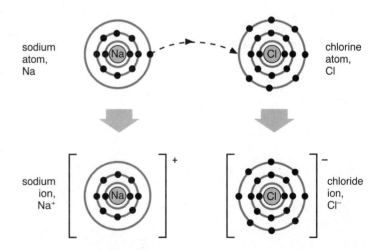

sodium
atom,
Na

chlorine
atom,
Cl

sodium
ion,
Na$^+$

chloride
ion,
Cl$^-$

■ **Figure 2.24** The transfer of an
electron from a sodium atom to
a chlorine atom.

Elements which form negative ions are those whose outer shells are almost full. These are found on the right of the Periodic Table and therefore they are non-metals. However, elements in the middle of the Periodic Table are also non-metals and these do not readily form negative ions.

Ionic compounds are therefore formed between metals and non-metals on the right of the Periodic Table.

*upplement*

Ionic crystals

The positive and negative ions present in ionic compounds are held together by electrostatic forces of attraction. You will remember from your physics that opposite charges attract each other. The ions are not held together just in pairs, however, they form what are called 'giant structures' with millions of ions arranged in rows in three dimensions with opposite charges next to each other. Figure 2.25 shows the arrangement of sodium and chloride ions in sodium chloride.

Each salt crystal in Figure 2.26 is only one single structure. It is a giant ionic structure made of sodium and chloride ions next to each other in what we call a **crystal lattice**. A salt crystal as small as 1 cubic millimetre is a giant structure made of around 10 million million million ions!

The small spheres in Figure 2.25 represent the sodium ions, which are much smaller than the chloride ions. (Can you think why?)

Because of this arrangement of the ions, ionic compounds are crystalline. They form regularly shaped crystals and the shape depends on the arrangement of the ions. It is easy to see from Figure 2.25 why table salt, sodium chloride, forms crystals which are cubes (Figure 2.26).

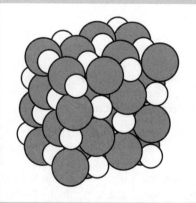

■ **Figure 2.25** Model showing how sodium ions and chloride ions are arranged in a crystal of sodium chloride. The small spheres represent the sodium ions.

■ **Figure 2.26** Crystals of table salt are cubes.

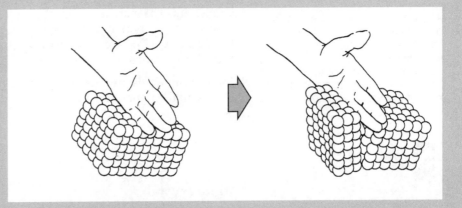

Figure 2.27
Model of cleaving a crystal.

One property of crystals is that they can easily be cleaved or split to form smaller crystals which have smooth parallel sides. This can be done with a knife blade if you hold it parallel to one of the edges of the crystal and give it a sharp tap. Figure 2.27 shows a model of this.

Because crystals can only be cleaved in this regular way, and the cleaved crystal has a perfectly flat and smooth surface, some natural ionic crystals are valued as gemstones (see Figure 2.28).

■ **Figure 2.28** The smooth surfaces and straight edges of this aquamarine are caused by the regular arrangement of ions in the crystal.

In Investigation 2.2 at the beginning of this section you were asked to classify materials according to their properties. A knowledge of the way in which the atoms join together in these materials helps us understand why the materials have these properties. Table 2.12 shows typical properties of ionic and covalent compounds and the reasons for these properties.

Macromolecules

You have seen that compounds such as water, and elements such as hydrogen and oxygen, are made up of particles that are small molecules. These molecules are made of only a few atoms joined together with covalent bonds. There are some substances that consist of very large numbers of atoms joined together in this way. These substances are called **macromolecules**.

One class of macromolecules that you will meet again in Chapter 9 are called **polymers**. These are very common and there are natural ones (like the chemicals that make up our skin or wood) and man-made ones (like nylon, polythene and other plastics). Polymers are large molecules made up of a small group of atoms that is repeated many times like bricks making up a house (see Figure 2.29).

Another example of a macromolecule is the element carbon. Carbon exists in two forms, graphite and diamond. Each form has a different structure. We call these two different structures of carbon, **allotropes** of carbon. Other elements, such as sulphur and tin, also show **allotropy**.

Properties of typical ionic compounds	Reasons for ionic compounds having these properties
Crystalline solid	Due to regular arrangement of ions, resulting from strong attractions between opposite charges
Conduct electricity when molten	On melting, ions are set free. These ions move to an oppositely charged electrode when a voltage is applied (see Chapter 5)
High melting points, high boiling points, high heats of fusion, high heats of vaporisation	These high values indicate that the ions are held together strongly and therefore lots of energy is needed to separate them
Properties of covalent compounds	**Reasons for covalent compounds having these properties**
Most are liquids or gases at room temperature	They consist of small molecules with weak attractive forces between them
Low melting and boiling temperatures, low heats of fusion and vaporisation	Due to weak intermolecular forces (attractive forces between the molecules)
Some are soluble in water, while some are soluble in organic solvents such as methylbenzene	Covalent molecular substances dissolve in covalent solvents
Do not conduct electricity when molten	Due to the absence of ions

The two forms of carbon are very different from each other. Diamond is the hardest substance known; graphite is very soft. Both forms occur naturally. Diamonds occur in certain kinds of rock that have been under very high pressure when they were very hot and molten. Under these conditions, the diamond crystals form. Because diamond is so hard, it has many uses. Diamond-tipped saws are used for cutting rocks and diamond-tipped drills are used for drilling through rocks. Glass engravers used diamond-tipped pencils to do their work (see Figure 2.30).

a

b

polythene

■ **Figure 2.29** (a) Polythene bag. (b) Structure of polythene made by repeating CH_2–CH_2 units

a

b

■ **Figure 2.30** (a) Glass engraver at work. (b) An artist using graphite.

Graphite is so soft that it will mark paper and is used mixed with clay to make pencil 'lead'. It has a very slippery surface and is used in 'graphited' lubricating oils. It has one unusual property for a non-metal; it conducts electricity. Because of this it is used in dry cells and in electric furnaces for smelting iron and aluminium (see Chapter 4).

We can explain these differences in property between diamond and graphite very easily if we look at the structures (see Figure 2.31).

In diamond, each carbon forms four bonds in different directions. Each bond joins onto another similar carbon atom. The structure goes on indefinitely. There is no such thing as a single molecule like a molecule of water or oxygen. The whole diamond crystal is one large molecule! Because the bonds are very strong and in all three dimensions, diamond is very hard.

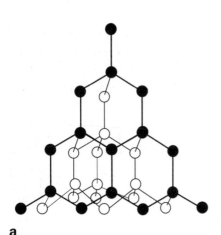

a

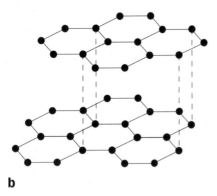

b

■ **Figure 2.31** Structures of (a) diamond and (b) graphite.

id you know?

The largest diamond in the world was found in South Africa in 1905. It is called the Cullinan diamond and is now part of the British Crown Jewels kept in the Tower of London. It weighs 620 grams. The diamond is one single molecule made of around 30 000 000 000 000 000 000 000 000 atoms of carbon!

The structure of graphite is different. Each carbon is joined to two others in six-sided rings that look rather like chicken wire. This structure is then repeated in layers. The bonds holding the atoms in each layer are strong. They are normal covalent bonds. The bonds holding the layers together are much weaker. Because of this, the layers can easily slide over each other or break apart. This is why graphite can mark paper; little bits of it easily flake off.

One very important point to remember is that, chemically, graphite and diamond are identical. They both have the same chemical properties. It is easy to make carbon dioxide by burning graphite in air. You can also make carbon dioxide by burning diamonds. (But it is rather an expensive way of making the gas!)

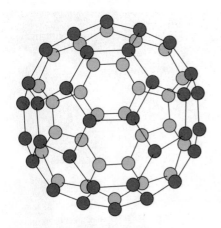

■ **Figure 2.32** C$_{60}$ fullerene, a third allotrope of carbon.

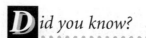

id you know?

There is a third form of carbon which has only been discovered very recently. In this form the atoms are joined together like graphite. They are not joined in flat sheets, however, but in a sphere that looks rather like a football and has 60 carbon atoms in it (see Figure 2.32). This form of carbon is called fullerene after the famous modern American architect called Buckminster Fuller who designed buildings shaped like this. Some chemists don't call these macromolecules fullerenes; they prefer to call them buckyballs! Three chemists, Robert Curl, Richard Smalley and Harry Kroto were awarded the 1996 Nobel Prize for their discovery of fullerene.

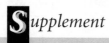

upplement

Silicon dioxide, another macromolecule

Look at Group IV of your Periodic Table. The first element is carbon. The second one is silicon. You might expect the oxides of these two elements to be similar and *chemically* they are indeed similar. *Physically*, however, they are very different. This is because carbon dioxide exists in the form of single small molecules, but silicon dioxide forms giant macromolecules.

Silicon dioxide is very well known. Sand, quartz and flint are all forms of silicon dioxide. They are all very hard substances; sand is used to make sandpaper, and flint was used by people to make sharp tools before they learnt how to make iron.

■ **Figure 2.33** Structure of silicon dioxide.

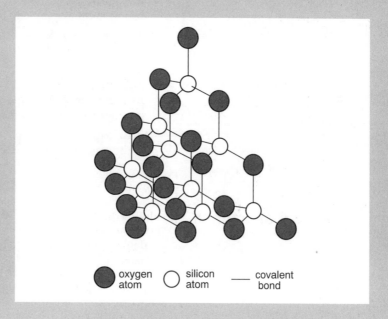

● oxygen atom ○ silicon atom ― covalent bond

The reason why silicon dioxide is hard is because of its structure (see Figure 2.33). It has a similar structure to diamond. Instead of carbon atoms there are silicon atoms and half-way between each silicon there is an oxygen atom.

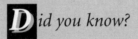

id you know?

Quartz macromolecules have an interesting electrical property. They vibrate very fast at a regular rate when a small electrical current is passed through them. This vibration of the crystal is used to control some clocks and watches. Such clocks keep very accurate time.

Metallic bonds

You will learn in Chapter 4 of a rather different kind of bond called the metallic bond. This is the bond that holds the atoms together in a metal. You will see that, if you understand what this bond is like, you can explain many important properties of metals such as their good electrical and heat conductivity.

uestions

2.6 Classify the following compounds as covalent or ionic:
$NaBr$, $MgCl_2$, PH_3, $FeCl_3$, H_2S, CuO

2.7 Show, using diagrams, how the elements lithium and bromine can combine to form an ionic compound.

2.8 Draw the electronic structures of ammonia (NH_3) and hydrogen chloride (HCl). Draw the structural formulae of these compounds.

2.9 Sulphur is in Group VI. How many electrons are there in its outer shell? Draw the structure of the compound (called hydrogen sulphide) formed between hydrogen and sulphur.

2.10 What is the formula of the compound formed between carbon and chlorine? Give a reason for your answer.

Chemical shorthand

Chemists have a convenient way of showing what happens in a chemical reaction in a form of shorthand. You already know that elements can be represented by symbols; carbon is represented by C and oxygen by O, for example. You also know that CO_2 is the shorthand for carbon dioxide, and it tells you that a molecule of carbon dioxide is made of one atom of carbon joined to two atoms of oxygen.

But what does this tell you?

$$C + O_2 \rightarrow CO_2$$

- It tells you about the reaction between carbon and oxygen.
- It tells you that carbon reacts with oxygen to form carbon dioxide.
- It also tells you that *one atom* of carbon reacts with *one molecule* of oxygen to form *one molecule* of carbon dioxide.

This is clearer if we draw the atoms.

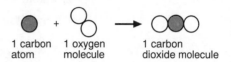

1 carbon atom   1 oxygen molecule   1 carbon dioxide molecule

Think about another reaction. Hydrogen burns in oxygen to form water.

Hydrogen + oxygen → water

We can write the shorthand symbols for these molecules:

$$H_2 + O_2 \rightarrow H_2O$$

This equation, however is not correct. Can you see why? If we draw the atoms, it looks like this.

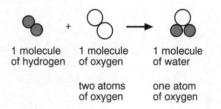

1 molecule of hydrogen   1 molecule of oxygen   1 molecule of water

two atoms of oxygen   one atom of oxygen

You can see that there are two oxygen atoms on the left but only one on the right. We say that this equation is not **balanced**. A balanced equation has the same number of atoms of each element before the reaction (the left) as there are after the reaction (the right).

To balance the equation, we will need two molecules of hydrogen, and two molecules of water will be produced .

2 molecules of hydrogen   1 molecule of oxygen   2 molecules of water

The balanced equation showing this reaction is this:

$$2H_2 + O_2 \rightarrow 2H_2O$$

The *large* numbers to the left of symbols tell you about the *number of molecules involved in the reaction.*

The *small* numbers to the right of symbols tell you about the *number of atoms in the molecule.*

State symbols

More information can be added to these equations if the state (solid, liquid or gas) is added to the formula for each substance. To do this, we put state symbols after the formula for the substance. The useful state symbols are these:

(s) – solid

(l) – liquid

(g) – gas

(aq) – aqueous solution (solution in water)

The two equations above will then become:

$$C(s) + O_2(g) \rightarrow CO_2(g)$$

$$2H_2(g) + O_2(g) \rightarrow 2H_2O(l)$$

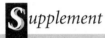 *Supplement*

We can use equations to show us what happens when sodium reacts with chlorine. The overall reaction is this:

Sodium + chlorine → sodium chloride
    $2Na + Cl_2 \qquad \rightarrow 2NaCl$

We can write **ionic** equations to show what happens to the sodium and to the chlorine. The symbol for an electron is 'e' and, of course, it has a negative charge.

Sodium atom → sodium ion + electron
Na $\rightarrow Na^+$ $+ e^-$

Chlorine molecule + 2 electrons → 2 chloride ions
Cl_2 $+ 2e^-$ $\rightarrow 2Cl^-$

The sodium atom loses only one electron and so it has a single positive charge. Magnesium, however, is in Group II and has two electrons in its outer shell. Magnesium can form an ion by losing two electrons and this means that it has not one charge but two. The ionic equation shows this:
$Mg \rightarrow Mg^{2+} + 2e^-$

Elements like chlorine in Group VII gain one electron when they form an ion. Elements in Group VI must gain two electrons to get a full outer shell and form an ion. Oxygen is in Group VI and the ion it forms is called the oxide ion. We can show this by an ionic equation like this:

$O_2 + 4e^- \rightarrow 2O^{-2}$

Each of the two atoms in the oxygen molecule gains two electrons.

We write the formula of the ionic compound sodium chloride as NaCl. This is because the charge on one sodium ion (+1) is exactly balanced by the charge on one chloride ion (−1). An ion of magnesium has two positive charges (+2). To balance this, two chloride ions are needed. The formula of magnesium chloride is therefore $MgCl_2$. The oxide ion has two negative charges (–2) and so the formula of magnesium oxide is MgO because the charge on the magnesium ion (+2) balances the charge on the oxide ion (–2).

The aluminium ion has a charge of three (+3). Can you write the formula of aluminium chloride? Can you also write the formula of aluminium oxide (it is more difficult)?

uestions

Write balanced equations, including state symbols, for the following reactions.

2.11 Magnesium + oxygen → magnesium oxide (MgO(s))

2.12 Carbon dioxide + limewater ($Ca(OH)_2$(aq)) → water + calcium carbonate ($CaCO_3$(s))

2.13 Methane (CH_4(g)) + oxygen → carbon dioxide + steam

2.14 Iron(III) oxide (Fe_2O_3(s)) + carbon monoxide (CO(g)) → iron + carbon dioxide.

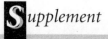upplement

Radioactivity

About 100 years ago, a French scientist called Henri Becquerel made a chance discovery. He had some photographic plates carefully wrapped so that light could not spoil them. He stored them near a sample of the element uranium that had recently been purified. When the plates were developed, they were black, just as if some light had reached them. Becquerel suggested that some kind of invisible radiation must have been given off by the uranium and had passed through the wrapping round the plates.

Pierre and Marie Curie, two other French scientists who investigated this further, called the effect **radioactivity**. All three shared the 1903 Nobel prize for chemistry.

We now know that, when an isotope of an element is radioactive, it has an unstable nucleus. The nucleus breaks down giving off the radiation and forming a new element with a different number of protons and neutrons. Only a few isotopes are radioactive. The best known ones are isotopes of the heavier elements such as uranium (92 protons and 146 neutrons) but there are radioactive isotopes of almost every element though they usually occur naturally in very small amounts. There is even a radioactive isotope of hydrogen; it has one proton and also two neutrons in the nucleus and it has a special name, tritium.

The radiation given off by radioactive isotopes is dangerous. (It killed Marie Curie who did not realise this.) Because of this the isotopes must be handled and stored with great care. However, radioactive isotopes can also be useful. Table 2.13 shows some examples of this. They are used in medicine, in measuring devices and in nuclear power stations.

■ Table 2.13 Uses of some radioisotopes.

Isotope	Use
Uranium-235 and -238	Nuclear power stations. A lot of energy is given off when these decompose. This can be used to make electricity
Iodine-131	Medical use. It can be used to test for abnormal functioning of the thyroid gland in the neck. Iodine is used in the thyroid gland and if radioactive iodine is introduced into the body the radiation from it will show whether the thyroid gland is using iodine correctly. Other isotopes are used to treat cancer. The radiation kills the cancer cells more easily than it kills normal cells.
Caesium-137	Used to detect whether a can of beer is full or not as it comes off the production line. A full can does not allow as much radiation from the caesium through as an empty one does. This isotope can also be used to check whether paper is being made to the correct thickness.

Review questions on this chapter can be found on pages 237–8.

The Periodic Table

Mendeleev's Periodic Table is now a little over a century old. More than any other discovery it has helped chemists understand the world about us. You have seen how the pattern that Mendeleev discovered by looking at the chemical properties of the elements can be explained by the electronic structure of the elements. In this chapter we will study the properties of some of the groups of elements in more detail.

Figure 3.1 shows a modern form of the Periodic Table. It is possible to classify elements into four blocks in the Table. In each block the elements have similar properties. These blocks are:

- Groups I and II on the left . Group I elements are called the **alkali metals** and Group II elements the **alkaline earth metals**
- The **transition metals** between Groups II and III.
- The group of metals on the right of the transition metals. These are called the **B-metals**
- The group of **non-metals** to the right of the Periodic Table.

Within these groups it is possible to identify trends in both the physical and chemical properties. It is this that makes the Periodic Table so useful because it allows us to predict the properties of elements we have not seen. One very important trend across the whole Table is the change from metals to non-metals from left to right. This does not happen suddenly at the black, stepped line but is gradual. Metallic elements near the line show some non-metal characteristics and non-metals near the line show some metallic characteristics.

Groups I and II, alkali and alkaline earth metals

This block on the left of the Table contains reactive metals which form colourless ionic compounds, most of which are soluble in water. These metals become more reactive as you go down the Groups. Reactivity decreases from Group I to Group II.

Transition metals

This block contains hard, strong, dense metals which have many important uses (see Figure 3.2). They often form coloured compounds. The block includes two sets of elements called the

■ **Figure 3.2** This was the first bridge made out of a metal. It is made of the transition metal iron. It was constructed in 1779 and it crosses the river Severn in England.

The Periodic Table

Non-metals
Form compounds with each other. Some form negative ions

B-metals
These metals also show some non-metal properties

Lanthanides and Actinides
Rare metallic elements, very similar to each other

The transition metals
Hard, strong, dense metals, form coloured compounds

The alkali metals and alkaline earth metals
Reactive metals that form colourless ionic compounds

Key:
H — symbol
Hydrogen — name
1 — atomic number

Group	I Alkali metals	II Alkaline earth metals
Period 1		
2	Li Lithium 3	Be Beryllium 4
3	Na Sodium 11	Mg Magnesium 12
4	K Potassium 19	Ca Calcium 20
5	Rb Rubidium 37	Sr Strontium 38
6	Cs Caesium 55	Ba Barium 56
7	Fr Francium 87	Ra Radium 88

H Hydrogen 1

Transition metals:

Sc Scandium 21	Ti Titanium 22	V Vanadium 23	Cr Chromium 24	Mn Manganese 25	Fe Iron 26	Co Cobalt 27	Ni Nickel 28	Cu Copper 29	Zn Zinc 30
Y Yttrium 39	Zr Zirconium 40	Nb Niobium 41	Mo Molybdenum 42	Tc Technetium 43	Ru Ruthenium 44	Rh Rhodium 45	Pd Palladium 46	Ag Silver 47	Cd Cadmium 48
57—71 See below	Hf Hafnium 72	Ta Tantalum 73	W Tungsten 74	Re Rhenium 75	Os Osmium 76	Ir Iridium 77	Pt Platinum 78	Au Gold 79	Hg Mercury 80
89—103 See below	Du Dubnium 104	Jl Joliotium 105							

Groups III–VIII:

III	IV	V	VI	VII Halogens	VIII Noble gases
					He Helium 2
B Boron 5	C Carbon 6	N Nitrogen 7	O Oxygen 8	F Fluorine 9	Ne Neon 10
Al Aluminium 13	Si Silicon 14	P Phosphorus 15	S Sulphur 16	Cl Chlorine 17	Ar Argon 18
Ga Gallium 31	Ge Germanium 32	As Arsenic 33	Se Selenium 34	Br Bromine 35	Kr Krypton 36
In Indium 49	Sn Tin 50	Sb Antimony 51	Te Tellurium 52	I Iodine 53	Xe Xenon 54
Tl Thallium 81	Pb Lead 82	Bi Bismuth 83	Po Polonium 84	At Astatine 85	Rn Radon 86

Lanthanides:

La Lanthanum 57	Ce Cerium 58	Pr Praseodymium 59	Nd Neodymium 60	Pm Promethium 61	Sm Samarium 62	Eu Europium 63	Gd Gadolinium 64	Tb Terbium 65	Dy Dysprosium 66	Ho Holmium 67	Er Erbium 68	Tm Thulium 69	Yb Ytterbium 70	Lu 71
Ac Actinium 89	Th Thorium 90	Pa Protactinium 91	U Uranium 92	Np Neptunium 93	Pu Plutonium 94	Am Americium 95	Cm Curium 96	Bk Berkelium 97	Cf Californium 98	Es Einsteinium 99	Fm Fermium 100	Md Mendelevium 101	No Nobelium 102	Lr Lawrencium 103

■ **Figure 3.1** Periodic Table.

Lanthanides (sometimes called the 'rare earth elements') and the Actinides which are all very rare and very similar to each other.

The metals become less reactive from left to right in the Table, like Groups I and II. Reactivity also decreases from top to bottom of the Table, the opposite of Groups I and II. This means that the least reactive metals, such as gold, are found at the bottom right of this block.

The B-metals

This block of metals is next to the non-metals. Their metallic properties such as electrical conductivity and heat conductivity are not as good as those of the transition metals and they also show some non-metallic properties.

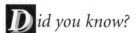

D id you know?

Tin is a well-known B-metal. It is unreactive and is used for lining food cans made of steel so that the food is not contaminated with rust. There is, however, another form (or allotrope) of tin which is not a metal at all but a grey powder rather like graphite but lighter in colour. This form does not conduct electricity. You can see that tin is very close to the borderline between metals and non-metals.

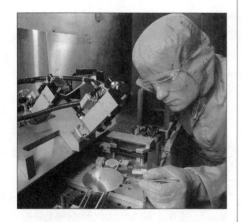

■ **Figure 3.3** Silicon is an important non-metal. It is made in large, very pure crystals which are then sliced into these thin 'wafers'. These are then used to make the electronic components found in everything from watches to computers.

Non-metals

Elements in this block vary a lot in their properties. Some are gases, one is a liquid and some are solids at room temperature. They only have one thing common to all of them; they are not metals. An example is shown in Figure 3.3. They form covalent compounds with each other and the ones on the right of the Table form ionic compounds with metals.

Group VIII, the inert gases (often also called Group O), are a special group of non-metals. Their most interesting property is that they do not usually react with other elements.

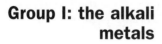

Group I: the alkali metals

These elements (Figure 3.4) occur in Group I of the Periodic Table . They are soft metals, easily cut with a knife. Table 3.1 shows trends in the physical properties of these metals. The melting and boiling points decrease down the Group. Caesium is classified as a solid but in many countries it will be a liquid. Many of the metals have densities less than 1 g cm^{-3} which means they float on water.

Group I metals	
Lithium	Li
Sodium	Na
Potassium	K
Rubidium	Rb
Caesium	Cs
Francium	Fr

Figure 3.4 List of all Group I metals.

chlorine

lithium
sodium
potassium

Table 3.1 Physical properties of alkali metals.

Name	Melting point (°C)	Boiling point (°C)	Density (g cm⁻³)
Lithium	180	1330	0.53
Sodium	98	890	0.97
Potassium	64	774	0.86
Rubidium	39	688	1.53
Caesium	29	690	1.90

Investigation 3.1

The properties of alkali metals

This investigation **MUST** be done by the teacher.

You will need:

- samples of lithium, sodium and potassium
- a glass trough or bowl
- a sheet of glass to go over the trough
- a knife
- gas jars of oxygen and chlorine
- combustion spoons
- red litmus paper.

The metals are all stored under paraffin to prevent them reacting with the air. When they are used, they should be cut and then cleaned with filter paper to remove the paraffin and then used immediately.

1 Cut off a small piece of each metal. Note that they all cut easily with the knife and that the freshly cut metal is shiny but soon goes dull or tarnishes.

2 Put water in the trough. Put a small piece of lithium in the water. Cover the bowl with the sheet of glass. Watch what happens to the metal. When the reaction is over, test the water with red litmus paper.

3 Repeat this experiment with the other two metals. Take care with this experiment; do not use a large piece of the metal (a cube with 2 mm sides is about the right size) or it can explode and pieces will jump out of the bowl if you do not have the lid on.

4 Put a piece of one of the metals in a combustion spoon. Set fire to it and lower it into a jar of oxygen. Note the colour and brightness of the flame. Repeat the experiment with the other metals.

5 Do experiment **4** gas jars of chlorine. Again, note the flame colour. Note also the smoke produced.

■ Table 3.2 Chemical properties of alkali metals.

Element	Reaction with water	Reaction with oxygen	Reaction with chlorine	Flame colour	Symbol of ion	Salts (e.g. nitrates, sulphates, carbonates)
Li	Reacts with cold water to give hydrogen and an alkali, lithium hydroxide (LiOH(aq))	Burns to form a white solid, lithium oxide ($Li_2O(s)$)	Reacts on heating to give white lithium chloride (LiCl(s))	Crimson red	Li^+	White crystalline solids which are soluble in water
Na	Reacts vigorously with cold water to give hydrogen and an alkali, sodium hydroxide (NaOH(aq))	Burns to form a white solid, sodium oxide ($Na_2O(s)$)	Vigorous reaction on heating to give white sodium chloride (NaCl(s))	Bright yellow	Na^+	White crystalline solids which are soluble in water
K	Reacts violently with cold water to give hydrogen and an alkali, potassium hydroxide (KOH(aq))	Burns to form a white solid, potassium oxide ($K_2O(s)$)	Very vigorous reaction to give white potassium chloride (KCl(s))	Mauve	K^+	White crystalline solids which are soluble in water

Table 3.2 summarises the properties of the alkali metals and includes many of the points you will have found out in the investigation.

In the investigation, you made the oxide, hydroxide and chloride of the three metals. The three reactions are described by these equations:

Sodium + oxygen → sodium oxide

Lithium + water → lithium hydroxide + hydrogen

Potassium + chlorine → potassium chloride

$$4Na(s) + O_2(g) \rightarrow 2Na_2O(s)$$

$$2Li(s) + 2H_2O(l) \rightarrow 2LiOH(aq) + H_2(g)$$

$$2K(s) + Cl_2(g) \rightarrow 2KCl(s)$$

Only one equation is shown for each reaction. The equation for the other two metals is exactly the same, except that the name and symbol of the metal are changed.

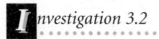

*I*nvestigation 3.2

Showing that hydrogen is produced when a Group I metal reacts with water

This investigation **MUST** be done by the teacher.

sodium

When you added the alkali metal to water in Investigation 3.1, you could not see the hydrogen produced because the metal floats. This investigation allows you to collect the hydrogen and test it (see Figure 3.5).

You will need:

- sodium
- a small piece of iron or copper gauze
- beaker and boiling tube.

1 Fill a boiling tube with water and invert it in a beaker of water.

2 Cut up a small piece of sodium and wrap it in a piece of iron gauze.

3 Drop the sodium in the gauze in the beaker. It will sink. Using the boiling tube, collect the gas that comes off it as it reacts with the water.

4 Test the gas in the boiling tube by setting fire to it. Note what happens. Look for signs of condensation on the inside of the tube.

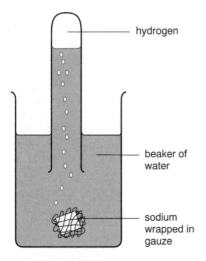

hydrogen

beaker of water

sodium wrapped in gauze

■ **Figure 3.5** Collecting the hydrogen produced by the reaction betweeen sodium and water.

The reaction of sodium with water is interesting. You saw in Investigation 3.1 that the metal stayed on top of the water. This shows that it has a density less than the density of water ($1\,\mathrm{g\,cm^{-3}}$). When it reacts with the water, enough heat is produced to melt the metal.

Investigation 3.2 showed that hydrogen is produced by the reaction. In Investigation 3.1 the reaction produced the gas hydrogen where the metal touched the water underneath it. This caused the metal to move over the surface of the water, floating like a hovercraft on a cushion of the gases hydrogen and steam.

The metal hydroxide that was formed by the reaction with water is soluble. It dissolves in the water, making the water alkaline. When red litmus paper is dipped in the water, it turns blue because the water is alkaline. You will read more about this in Chapter 5.

Group I compounds are all ionic. The ion formed by all the elements in the Group has one positive charge and so the formulae of the compounds are all very similar (see Table 3.3). All Group I compounds are colourless, crystalline solids which are soluble in water.

The test for hydrogen

Hydrogen gas burns in air to form water. If it is mixed with air before it is ignited, it will explode with a 'pop' when a flame is brought near it. The water formed by the reaction can often be seen as condensation on the inside of the tube.
$$2H_2(g) + O_2(g) \rightarrow 2H_2O(l)$$

■ **Table 3.3 Group I compounds.**

Metal	Chloride	Nitrate	Sulphate	Carbonate
Lithium	LiCl	$LiNO_3$	Li_2SO_4	Li_2CO_3
Sodium	NaCl	$NaNO_3$	Na_2SO_4	Na_2CO_3
Potassium	KCl	KNO_3	K_2SO_4	K_2CO_3

Group I reactivity

The investigation showed that the reactivity of the Group I metals increases down the group (see Figure 3.6). This is shown clearly by the reaction with water; so much heat is produced when potassium reacts that the hydrogen produced catches fire.

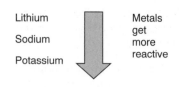

Lithium

Sodium

Potassium

Metals get more reactive

■ **Figure 3.6** Reactivity of Group I metals.

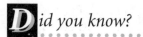

*D*id you know?

If you add a lump of caesium to water in a glass trough, the reaction is so vigorous that the trough will shatter into small pieces

Uses of Group I elements and compounds

Compounds of Group I elements are very common and have many uses but the elements themselves are rare. This is because they are difficult and expensive to obtain from their compounds because they are so reactive.

Sodium chloride, **salt**, is a very important raw material of the chemical industry. It is the chemical on which the 'alkali' industry is based. The alkali industry produces, among other things, all the soaps and detergents we use. This industry has grown up wherever the following can be found:

• large deposits of sodium chloride
• a readily available energy source such as coal
• a market for the products.

The salt deposits were formed when seas dried up millions of years ago. Salt is also extracted from the sea in parts of the world where the sun can be used to evaporate the sea water (see Figure 3.7).

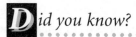

*D*id you know?

Salt is a very good road-making material. It forms a hard surface that is not broken up when vehicles travel along it. The only problem is that it dissolves when it rains! It can only be used in desert roads such as the roads around Walvis Bay in the Namib desert. Occasionally, it rains in the Namib and this causes severe rusting of the cars that are driven on the wet roads.

■ **Figure 3.7** Walvis Bay in Namibia is a good place to produce salt from sea water. It is warm, sunny and it is on the coast of the Namib desert where it hardly ever rains. This salt has been made by the evaporation of sea water by the sun. The salt is used in the southern African alkali industry.

Glass is an important material made from sodium carbonate (a product of the alkali industry). The common window glass is made by melting together sodium carbonate, calcium carbonate (crushed limestone) and sand.

Sodium metal is used in the very bright yellow street lights seen in the cities of the world. When you burnt sodium, you will have seen the bright yellow flame. This yellow colour is produced in fluorescent bulbs that contain small quantities of sodium metal vapour.

3.1 Using Table 3.1, plot a graph showing how the boiling and melting points of the elements of Group I vary with proton number (*x* axis). Use the graph to predict the melting and boiling points of francium (proton number 87).

3.2 Rubidium is the fourth element in Group I. Predict the following properties of rubidium and its compounds:

• appearance

• hardness

• reaction with water

• appearance and solubility of rubidium chloride

• electrical conductivity.

3.3 Sodium is a very good conductor of electricity and scientists are working on ways of using it to make electrical wires. What are the main problems the scientists must try to solve before sodium can be used in this way?

Group VII: the halogens

The halogens are the elements in Group VII (see Figure 3.8). They are all non-metals. Fluorine and chlorine are gases, bromine is a liquid and iodine is a solid (see Table 3.4). The elements are all poisonous but their ions are essential to life. This is why athletes who sweat a lot have to take salt tablets; without these they could get severe muscle cramps

■ Table 3.4 Physical properties of the halogens.

Name	Symbol	Melting point (°C)	Boiling point (°C)	State at room temperature (15 °C)	Colour
Fluorine	F	−220	−188	Gas	Yellow
Chlorine	Cl	−101	−35	Gas	Green
Bromine	Br	−7	59	Liquid	Brown
Iodine	I	114	184	Solid	Purplish/black

Group VII elements	
Fluorine	F
Chlorine	Cl
Bromine	Br
Iodine	I
Astatine	At

■ **Figure 3.8** List of all Group VII elements.

   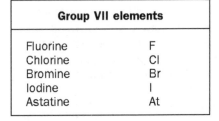

chlorine   potassium   concentrated
                  permanganate   hydrochloric
                                      acid
                                      concentrated
                                      sulphuric
                                      acid

*I*nvestigation 3.3
· · · · · · · · · · · · · · · · · · · ·

Preparation and reactions of chlorine

This investigation **MUST** be done by the teacher. Chlorine is a poisonous gas. The preparation must be done in a fume cupboard.

You will need:

• potassium permanganate

• concentrated hydrochloric acid

• apparatus in Figure 3.9.

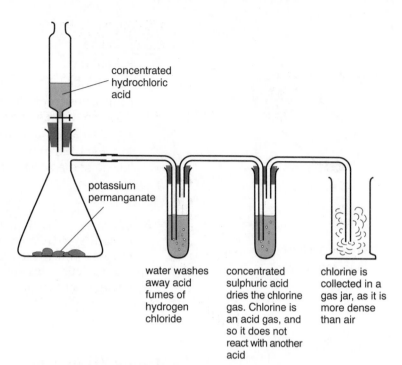

concentrated hydrochloric acid

potassium permanganate

water washes away acid fumes of hydrogen chloride

concentrated sulphuric acid dries the chlorine gas. Chlorine is an acid gas, and so it does not react with another acid

chlorine is collected in a gas jar, as it is more dense than air

Figure 3.9 Preparation of chlorine.

1 The glassware is put together as shown in the diagram. The two wash bottles are not necessary for this experiment, but they are shown in the diagram to illustrate how a sample of pure dry chlorine is made.

2 Allow a small quantity of concentrated hydrochloric acid to drop onto the potassium permanganate. Watch what happens.

3 Chlorine is heavier than air and so can be collected in a gas jar as shown. This method of collecting gases is called downward delivery. The chlorine sinks to the bottom of the jar.

4 When the jar looks full, put a top on it and replace it with another.

5 Carry out the following tests with chlorine.

• Observe the colour.

• Burn some sodium in a combustion spoon and lower it into the gas (this was done in Investigation 3.1).

• Heat some iron wool until it is glowing and lower it quickly into the gas. Note what happens.

• Put some moist litmus paper into the gas.

Write the results in a table.

Test for chlorine
Hold a piece of moist blue litmus paper in the gas. It will first turn red and then will be bleached if the gas is chlorine.

iodine vapour

*I*nvestigation 3.4

A reaction of iodine

Iodine is a solid which easily sublimes when it is heated. In this reaction iodine vapour reacts with hot iron (see Figure 3.10).

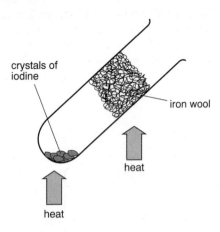

crystals of
iodine

iron wool

heat

heat

■ **Figure 3.10** Heating iron wool
in iodine vapour.

You will need:
• iodine
• iron wool
• test tube.

1 Put a few crystals of iodine in the bottom of a test tube and a piece of iron wool half-way up the tube.

2 Heat the iodine gently until it sublimes. At the same time heat the iron wool. Watch carefully what happens. Do you see any sign of a reaction?

These investigations show that the halogens are non-metals that react readily with metals. The products formed are ionic compounds and these appear in the form of a smoke. One important reaction that you carried out showed that chlorine was a **bleaching agent**; moist litmus paper placed in chlorine was bleached colourless. This is a test for chlorine gas.

Group VII compounds

As you learnt in Chapter 2, Group VII elements form two kinds of compounds:

• ionic compounds with metals
• covalent compounds with non-metals.

The ionic compounds formed with metals are hard, crystalline substances. They contain the negative ions such as chloride (Cl^-) or iodide (I^-). A typical one is sodium chloride, table salt. In these investigations you also made iron chloride which has orange-coloured crystals. Iron iodide is also a deep orange-coloured solid. We call the Group VII elements the halogens and we call their ions the **halide** ions. The reactions in the investigations can be represented by equations:

Sodium + chlorine → sodium chloride

Iron + chlorine → iron chloride

Iron + iodine → iron iodide

$$2Na(s) + Cl_2(g) \rightarrow 2NaCl(s)$$
$$2Fe(s) + 3Cl_2(g) \rightarrow 2FeCl_3(s)$$
$$2Fe(s) + 3I_2(g) \rightarrow 2FeI_3(s)$$

Most halides are soluble. This is why the main source of the halogens is sea water. Over millions of years, the rain has washed the soluble halides out of rocks and into the seas. We obtain chlorine and bromine from deposits of salt left when ancient seas dried up. We obtain iodine from seaweed. The seaweed takes in iodide compounds from the sea water and we can recover them by harvesting the seaweed, drying it, burning it and getting the iodide compounds from the ash.

Some halides are insoluble. They are the halides of some of the transition metals and B-metals such as lead. They can be used as tests for the halide ions; a white precipitate of silver chloride is formed when silver ions are added to chloride ions and yellow lead iodide is formed when iodide ions are added to a solution containing lead ions.

The compounds between halogens and hydrogen

The halogens form covalent compounds with hydrogen. These are all gases with a very unpleasant choking smell. They have a very important property; they are very soluble in water and the product is an acid. **Hydrogen chloride**, for example, is a gas which is very soluble in water to give **hydrochloric acid**. These hydrogen halides are all covalent gases but when they mix with water, halide ions are formed in the water. This is summarised in Table 3.5 and you will learn more about the properties of these very useful acids in Chapter 5.

■ Table 3.5 The hydrogen halides.

Covalent gases		Product when the gas is mixed with water	
Hydrogen chloride	HCl	Hydrochloric acid	$H^+ Cl^-$ (aq)
Hydrogen bromide	HBr	Hydrobromic acid	$H^+ Br^-$ (aq)
Hydrogen iodide	HI	Hydroiodic acid	$H^+ I^-$ (aq)

Group VII reactivity

Investigation 3.5

bleach
bromine water

Reactivity of halogens

You will need:

• dilute solution of a chlorine bleach or chlorine water (water that chlorine has been bubbled through)

• bromine water (water that has been shaken with a drop of bromine)

• solutions of sodium chloride, sodium bromide and sodium iodide

• starch solution.

1 Put a small quantity of sodium chloride solution in a test tube. Add a few drops of the chlorine solution. Do you see any change? Then add a drop of starch solution and note any change.

2 Repeat with sodium bromide solution and then again with sodium iodide solution.

3 Repeat the whole procedure using bromine solution instead of chlorine solution.

4 Identify the halogen present in the test tube in each case. This list will help you:

Fluorine

Chlorine

Bromine

Iodine

Elements get **more** reactive up the group

■ **Figure 3.11** Reactivity of the halogens.

• If iodine is present, the solution will be a brown colour and will turn black when starch is added.

• If bromine is present, the solution will be a brown colour but starch will have no effect on it.

• If only chlorine is present, no colour will be seen (except perhaps a slight green).

5 Write your observations down in a table. In the table note which halogens you found in each case.

This investigation shows the reaction between halogens and other halide ions. It shows that, when a halogen high in the group is added to a solution containing the ions of one lower down, there is a reaction. For example, if chlorine solution is added to sodium iodide solution, there is a reaction and iodine is produced.

Chlorine + sodium iodide → sodium chloride + iodine

This is because chlorine is more reactive than iodine. It competes with the iodine for the sodium ion and wins. If bromine solution is added to a solution of sodium chloride, there is no reaction because bromine is less reactive than chlorine.

The equations below summarise the reactions in Investigation 3.5.

Chlorine + sodium chloride → no reaction

Chlorine + sodium bromide → sodium chloride + bromine

Chlorine + sodium iodide → sodium chloride + iodine

Bromine + sodium chloride → no reaction

Bromine + sodium bromide → no reaction

Bromine + sodium iodide → sodium bromide + iodine

These reactions show that the reactivity of the halogens decreases down the Group (see Figure 3.11). This is the opposite from Group I where reactivity increases down the group.

Uses of the halogens

Chlorine is a very important element industrially. It is made from sodium chloride and is one of the products of the 'alkali' industry (page 51). Some important uses of chlorine (see Figure 3.12) are:

• making the very common and useful plastic PVC
• making aerosol propellants and the liquid used in refrigerators
• making liquid bleach for use around the home
• bleaching wood pulp to make paper
• making chemicals such as drugs, insecticides and weedkillers
• purifying water.

You saw how chlorine bleached litmus paper in Investigation 3.3. This is a very useful property of the halogens. Substances which bleach are 'oxidising agents' and you will study these further in Chapter 5. Chlorine is a useful bleach which is widely used, particularly to bleach paper.

a

b

■ **Figure 3.12** Some uses of chlorine: (a) in a refrigerator and (b) chlorination tank in a water purification plant.

Another useful property of chlorine is that it is poisonous. It is particularly poisonous to bacteria and so it is used to make water safe to use. Enough chlorine is bubbled into water in a purification plant to kill most of the bacteria in the water. You can often smell chlorine in the water when you turn on the tap.

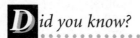

Did you know?

In some parts of the world, the water supply contains small amounts of fluorine compounds. It was found that, in these areas, people did not suffer much from tooth decay. This is because compounds of fluorine protect teeth from decay. This is why many toothpastes contain fluorine compounds.

Questions

3.4 From the information in Table 3.4 (page 52), plot a graph showing how the melting point of the halogens changes with proton number (*x* axis). Use the graph to predict the melting point of the halogen astatine (proton number 85).

3.5 What, if anything, would you expect to see in the following reactions:

a Bromine water is added to a solution of sodium fluoride.

b Iodine solution is added to a solution of sodium chloride.

c Fluorine is bubbled through a solution of sodium bromide.

Explain your answers.

3.6 Hydrogen combines explosively with fluorine. Give the formula of the product. Is the product a solid, liquid or gas? What would be produced if the product were bubbled through water?

3.7 If you were to warm a drop of bromine gently in a test tube which also contained some aluminium foil, what would you expect to happen, if anything?

The inert gases

The most interesting thing about the Group VIII elements is that they are chemically very uninteresting. They do not usually react with anything. We say they are inert (see Figure 3.13).

They are sometimes called the **noble gases**. They are called this because the metals that do not tarnish – like gold and silver – were called the noble metals. The ones that easily rust or corrode were called 'base' metals. 'Noble' and 'base' mean the opposite of each other and the words were once applied to people as well as metals!

You saw in Chapter 2 that the reason for the unreactivity of the inert gases is that they have a full outer shell of electrons and therefore do not need to combine with other elements in order to achieve this.

Group VIII elements	
Helium	He
Neon	Ne
Argon	Ar
Krypton	Kr
Xenon	Xe
Radon	Rn

■ **Figure 3.13** List of all Group VIII elements

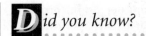
Table 3.6 shows some physical properties of these gases. You can see from the table that the melting and boiling points and the densities increase down the Group. As you go down the Group, the atoms get bigger and so it is not surprising that the density increases. As the atoms get bigger, they will require more energy to make them move and so you would expect an increase in melting and boiling points.

■ **Table 3.6 Group VIII elements.**

Name	Symbol	Melting point (°C)	Boiling point (°C)	Density (g dm^{-3})
Helium	He	–270	–269	0.17
Neon	Ne	–249	–246	0.84
Argon	Ar	–189	–186	1.66
Krypton	Kr	–157	–152	3.46
Xenon	Xe	–112	–108	5.5

Uses of the inert gases

Because they are unreactive, the inert gases are very useful. Table 3.7 shows some of their uses and the reasons for them.

■ **Table 3.7 Uses of the inert gases.**

Gas	Use	Reason
Helium	Filling airships and balloons	Very low density, not flammable
Helium	Mixing with oxygen to form a gas for divers to breathe	If a diver breathes air, nitrogen dissolves in the blood and can cause a dangerous problem called 'nitrogen narcosis' in which the diver has symptoms similar to drunkenness
Neon	Fluorescent lights	When an electric current is passed through neon, it gives off a bright light
Argon	Filling light bulbs	It is unreactive and so the filament does not burn away

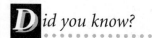

id you know?

Radon is a radioactive gas that is slowly given off by certain rocks such as granite. Houses built on granite can build up dangerous levels of radon in the rooms if they are not well ventilated. If too much radon is breathed in, it can cause lung cancer.

uestions

3.8 Explain why the inert gases do not react with other elements.

3.9 Use Table 3.6 to plot a graph showing how the boiling points of the inert gases change as the proton number increases. Explain the general shape of the curve. Use the curve to predict the boiling point of the inert gas radon (proton number 86).

The transition metals

The transition metals are found in the centre block of the Periodic Table. Although they are not all in the same Group like the halogens or the alkali metals, they all have similar properties and so it is useful to study them together. Table 3.8 shows some of the properties of the first row of transition metals.

■ **Table 3.8 The first row of transition metals.**

Name	Symbol	Melting point (°C)	Boiling point (°C)	Density (g cm^{-3})
Scandium	Sc	1540	2730	3.0
Titanium	Ti	1675	3260	4.5
Vanadium	V	1900	3000	6.0
Chromium	Cr	1890	2482	7.2
Manganese	Mn	1240	2100	7.2
Iron	Fe	1535	3000	7.9
Cobalt	Co	1492	2900	8.9
Nickel	Ni	1453	2730	8.9
Copper	Cu	1083	2595	8.9
Zinc	Zn	420	907	7.1

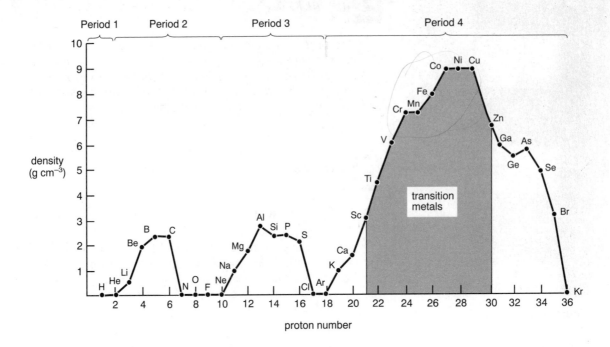

These metals are much more dense than other elements you have studied. The graph in Figure 3.14 shows this clearly. It also shows how density is a **periodic property** of elements. What this means is that there is a pattern of densities increasing and then decreasing across each Period. This pattern is then repeated across the next Period.

Other physical properties such as melting and boiling points show a similar periodic change. Try plotting similar graphs for these using the data in Table 1.2 on page 15.

Transition metals form coloured compounds. Table 3.9 shows a number of compounds that are well known, together with the transition metal present in them and also their colour.

■ **Table 3.9 Colours of some transition metal compounds.**

Name	Formula	Colour
Potassium chromate	K_2CrO_4	Yellow
Potassium manganate(VII)	$KMnO_4$	Purple
Iron(II) chloride	$FeCl_2$	Green
Copper(II) sulphate	$CuSO_4 \cdot 5H_2O$	Blue
Iron(III) chloride	$FeCl_3$	Orange/brown
Cobalt(II) chloride	$CoCl_2$	Blue
Khaki dye (iron)	–	Brown
Haemoglobin in blood (iron)	–	Red

The presence of transition metal compounds in some natural crystals causes them to have attractive colours which makes them

Figure 3.15 The precious stones in this necklace are coloured by the presence of transition metal compounds. The stones are set in gold, a transition metal. Transition metals are very resistant to corrosion.

valuable as gemstones. The colours in jewels such as sapphire, emerald and amethyst are all caused by transition metals (see Figure 3.15).

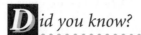

The colour of hair is caused by the presence of transition metal compounds in the hair. Brown hair contains iron or copper compounds, blonde hair contains compounds of titanium and if you are a redhead, it is because of the presence of molybdenum compounds.

Uses of transition metals

Two properties of transition metals make them very useful. They are usually hard and strong and they are not easily corroded. For this reason they are very widely used and you will learn more about this in the next chapter.

One important use of many transition elements is as catalysts in many industrial processes. A catalyst is a substance that speeds up a chemical reaction. The catalyst helps the reaction to take place without itself being changed. Most industrial processes use catalysts. Many of the catalysts are kept secret by the companies that invented them. Table 3.10 lists some industrial reactions and the catalysts that are used in them.

■ **Table 3.10 Catalysts used in some industrial processes.**

Process	Transition metal in catalyst
Making ammonia	Iron
Making sulphuric acid	Vanadium
Making nitric acid	Platinum
Making margarine	Nickel
Making polythene	Titanium

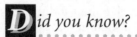

Many countries now require by law that exhaust fumes from vehicles should not contain substances that cause pollution of the air. To destroy these substances produced by the engine, a transition metal catalyst is placed in the exhaust pipe. The transition metal in the catalyst is platinum. The catalyst breaks down oxides of nitrogen and also helps any unburned hydrocarbons to change to carbon dioxide and water.

3.10 What are the transition metals? List their characteristic properties.

3.11 How does the reactivity of the transition metals change **a** across Periods and **b** down Groups?

Predicting properties of elements using the Periodic Table

The Periodic Table can be most useful in predicting properties of elements. You have already seen how accurately Mendeleev himself predicted the properties of germanium which had not then been discovered.

Investigation 3.6

Predict some of the properties of the halogen astatine, which is below iodine in Group VII. You might need to look back at some of the properties of halogens. Copy and complete Table 3.11 about the element.

■ **Table 3.11 Properties of astatine.**

Property	Astatine
Metal or non-metal	
Solid, liquid or gas	
Colour	
Appearance and properties of compound with hydrogen	
Appearance and properties of compound with sodium	
Reaction with iron	
Reactivity compared with iodine	

Did you make these predictions? Astatine will be a dark-coloured solid which will react slowly with iron when heated. It will be less reactive than iodine. It will form a white, crystalline compound with sodium that is soluble in water. The compound with hydrogen will be a gas which is very soluble in water giving an acid solution.

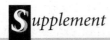

Supplement

Other families of elements

The kinds of trends that have been studied in Groups I, VII and VIII are also present in the other Groups. There are also patterns that can be seen if we look at elements across a Period. Table 3.12 shows the formulae and properties of the oxides of the elements of the third Period, sodium to argon.

It is easy to see trends in the formulae of the oxides, and trends in the reactions of the oxides as you go across the period.

With information like this, together with knowledge of trends in groups at both ends of the Periodic Table, it is possible to make predictions about many other elements that you have not studied.

■ Table 3.12 Properties of oxides across Period 3.

Element	Group	Formula of oxide	Properties of oxide
Sodium	I	Na_2O	White crystalline solid, soluble in water to give an alkaline solution
Magnesium	II	MgO	White crystalline solid, slightly soluble in water to give an alkaline solution
Aluminium	III	Al_2O_3	White crystalline solid, insoluble in water
Silicon	IV	SiO_2	White solid with giant covalent structure, insoluble in water
Phosphorus	V	P_2O_5	White solid with covalent structure which reacts with water to give an acid solution
Sulphur	VI	SO_2	Gas, soluble in water to give an acid solution
Chlorine	VII	Cl_2O	Unstable gas which reacts with water to give an acid solution
Argon	VIII	–	Does not form an oxide

Using Table 3.12, predict some of the properties of the Group II oxide calcium oxide, and the oxide of the Group VII element selenium.

Did you predict these properties?

• You would expect calcium oxide to have a formula CaO, like magnesium oxide. It should be a white solid and be only sparingly soluble in water to give an alkaline solution.

• Selenium dioxide, SeO_2, might be a gas which dissolves in water to give an acid solution.

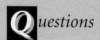uestions

3.12 Strontium is in Period 4 of Group II, the same Group as magnesium. What is the symbol for the strontium ion?

3.13 What would you expect to happen if you heated some strontium in a flame? Write an equation for the reaction.

3.14 What would you expect to happen if you put a piece of strontium in water? Write an equation for the reaction.

3.15 Strontium reacts readily with chlorine. What is the name, formula and colour of strontium chloride? Would you expect it to be soluble in water?

Give reasons for all your answers.

Review questions on this chapter can be found on pages 238–9.

4 *Metals*

Metals are extremely useful materials. In order to make the best use of them, we must understand their properties. We also need to know how to extract them from their ores without doing too much damage to the environment. In this chapter you will study the physical and chemical properties of metals and what use we make of them.

Metals around us

Figure 4.1 shows some uses of metals. You can think of many more. Think about what properties of metals made them useful for making the metal parts in the picture. The wires carrying electricity are made mainly out of aluminium because aluminium is light, it is a good conductor of electricity and it does not corrode much in air. Yet the pylons that carry the wires are made out of steel and not aluminium. Why is this?

Look carefully at the surface of a piece of new galvanised iron. Galvanised iron is made out of thin steel which has been dipped in molten zinc. The coating of zinc prevents the iron from rusting. When it is new, you can see that the zinc is not one smooth coat but is a lot of small patches (called grains). Each patch is a single crystal of zinc spread out on the iron. In each crystal, the zinc atoms are arranged in rows and the rows are arranged in layers like the ions in an ionic crystal. However, there are some important differences between ionic crystals and metal crystals and these explain the differences in the properties between ionic and metal crystals.

■ **Figure 4.2** This photomicrograph shows crystals of zinc.

■ **Figure 4.1** Electricity pylons.

Metals usually have:
- high melting points
- high boiling points
- high densities

Metals usually are:
- good conductors of electricity
- good conductors of heat
- easily pulled out into wires (ductile)
- easily hammered into different shapes (malleable)

■ **Figure 4.3** Some physical properties of metals.

To understand more about the properties of metals, we have to know more about the atoms that make up the metals. The *chemical* properties of the metals depend on the arrangement of the *electrons* in the metal atoms. The *physical* properties of the metals depend on the way the atoms are arranged together in the metal crystals of the metal and also on the size of the metal crystals. Figure 4.2 shows crystals in a metal greatly magnified.

What are the physical properties of metals that make them so useful to us (see Figure 4.3) ?

Melting and boiling points

If a substance has a high melting point, it means that a lot of energy is needed to pull the particles of the substance apart. Metal atoms are held strongly together. This means that a lot of energy is needed to pull the ions apart and so metals have high melting and boiling points as shown in Table 4.1.

■ **Table 4.1 Physical properties of metals.**

Metal	Density (g cm^{-3})	Melting point (°C)	Boiling point (°C)
Aluminium	2.7	659	2447
Gold	19.3	1063	2600
Iron	7.9	1540	3000
Magnesium	1.7	650	1110
Tungsten	19.4	3410	5930
Zinc	7.1	420	908

 id you know?

Filaments of electric light bulbs are made out of tungsten because it has a particularly high melting point. The filament must be white hot but it must not melt.

Density

Because the metal atoms are held together very strongly, the atoms are packed close together and so metals have a high density. As you can see from Table 4.1, most metals have a high density compared with typical non-metallic elements and compounds (remember that the density of water, for example, is 1 g cm^{-3}).

Some metals, like aluminium and magnesium, have a relatively low density. Sodium has an even lower density; it floats on water and this tells us that its density is less than 1 g cm^{-3}. As you discovered in the last chapter, the lower density metals are all on the left-hand side of the Periodic Table whereas the ones with higher densities are all transition metals. The metals with the lower densities in Groups I and II are also all rather reactive, which is a pity because we often need to use metals that are light for making such things as electricity cables and aircraft parts. In the section on *alloys* later in this chapter, you will find out how we can design metals that are both light in weight and unreactive.

Electrical conductivity

An electric current in a metal is caused by electrons moving through the metal. This can happen because the outer electrons in the metal atoms easily become detached from the atoms. These electrons can then move away from the negative terminal in a circuit and towards the positive terminal.

Table 4.2 shows that some metals are much better conductors than others. The good conductors are useful for making electrical wires and components. The filament of an electric fire is made from a metal mixture called nichrome which has a rather poor conductivity. This means that it has a fairly high resistance and so it gets hots as the current passes through it. Can you think of two reasons why we do not make electric cables out of iron?

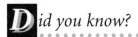

*D*id you know?

The elements such as silicon and germanium in the centre of the Periodic Table are known as semiconductors. They do not conduct as well as metals but they are much better conductors than non-metals. Very pure crystalline silicon is the basis of modern electronic 'chips'.

Conductivity of heat

Heat is quickly conducted through a solid when the particles are close together. This allows the kinetic energy in a vibrating particle to be passed on to the next particle easily when the two hit each other. In a metal this energy can also be transferred by the moving electrons and so metals are the best solid conductors of heat.

Malleability and ductility

The bonds holding the ions together in a crystal of sodium chloride are strong but they are also rigid. The bonds between metal atoms are also strong but not rigid. Because of this, if you hit a crystal of sodium chloride with a hammer it will crush, but if you hit a metal with a hammer it will not crush, it will deform. Figure 4.4 shows what happens. The layers of atoms do not move apart, they slide over each other. After they have moved, the close-packed structure is still there. This is also what happens when a metal is pulled out into a wire.

It is much easier to hammer a metal into a different shape when it is hot than when it is cold. When the metal is hot, the particles have more energy and are vibrating faster and further away from each other. It is easier to push them over each other when this is happening.

■ **Table 4.2 Electrical conductivities of substances.**

Substances	Conductivities (mho)
Aluminium	3.7×10^7
Copper	5.9×10^7
Nichrome	9.0×10^5
Silver	6.3×10^7
Iron	1.1×10^7
Silicon	4.3×10^{-4}
Glass	10^{-10} to 10^{-14}

The larger the number, the better the conductivity.

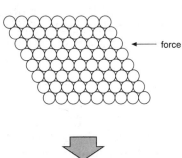

← force

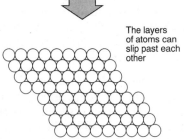

The layers of atoms can slip past each other

■ **Figure 4.4** Metal particles before and after hammering.

Questions

4.1 Explain the words *ductile* and *malleable*.

4.2 You are given a sample of an element you have never heard of before. Describe three tests you could do to find out if it is a metal or a non-metal.

4.3 Explain why metals are good conductors of electricity and have high densities and melting points.

4.4 Mercury is an unusual metal because it is a liquid at room temperature. Explain why it is particularly useful in thermometers and for making electrical switches for high voltages where sparking could easily occur.

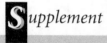

The metallic bond

Metal atoms are held strongly together by what are called **metallic bonds** (see Figure 4.5). The outer electrons of each metal atom in the crystal can move around freely between the atoms. This means that the metal is made of rows of positive ions surrounded by a 'sea' of moving electrons. This 'sea' of (negative) electrons attracts the positive ions strongly together.

The metallic bond explains a number of the properties of metals.

Because the atoms are held together very strongly, they are close together and a lot of energy is needed to pull them apart. This explains why the melting points and densities of most metals are high. If you look at Table 4.1 on page 65, you can see that metals with a rather low density also have rather low melting points. Can you explain this?

We know that an electric current in a metal is caused by electrons moving through the metal. This can happen because the outer

■ **Figure 4.5** Metallic bonding.

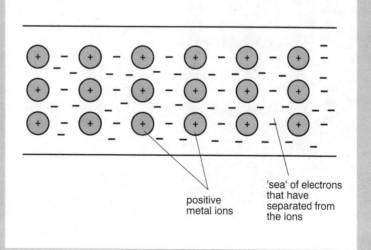

positive
metal ions

'sea' of electrons
that have
separated from
the ions

electrons in the metal atoms easily become detached from the atoms to form the 'sea' of electrons. These electrons will then move away from the negative terminal in a circuit and towards the positive terminal. The moving electrons can also take heat energy through the metal and so metals are good conductors of heat.

It is the 'sea' of electrons that makes the metallic bond strong but not rigid and so it will deform, not crush when it is hit.

Questions

4.5 Explain how metals can conduct electricity.

4.6 Metals that conduct electricity well usually also conduct heat well. Explain why this is so.

A pattern of metals – the reactivity series

magnesium
calcium

■ **Figure 4.6** Gold mask from the Egyptian tomb of Tutankhamen.

Figure 4.6 shows a metal mask made over 3000 years ago and yet it looks almost new. This is because it is made of gold, which does not react with air, water or dilute acids. However, very few metals are this unreactive. The reactivity of metals can easily be investigated.

Investigation 4.1

How do metals react with air and oxygen?

You will need:

- gas jars of oxygen
- combustion spoon
- burner
- steel wool
- samples of the metals calcium, copper, iron (wool), magnesium, zinc.

1 Clean the samples of metals with steel wool until they shine and then leave them for a few days and look at them again.

2 Heat a small quantity of a metal on a combustion spoon in air. When it is hot, lower it carefully into a gas jar of oxygen as shown in Figure 4.7.

CARE Some of these metals may burn with a very hot flame. Take care not to touch the sides of the jar with the burning metal or it may crack.

Unlike the gold mask, most metals will tarnish when they are left in air; the surface gradually becomes dull. This is because the metal slowly reacts with oxygen in the air. The metals react much faster with pure oxygen, particularly if they are heated. Many metals will react with oxygen under these conditions. The investigation shows that some metals react more vigorously with oxygen than others.

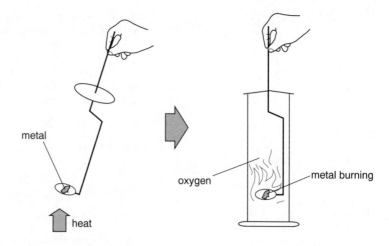

■ **Figure 4.7** Burning metals in oxygen.

• Sodium, potassium, calcium and magnesium will burn in air and will burn very brightly in oxygen. Sodium and potassium are stored under oil because they react so readily with the oxygen in the air.

• Aluminium, zinc and iron will also burn in oxygen if they are in the form of a powder or a 'wool'.

• Copper will not burn but it becomes covered in a black coating.

In all these cases the product of the reaction is the metal oxide.

The reaction can be represented by an equation such as this.

Magnesium + oxygen → magnesium oxide

$$2Mg(s) + O_2(g) \rightarrow 2MgO(s)$$

Many metals will react with water. In the last chapter you studied the reaction of Group I metals with water. In the next investigation you will study more metals.

_I_nvestigation 4.2

How do metals react with water?

You will need:

• samples of the metals calcium, copper, iron (nails), magnesium, zinc

• test tubes

• steel wool.

1 Clean the metals carefully with steel wool.

2 Leave sample of metals in test tubes of water for several days. Some metals will react quite rapidly with water but others take some time and still others show no signs of a reaction even after several weeks.

3 Record your observations over several days in a table.

magnesium
calcium

Not all metals react with water and some react much faster than others. Table 4.3 summarises the results.

In all these reactions the water is split up by the metal. You may have noticed bubbles of a gas in many of the reactions. You can show that the bubbles are hydrogen gas by bringing a flame near to the test tube. A small explosion can be heard.

The reaction can be represented by an equation like this:

Calcium + water → calcium hydroxide + hydrogen

$$Ca(s) + 2HOH(l) \rightarrow Ca(OH)_2(s) + H_2(g)$$

The equation shows how the metal splits up the water, combining with part of it to form the white solid calcium hydroxide ($Ca(OH)_2$) and releasing the hydrogen. (The formula of water has been written as HOH and not H_2O to make this clearer.)

■ **Table 4.3 Reactions between metals and water.**

Metal	Reaction
Potassium	Reacts very rapidly with water. It floats on the water and the heat of the reaction causes it to melt into a ball which skims across the surface getting smaller as it reacts. Will burn if it is placed on a piece of ice
Sodium	As potassium but will not burn on contact with ice
Calcium	Reacts rapidly with water producing bubbles of hydrogen
Magnesium	Reacts slowly with cold water. After a few minutes a few bubbles can be seen on the metal surface. Will burn in steam
Zinc and iron	Will show signs of reacting with water after a few days. Can be made to burn in steam
Aluminium	Will not react with water but if your water is rather impure, some corrosion may be seen
Copper	Will not react at all with water

*I*nvestigation 4.3

How do metals react with dilute acids?

You will need:

- samples of the metals calcium, copper, iron (nails), magnesium, zinc
- dilute hydrochloric acid
- test tubes.

magnesium
calcium

dilute
hydrochloric acid

The reaction between metals and acids can be investigated in the same way as with water. Place a piece of the metal in dilute acid and observe what happens. (**CARE** The reaction between alkali metals such as sodium and potassium with acids is so vigorous that it is dangerous and should not be tried.)

When the metal reacts with the acid, hydrogen is produced. The reaction is exothermic. The amount of heat that is given off depends on how reactive the metal is. The reaction between metals and acid is very similar to the reaction with water but more vigorous.

The reaction can be represented by an equation like this.

Zinc + hydrochloric acid → zinc chloride + hydrogen

$$Zn(s) + 2HCl(aq) \rightarrow ZnCl_2(aq) + H_2(g)$$

You will learn in the next chapter that all acids – and water – contain hydrogen. You can see from the equation that the metal replaces the hydrogen in the acid. A substance called a salt is formed. The salt in this case is zinc chloride.

We can summarise the reactions of common metals with oxygen, water and acids in Table 4.4.

■ **Table 4.4 The reactivity series for metals.**

Metal	Reaction with oxygen in air	Reaction with cold water	Reaction with steam	Reaction with dilute hydrochloric acid	Symbol
Potassium Sodium Calcium	Burn in air on heating to form the metal oxide	React with cold water to form hydrogen and the metal hydroxide	React with steam to form hydrogen and the metal oxide	Violent reaction to give hydrogen	K Na Ca
Magnesium	Do not burn but react to form the metal oxide on heating			React to form hydrogen and the chloride of the metal	Mg
Zinc Iron		React slowly with cold water			Zn Fe
Lead Copper		Do not react with cold water	Do not react with steam	Do not react	Pb Cu

The table shows that, for each of these reactions, the **order of reactivity** of the metals is the same. We call this the **reactivity series** for metals. You can see a pattern in this reactivity series. The most reactive metals are those in Group I of the Periodic Table. The next in the series are the Group II metals. The transition metals are among the least reactive metals.

Can you also see that, in Groups I and II, the reactivity increases down the Group? You will remember this from Chapter 3 on the Periodic Table. Where would you place the metal caesium in the reactivity series?

Aluminium has not been included in the series because, as you have found, it seems to be unreactive and yet it is not a transition metal. We will come back to aluminium later in the chapter.

Something to think about

The metals at the bottom of Table 4.4 have been known and used for thousands of years. The ones at the top were first extracted in the 19th century. Can you think why this should be so? The answer will be given later in the chapter.

 uestions

4.7 What is meant by the reactivity series?

4.8 Titanium is a metal that reacts quite rapidly with acids but hardly at all with water or steam. Where would you place titanium on the reactivity series?

4.9 a Look at the reactivity series (see Table 4.4). Then look at the Periodic Table. Can you see any similarities?

b Barium is low down in Group II. Where would you place it on the reactivity series?

c Describe two experiments you could do with barium to find out whether you have put it in the correct place. What results do you predict for your experiments?

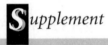 upplement

How readily will a metal form its positive ion?

Look at all the reactions of metals you have studied. In every case when the metal has reacted, it has formed an ionic compound containing the positive ion of the metal. Think of the reaction between zinc and dilute hydrochloric acid.

$$Zn(s) + 2HCl(aq) \rightarrow ZnCl_2(aq) + H_2(g)$$

In this reaction zinc atoms have become zinc ions.

$$Zn \rightarrow Zn^{2+} + 2e^-$$

What has happened to the two electrons? The equation shows that two hydrogen ions in the acid change into a hydrogen molecule. Hydrogen ions have no electrons but the hydrogen molecule has two. The electrons from the zinc have been given to the hydrogen

$$2H^+ + 2e^- \rightarrow H_2$$

Copper is near the bottom of the reactivity series. This means that, unlike zinc, copper atoms will not readily give up their electrons to form copper ions. The reactivity series (Figure 4.8) therefore shows us how readily metals will give up electrons to form ions.

The next two investigations will illustrate this further.

Figure 4.8 Reactivity series showing tendency of metals to form positive ions.

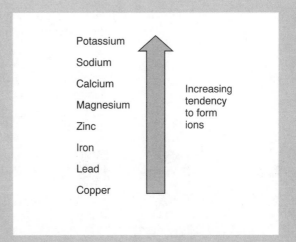

Potassium

Sodium

Calcium

Magnesium

Zinc

Iron

Lead

Copper

Increasing tendency to form ions

magnesium

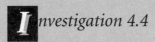 *nvestigation 4.4*

Will metals react with solutions of the ions of other metals?

You will need:

• samples of the metals copper, iron (nails), magnesium, zinc

• solutions of compounds containing the four metals, that is, solutions of the four metal ions

• test tubes.

1 Put a piece of zinc in a small sample of the solution of copper ions. Watch carefully for any reaction.

2 At the same time put a piece of copper in a solution of zinc ions and watch it carefully.

3 Do the same with all the possible combinations of metals and ions and write the results in a table (metals down the side and ions across the top).

You will have seen that, when the metal you used was higher in the reactivity series than the ion, there was a reaction but when it was lower, nothing happened. When you put zinc in the solution of copper ions, you saw copper forming on the zinc. You may also have noticed that the blue (or green) colour of the solution became fainter. This is because the zinc atoms were forming ions and dissolving in the solution and the copper ions (responsible for the blue colour) in the solution were forming atoms. Zinc and copper compete to form ions and the zinc, being more reactive, wins. The equations show what happens:

$$Cu^{2+} + 2e^- \rightarrow Cu$$

$$Zn \rightarrow Zn^{2+} + 2e^-$$

or, combining them:

$$Cu^{2+} + Zn \rightarrow Cu + Zn^{2+}$$

On the other hand, when you put copper into the solution of zinc ions, nothing happened:

$$Cu + Zn^{2+} \rightarrow \text{No reaction}$$

lead nitrate solution

silver nitrate solution

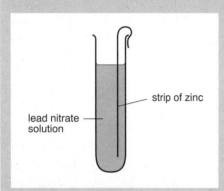

Figure 4.9 The reaction between zinc and lead nitrate solution.

strip of zinc

lead nitrate solution

Investigation 4.4 (continued)

You will need:

- strips of zinc and copper
- solutions of lead nitrate and silver nitrate
- test tubes.

4 Set up a tube of lead nitrate solution with a strip of clean zinc dipping in it. Place it on one side and do not disturb it. Watch the crystals of lead growing (see Figure 4.9).

5 For even better crystals, try a strip of zinc or copper dipping into a solution of silver nitrate.

These two reactions show not only that more reactive metals will displace less reactive ones from solution but that metals are naturally crystalline. The crystals of lead and silver can clearly be seen growing in these experiments.

Write equations for the other reactions you observed.

Investigation 4.5

magnesium powder
zinc powder

Will metals react with the oxides of other metals?

You will need:

- tin lid
- safety spectacles
- burner
- magnesium, zinc, iron and copper in powder form
- magnesium, zinc, iron and copper oxides.

Be very careful with the powders as the more reactive metal powders can catch fire easily. (Always remember to replace the storage bottle top after you have taken small samples out.)

1 Mix together equal amounts of zinc powder and copper oxide so that you have about as much of the mixture as would cover a small coin. Put the mixture on a tin lid and heat it strongly from below. (Remember to wear your safety spectacles.) Watch what happens.

2 Do the same with a mixture of zinc oxide and copper. Can you predict what will happen when you heat it?

3 Repeat the experiment with all the other mixtures you can make and write the results down in a table similar to the one in the last investigation.

Some of these mixtures will react very vigorously and leave behind a lump of molten metal. As before, you will observe that, when the metal you used was higher in the reactivity series than the metal in the oxide, there will be a reaction but when it is lower, nothing happens. This can be shown using equations:

$$Zn + CuO \rightarrow ZnO + Cu \quad \text{reaction}$$

But

$$Cu + ZnO \rightarrow \text{no reaction}$$

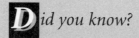id you know?

A form of this reaction, using aluminium powder and iron oxide, was once used for welding tram lines in the days before portable oxy-acetylene torches. The lump of molten iron produced welded the lines. The mixture was called the 'thermit' mixture.

How stable are metal compounds?

Some metal compounds are very stable but others are easily decomposed by heat. The next activity shows this. Look at the results and see if there is a pattern related to the Periodic Table.

potassium nitrate

*I*nvestigation 4.6

Heating some metal compounds

You will need:
- copper nitrate
- magnesium or calcium nitrate
- sodium or potassium nitrate
- test tubes
- burner
- spill.

Test for oxygen
Light a spill. Blow it out so that it is glowing. Put it in the gas. If the spill relights, the gas is oxygen.

1 Take a *small* amount copper nitrate in a test tube and heat it. Watch carefully what happens. Test any gas evolved with a glowing spill. The test for oxygen gas is that it will relight a glowing spill put into it.

2 Repeat the same experiment with calcium or magnesium nitrate. You will have to heat these nitrates much more to see a reaction.

3 Repeat the experiment a third time with sodium or potassium nitrate. This time the reaction will be different. You may notice that the crystals still break up if you heat very strongly and if you put a glowing spill in the tube, it will relight.

In the first two experiments you will see a brown gas coming off as the crystals decompose. This gas, nitrogen dioxide, has a very unpleasant smell and is rather poisonous, so do not continue heating for long. Note that the substance left behind in the first experiment is black; it is copper oxide. The oxide is also produced in the second experiment but in the third one the substance left behind is called sodium nitrite.

In all three reactions you should also be able to detect oxygen being given off.

The reactions that occur when nitrates are heated can be summarised in these equations:

$$2Cu(NO_3)_2(s) \rightarrow 2CuO(s) + 4NO_2(g) + O_2(g)$$

$$2Mg(NO_3)_2(s) \rightarrow 2MgO(s) + 4NO_2(g) + O_2(g)$$

$$2NaNO_3(s) \rightarrow 2NaNO_2(s) + O_2(g)$$

This work shows that the nitrates become less stable down the reactivity series. It also shows that Group I nitrates decompose in a different way from the nitrates of Group II and transition metals. These decompose to the oxide giving off both oxygen and nitrogen dioxide whereas Group I nitrates do not lose nitrogen dioxide.

We can obtain similar results if we heat the hydroxides of the metals. Group I hydroxides are stable to heat but the others decompose to the oxide and water. The hydroxides of the transition metals near the bottom of the reactivity series decompose most easily.

The results for all these experiments are summarised in Table 4.5.

■ **Table 4.5 The effect of heating some metal hydroxides and nitrates.**

	Group I metals	Group II metals	Transition metals
Nitrates	Decompose to nitrite and oxygen	Decompose to oxide, nitrogen dioxide and oxygen	Decompose easily to the oxide, nitrogen dioxide and oxygen
Hydroxides	No effect on heating	Decompose to oxide and water	Decompose easily to oxide and water

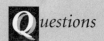
4.10 If some zinc is placed in a solution of manganese sulphate, there is a reaction and manganese metal is produced. If manganese is placed in a solution of iron(II) sulphate, iron is produced. Where would you place manganese on the reactivity series? Explain your answer.

4.11 What would you expect to see if you put some copper in silver nitrate solution? What would happen to the colour of the solution? Explain your answers.

4.12 Nickel is just above copper in the reactivity series whereas scandium is just below magnesium. Describe what you would expect to see if you heated the nitrates and the hydroxides of scandium and nickel.

Getting metals from their ores

Figure 4.10 This uranium mine in Gabon shows how large scale quarrying for ores can cause serious damage to the environment.

We obtain the metals we need from rock which contains them (see Figure 4.10). We call the rock that contains the metal the **ore**. Ores often have strange sounding names; haematite is an important ore of iron, galena is a lead ore and bauxite is an ore of aluminium.

There are three steps in the process of obtaining metals from their ores:

- mining and concentrating the ore
- reducing the ore to the metal
- refining the metal further if this is needed (as in the case of copper).

Mining and concentrating the ore

Often the amount of ore in the rock is so low that it has to be separated from the other minerals and concentrated before it can be extracted. Most of the rock is therefore not wanted. It is often possible to get rid of much of the unwanted material by physical processes like **flotation**. In this process the crushed rock is mixed with a mixture of oils and water. The mixture is carefully designed so that the particles of the ore stay floating but the impurities, such as sand, sink to the bottom. The ore particles are held in the liquid by electrostatic forces.

Because most rocks only contain a small amount of the metal, quarries are often very large, as shown in the picture. The process of extracting the metal leaves a lot of waste and this is often poisonous to plants. This means that extracting metals can do much damage to the environment.

Some metals occur uncombined in nature. Gold is one of these. The uncombined gold is sometimes washed down rivers and is found in river beds. It can be extracted by an old process called 'panning'. The crushed material from the river bed is washed in running water. The impurities are washed away and the very dense pieces of gold are left behind.

Reducing the ore to the metal

There are three important ways of doing this:

- heating the ore
- heating the ore with carbon
- electrolysis of the molten ore.

Heating the ore is only possible with certain metals. Mercury is an example. The common ore of mercury is mercury sulphide (called cinnabar). When it is heated in air, the sulphur combines with the oxygen leaving mercury behind.

Some copper ores can be treated in the same way. This is possible when the ore contains copper sulphide. Heating the ore produces copper and sulphur dioxide.

The equation shows what happens.

Copper sulphide + oxygen → copper + sulphur dioxide

$$CuS(s) + O_2(g) \rightarrow Cu(s) + SO_2(g)$$

Heating the ore with carbon is the most common method of extracting metals from their ores. The ores are the oxides of the metals. The form of carbon used in earlier times was charcoal. There are remains of furnaces all over the world which used charcoal. These furnaces were used to make lead, tin or iron. In modern times, instead of charcoal we use coke, a form of carbon made from coal. The process is called **smelting** the ore.

The ore is heated with the carbon in the furnace. The heat comes from the carbon which burns. One of the products of the burning of carbon is carbon monoxide. It is this carbon monoxide that reacts with the ore and changes it to the metal. The carbon monoxide combines with the oxygen in the metal ore and the metal is left behind.

The equation shows the reaction with iron oxide.

Iron oxide + carbon monoxide → carbon dioxide + iron

$$Fe_2O_3(s) + 3CO(g) \rightarrow 3CO_2(g) + 2Fe(l)$$

This process is called the **reduction** of the ore to the metal and carbon monoxide is called the **reducing agent**.

From earliest times limestone has been added to the reduction furnace. It helps to remove impurities from the ore. Limestone forms calcium oxide in the furnace and this is basic and will react with any acidic impurities in the ore. A common acidic impurity is sand, silicon dioxide. This forms calcium silicate which melts and can be run off at the bottom of the furnace.

Limestone (calcium carbonate) → calcium oxide + carbon dioxide

Calcium oxide + silicon dioxide → calcium silicate

$$CaCO_3(s) \rightarrow CaO(s) + CO_2(g)$$
$$CaO(s) + SiO_2(s) \text{ (sand)} \rightarrow CaSiO_3(s) \text{ (calcium silicate)}$$

Not all ores are in the form of oxides. Some are sulphides (such as galena, lead sulphide) and others are carbonates. These ores are heated in air first to convert them to the oxides. The oxides are then reduced with carbon. You can see from the equation below that the process of heating a sulphide ore in air produces sulphur dioxide. This is an unpleasant choking gas which damages plants and buildings as well as being poisonous to animals. The furnaces in which the sulphide ore is heated always have high chimneys so that the sulphur dioxide can be carried a long way in the air before it finally returns to the ground (see Figure 4.11).

These equations show how some ores are converted into the metal oxides by heating in air:

Lead sulphide + oxygen → lead oxide + sulphur dioxide

Zinc carbonate → zinc oxide + carbon dioxide

$$2PbS(s) + 3O_2(g) \rightarrow 2PbO(s) + 2SO_2(g)$$
$$ZnCO_3(s) \rightarrow ZnO(s) + CO_2(g)$$

Electrolysis of the molten ore is the process used to smelt ores that cannot be reduced by carbon. Metals such as sodium, magnesium and aluminium are extracted instead by electrolysis of a molten compound. Sodium, for example, is obtained by electrolysing molten sodium chloride.

As you will discover in Chapter 6, if an electric current is passed through an electrolyte, ions in the electrolyte are converted into atoms and so these elements appear at the electrodes.

Aluminium is made by electrolysing molten aluminium oxide and so the two products of the electrolysis are aluminium and oxygen. Aluminium appears at the cathode (negative electrode) and oxygen is collected at the anode. This process is described in more detail later on in this chapter.

Extraction of metals and the reactivity series

Look back at the reactivity series for metals on page 71. Can you see a pattern in the method used for extraction metals? Those metals that are least reactive form compounds that are easily broken down.

■ **Figure 4.11** This is the beginning of the flue (chimney) of an old lead smelter in England used 150 years ago to make lead from lead sulphide. The flue leaves the back of the furnace and runs along the ground for several kilometres to the top of a nearby hill. The long flue ensured that the sulphur dioxide from the smelter was taken well away. It also allowed lead vapour escaping from the furnace to condense in the soot. The flue was swept regularly (by small boys climbing inside it) and the soot was put back in the smelter.

This means that these metals are easily extracted. Those metals high in the reactivity series form strong bonds in their compounds. A lot of energy is needed to break these bonds. These metals are not extracted easily.

Table 4.6 summarises the methods used for extracting metals. You can see that the metals at the bottom of the reactivity series which can be extracted most easily have been known since ancient times. Notice also that these metals all have symbols taken from their Latin name (Fe – *ferrum*, Pb – *plumbum*, etc).

■ **Table 4.6 Reactivity series and method of extraction of metals.**

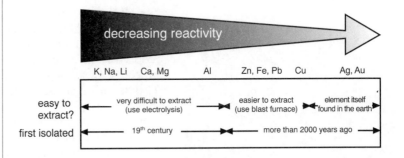

Questions

4.13 What method is most likely to be used for the extraction of the following metals:

a potassium

b zinc?

Give a reason for your answer.

4.14 Explain why copper smelters often have very tall chimneys and are often found in places where there are not many people.

4.15 Limestone is often added to the mixture in a furnace. Explain the reason for this.

4.16 List any environmental problems in your region caused by our use of metals. How could these problems be overcome?

Making iron and steel

Pure iron is very rare. It is rare for two reasons, firstly because it is very difficult to make and secondly it is not much use to us because it is very soft; a 1cm diameter bar can easily be bent by hand. When we talk about iron (such as when we talk about iron filings) we really mean steel. Steel is iron with a small percentage of carbon in it.

Steel is the most common and most useful metal. It is common partly because there is a lot of iron in the earth's crust (about 5% of the crust is iron) and partly because it is quite easy to extract. In 1990 we made 710 million tonnes of steel!

Extracting iron from iron ore

The iron is extracted using carbon in the form of coke heated either by electricity (the electric arc furnace, Figure 4.12) or by burning the coke (the blast furnace, Figure 4.13).

In the electric arc furnace the heat comes from the electrical sparks (arcs) jumping between large carbon electrodes lowered into the furnace. Scrap metal in the furnace helps the arcing process as it conducts electricity. The carbon from the electrodes burns away to form carbon monoxide which reduces the iron ore.

Carbon + oxygen $\rightarrow$ carbon monoxide

Carbon monoxide + iron oxide $\rightarrow$ iron + carbon dioxide

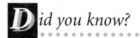

$$2C(s) + O_2(g) \rightarrow 2\,CO(g)$$
$$3CO(g) + Fe_2O_3(s) \rightarrow 2Fe(l) + 3CO_2(g)$$

In the blast furnace the reactions are the same but the heat is generated by burning coke (using a blast of air forced in near the bottom). Limestone is added to the contents of the furnace (called the 'charge') to react with impurities. Look back to page 78 for more about this reaction.

Look back to page 78 for more about this reaction.

D id you know?

A modern electric arc furnace takes a load of about 100–120 tonnes and consumes 70–90 megawatts at full power, which is about the same as a small town.

Because carbon is used in the extraction process, the metal that comes out of the blast furnace contains about 4% of dissolved carbon. It is called 'pig iron' or 'cast iron'. It is very hard but rather brittle. To make a more useful metal, steel, the amount of carbon in it must be reduced to between 0.5 and 2%. The electric arc furnace is used to make steel directly in one process as the amount of carbon that is allowed to enter the molten iron from the electrodes can be carefully controlled.

Converting pig iron from the blast furnace into steel

To make steel, the carbon in the pig iron is partly burnt away using oxygen in a basic oxygen furnace (see Figure 4.14). An oxygen pipe (called a lance) is put into the molten pig iron and exactly the right amount of oxygen is blown through. The carbon burns off at the top of the furnace in a very spectacular way. The molten metal is then poured out and cast into blocks called ingots. While the metal is in this furnace, any other additives can be put in to make 'special' steels. You will learn more about these later on in the chapter.

There are many different kinds of steel. The hardness of steel depends on how much carbon remains dissolved in it. To make steel for a particular purpose, it is important to know exactly how much

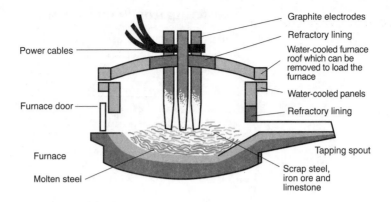

Figure 4.12 Electric arc furnace.

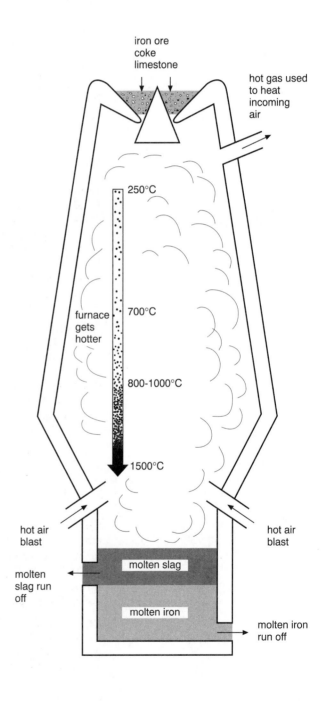

Figure 4.13 Blast furnace.

Figure 4.14 Basic oxygen furnace.

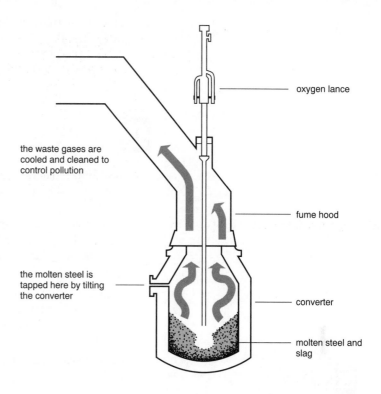

carbon there is in it and that is why exactly the right amount of oxygen is blown through the basic oxygen furnace so that not all the carbon is burnt off. Table 4.7 shows some steels and their uses.

■ Table 4.7 Uses of steels.

Kind of steel	What is added to the iron	Possible uses
Cast iron	4% carbon	Engine blocks, drain covers
Carbon steels		
Low carbon	Less than 0.3% carbon	Car bodies, rivets
Medium carbon	0.3–0.8% carbon	Railway lines, springs
High carbon	0.8–1.5% carbon	Knives, razor blades

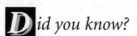 *id you know?*

The first bridge to be built of iron was constructed over the river Severn in England in 1779. It is made entirely out of cast iron and the place where it was built came to be known as Ironbridge. Because the techniques of welding and riveting were not known then, the kind of joints were those used in woodworking. The bridge is constructed in the form of an arch which makes use of the high *compressive* strength of cast iron. There is a picture of this bridge on page 45. Later steel bridges, such as the suspension bridge shown on page 1 (which also crosses the river Severn), make use of the high *tensile* strength of steel.

uestions

4.17 What materials are added to the blast furnace to make iron? Why does the product of the blast furnace contain 4% carbon?

4.18 How is the product of the blast furnace turned into steel? What are the advantages of the electric arc furnace over the older blast furnace for making steel?

4.19 What is the reducing agent in the blast furnace?

4.20 What is the purpose of the limestone added to the charge in the blast furnace and the electric arc furnace?

4.21 How do the properties of the steel depend on how much carbon is dissolved in it? Give one use for a high carbon steel (1.5% carbon) and one for a low carbon steel (0.3%).

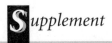upplement

Making zinc

The most common ore of zinc is called zinc blende and it is zinc sulphide. The sulphide ore is first converted to the oxide by roasting in air. This produces a lot of sulphur dioxide as an unpleasant by-product.

$$2ZnS(s) + 3O_2(g) \rightarrow 2ZnO(s) + 2SO_2(g)$$

The zinc oxide is then heated with coke to reduce it to zinc. Because zinc boils at only 913 °C it does not sink to the bottom of the furnace like iron but escapes with the waste gases as zinc vapour. The gases are cooled rapidly and the zinc condenses.

Zinc is usually extracted together with lead but the molten metals do not mix. The zinc floats on top of the lead and can be run off.

Zinc has many uses. It is used in ordinary torch cells where it is the case of the cell which is the negative terminal. It is also used to make a number of alloys (page 86). Perhaps the most important use of zinc is to coat steel to stop it rusting. This is a process called galvanising; clean sheets of iron are dipped into vats of molten zinc. The zinc stops the iron from rusting because it is more reactive than iron and so it reacts with air and water before the iron does. Only when all the zinc has corroded away does the iron underneath begin to rust badly.

Making aluminium

Aluminium is high on the reactivity series and is too reactive to be extracted with carbon. Instead electrolysis is used. However, aluminium oxide has a very high melting point (2015 °C) and so it is not possible to melt it easily. This is why aluminium was a very rare metal until quite recently when it was discovered that the oxide would dissolve in another aluminium compound called cryolite

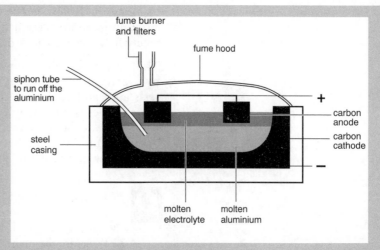

Figure 4.15 Electrolysis cell for producing aluminium.

(sodium aluminium fluoride) at a much lower temperature. This mixture is electrolysed in a cell with carbon electrodes (Figure 4.15).

The heat produced by the resistance of the electrolyte keeps the cell hot and molten aluminium collects at the bottom. This is siphoned off each day.

The reactions are these.

At the cathode $Al^{3+} + 3e^- \rightarrow Al$

At the anode $2O^{2-} \rightarrow O_2 + 4e^-$

The carbon anodes gradually burn away because the carbon reacts with the oxygen produced on them. They are replaced every 24 hours.

Because the electrolyte contains fluoride ions, the waste gases contain fluorine. This could cause damage to the surrounding countryside and so the gases are cleaned thoroughly before they leave the chimney.

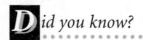 *id you know?*

The French Emperor in the early 1800s, Napoleon Bonaparte, had a very rare dinner set. It became well known because it was made of a metal much more expensive than silver. It was made out of aluminium! Aluminium was so expensive because it could not be extracted using electrolysis at that time. In 1990 we made around 25 million tonnes of aluminium. That would impress Napoleon.

If you look back at the reactivity series (Table 4.6, page 80) you will see that aluminium is quite high up. Aluminium *should* be a reactive metal, and yet it is not. It seems to be almost as unreactive as copper. The reason for this is that aluminium metal is always covered with a very thin layer of aluminium oxide. This layer of oxide is stuck firmly to the metal and is insoluble and unreactive and prevents further attack on the aluminium. This can be shown quite easily. If you remove the oxide coating by scratching the aluminium and putting it straight into some acid, it reacts quickly where it has been scratched.

This property of aluminium oxide is extremely useful. It allows us to use aluminium to make articles where lightness, corrosion resistance and good heat conductivity are important. The list of these articles is very long. It includes car engines, pans, kitchen foil, window frames and even some coins. If it were not for this property of aluminium oxide, all these items, left in air, would crumble into a hot heap of aluminium oxide in just a few minutes.

uestions

4.22 What are the main uses of aluminium?

4.23 Aluminium is high on the reactivity series and yet it is used to make items such as cooking pans which are often used with substances such as dilute acids and salt which cause corrosion of metals. Explain why aluminium can be used in this way.

4.24 Why is aluminium not extracted using a coke burning furnace?

4.25 The electrodes of the furnace used to make aluminium are made out of carbon. Why does the anode have to be replaced much more often than the cathode?

4.26 Much of our aluminium is made in countries such as Canada which have many hydro-electric power stations. Explain why this is so.

4.27 Zinc is not run off at the bottom of the furnace in which it is made. How is it removed? Why is it removed in this way?

Alloys

An alloy is a mixture of two or more metals. Alloys are useful because they often have properties that are different from the metals they are made out of. In particular, they are often stronger than the metals they are made out of. This allows us to take a rather weak, but light, metal, aluminium, and make it into a strong alloy with small amounts of other metals. The alloy, called duralumin, can be used to make aircraft (Figure 4.16).

It is quite easy to see how metals can be made stronger when they are mixed with a small amount of another metal which has atoms that are a different size. Figure 4.17 shows an alloy. Notice that the atom of the second metal is slightly larger than the atoms of the main metal. When a force is applied to the alloy at the point shown, the layers cannot move very far because the atom of the second metal stops them.

Copper is a very useful metal because it is resistant to corrosion. Unfortunately, it is rather soft and cannot be used for anything that requires strength. There are alloys of copper, however, which have the resistance to corrosion of copper but also have strength.

■ **Figure 4.16** Aircraft like this Boeing 747 which can carry over 400 passengers could not be made without the use of alloys.

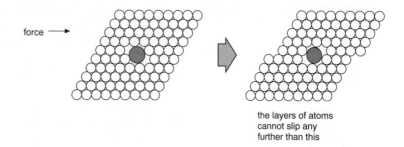

force →

the layers of atoms cannot slip any further than this

■ **Figure 4.17** An atom in an alloy preventing slipping of layers.

One alloy is bronze which is 97% copper and the remaining 3% tin and zinc. One important use for it is for casting ships' propellers which have to be very strong and be resistant to corrosion by the sea water. The second strong alloy of copper is brass.

Another way alloying makes the metal stronger is by making the individual metal crystals smaller. The atoms of the second metal prevent the metal forming large crystals as it cools because they stop the regular build-up of layers. The crystals are therefore smaller. Deforming can only happen inside a crystal. It cannot happen across the boundaries (called grain boundaries) between two crystals. This makes the alloy much stronger than the pure metal.

Table 4.8 shows some common alloys, their uses, and the metals they are made from.

Steel is the most widely used alloy. It is called an alloy even though the element mixed with the iron is not another metal but is the non-metal carbon. You have already seen on page 83 how the percentage of carbon in the steel alters its properties. These steels on page 83 contain only carbon and they are called 'carbon steels'. But we can mix steels with other metals to form 'alloy steels'. This allows us to make a great variety of steels with properties exactly suited to our needs. Table 4.9 shows some alloy steels.

■ **Table 4.8 Some alloys and their uses.**

Alloy	Main components	Some uses	Useful properties of alloy
Duralumin	Aluminium, copper, magnesium	Aeroplanes	Light and strong
Brass	Copper, zinc	Doorknobs, ornaments	Corrosion-resistant and hard Readily pressed into shapes
Bronze	Copper, tin	Ships' propellers, church bells, statues	Corrosion-resistant and hard Readily pressed into shapes
Cupro-nickel	Copper, nickel	'Silver' coins	Corrosion-resistant, looks like silver
Titanium alloy	Titanium, iron, carbon	Aeroplanes	Light and strong Low expansion when heated
Solder	Lead and zinc	Joining wires	Very low melting point (170 °C)

■ Table 4.9 Some alloy steels.

Type	Typical composition	Typical uses
Chromium steel	Up to 5% Cr	Ball bearings
Cobalt steel	Up to 10% Co	Magnets
Molybdenum steel	Up to 4% Mo	Gun barrels
Stainless steel	Often 18% Cr, 8% Ni	Sinks, cutlery
Tungsten steel	Up to 18% W	Tools, armour plate
Vanadium steel	Up to 2% V	Spanners, tools

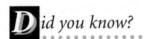

You do not have to add other metals to steel to make it harder. You can do it just by heating it. If you heat it up to red heat and then suddenly cool it by putting it in water, the surface becomes very hard. This is because, at red heat, the 'grains' (iron crystals) are small. When the steel is cooled suddenly, the grains do not have a chance to get bigger and a metal with small grains is hard because slippage of atoms cannot take place across the grain boundaries. This kind of hardening of steel is called 'case hardening'. Blacksmiths case harden horseshoes before they nail them on.

4.28 Pure iron (called wrought iron) is easily bent by hammering it when cold. Mild steel contains about 0.5% carbon and is much stronger but can be bent in a press and is used to make car bodies. Cast iron contains about 4% carbon and cannot be bent but breaks if hit hard. Explain how these different properties can arise.

4.29 Make a table showing the elements present in the following alloys. Show the use of each alloy in your table. Solder, bronze, duralumin, stainless steel, cupronickel.

4.30 Find out what the different coins in your country are made of. Why are they made of these alloys? Why are 'silver' and 'gold' coins no longer made of silver and gold?

Corrosion and its prevention

Metals left around in air become dull. Steel very often rusts. These processes are examples of corrosion. Corrosion of metals is an extremely expensive problem all over the world (see Figure 4.18). Much thought, time, effort and money is spent each year trying to prevent it.

In this investigation you will also give some thought to what causes it and which metals corrode the most.

■ **Figure 4.18** Some serious rusting.

magnesium

Investigation 4.7

What causes corrosion?

You will need:
- small steel nails
- magnesium ribbon
- copper turnings
- zinc granules
- steel wool or sandpaper
- jam jars or test tubes (one or two of which have tightly fitting lids)
- sodium chloride (salt)
- candle wax.

Experiment 1

1 Clean samples of all the metals with the steel wool.

2 Put some salt water in four jars and place a piece of a different metal in each. Set up another set with tap water. Set up a third set with no water at all.

3 Leave these jars for several days (or weeks). Look at them regularly and make a note of any change in the metals.

Experiment 2

4 Set up two jars containing a steel nail in each. The jars should have tightly fitting lids. One jar should contain water. The second jar should contain air only and should be as dry as you can make it. Warm it before screwing on the lid.

5 Boil some water in a test tube for several minutes. This will boil out as much as possible of the air dissolved in the water. Put a nail in the water before it cools. Add some candle wax (or oil). This will seal the water from the air by forming a layer at the top.

6 Leave these nails also for several days, noting any changes.

The first experiment will show:

- corrosion is worse if water is present than in dry air
- corrosion is much worse if the water is salty.

Corrosion is worse when the water is salty because the process is an ionic one. Reactions involving ions involve the movement of electrons; electrons can move better in salty water, which contains ions, than in pure water. We say that corrosion is an **electrolytic** process. You will learn more about this in Chapter 6.

The second experiment tells you something about the rusting of iron. (Rusting is the name given to the corrosion of iron.) The nail in the dry air does not rust at all. The nail in the water with no dissolved air does not rust either (there may be a little rust on it if you did not boil the water for long enough). The nail in both water and air will rust a lot. Rusting therefore needs both air (oxygen) and water to take place.

Preventing corrosion

There are two ways of preventing corrosion. The first is to prevent water and air getting to the metal by covering it with something such as paint or oil. The second method is to attach the metal to another that is more reactive. In this case the more reactive metal corrodes first. This is called 'sacrificial' protection, because the second metal is sacrificed to protect the first one. An example of sacrificial protection is galvanised iron which is coated with zinc. The zinc corrodes before the iron does. Table 4.10 shows examples of the prevention of corrosion by different methods.

■ **Table 4.10 Ways of preventing corrosion.**

Metal object	Method of preventing corrosion	Advantages of using this method
Car bodies	Paint	Easily applied, looks attractive
Bicycle chain	Oil	Protects moving parts – other coatings would wear off
Iron roofing	Galvanising. The steel is coated with a layer of zinc which corrodes away first	Long-lasting, easy to apply
Food can	Tin 'plating'. Steel is coated with a layer of tin	Tin does not easily corrode and is not poisonous
Silver plated cutlery	Silver electroplating (see Chapter 6)	The coating is very attractive, even, and hard-wearing

4.31 How would you prevent the following steel articles from rusting?

a A bicycle chain

b A car body

c A steel kettle

d A corrugated iron roof

e A food can

4.32 Galvanising is one way to stop iron rusting. This is known as 'cathodic protection'. Explain how it works.

4.33 Why do cars rust much more near coasts than they do if they are kept inland?

Caring for our planet – extracting metals

The photograph on page 77 shows how the extraction of metals can destroy large areas of land by quarrying. The one on page 79 shows the bottom of a long flue of an old lead smelter. This carries the poisonous sulphur dioxide gas high into the air so that it does not kill the vegetation in the valley. These are two examples of a serious problem which is caused by our need for metals. The processes of extracting metals damage the environment. Here are some more ways in which the process affects the environment.

• The electricity needed for electrolysis is obtained either by burning coal (which causes air pollution) or from hydroelectric schemes (which flood large areas of land).

• Waste metal such as rusting drink cans and car bodies cause unpleasant litter.

• Many of the processes of purifying ores and metals use a lot of water. This means that waste water is produced. This often contains substances dissolved in it that are very harmful to water life. Many of the rivers near factories that produce metals have no living things in them.

• The spoil heaps (the unwanted material left behind when ores are extracted) often contain a lot of substances that prevent plants from growing on them. Sometimes these substances are washed out into rivers and poison life in the water.

We need cheap metals. How can we make sure we have a supply of cheap metals without doing serious damage to our environment? One way is to re-use scrap metal. We call this 'recycling'.

What can we do to try and recycle more metals?

• We can make people aware of the need to recycle metals.

• We can organise collections of metals for sale to scrap metal dealers.

• Metal objects should be made so that they can be recycled easily.

Recycling drinks cans

Many drinks cans are made of two metals. The round part is made of steel but the top end is made of aluminium. In many countries this has now been made illegal and the whole can must be made of the same metal so it can be recycled easily. Have you noticed that the old pull-ring at the top of the can has been replaced with a new kind that does not come off when the can is opened? This allows the pull-ring to be recycled too.

Recycling expensive metals

Would you ever throw away a piece of gold? No, you would try and sell it. Already most metals that are expensive are not thrown away. They are sold for recycling. Copper, tin and mercury are examples of metals that are almost always recycled because they are quite expensive metals. As metal ores are used up, the metal becomes more expensive and more is recycled.

uestions

4.34 What is meant by 'recycling'? What steps can be taken to ensure that as much metal as possible is recycled?

Review questions on this chapter can be found on page 239.

5 Acids and alkalis

The word 'acid' originally meant a sour taste. Foods like vinegar, lemon juice and sour milk had an 'acid taste'. These days, the word means the class of substances that cause such a sour taste. There are very many compounds which cause this, but some of them would be very unpleasant indeed to taste! This chapter looks at the class of compounds we call acids and at their reactions.

What are acids and what do they do?

The easiest way to recognise an acid is to use an **indicator**. An indicator is a substance that changes colour when an acid is added to it. Litmus is a chemical that is extracted from a lichen and it is an indicator that has been known for over 400 years. In acid solutions it turns red. Many coloured extracts from plants will change colour when an acid is added to them; the red colour from red cabbage is a particularly good one.

Acids react in other ways also and the next investigation shows some of them.

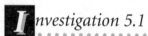

I nvestigation 5.1

Some reactions of acids

Three different acids are allowed to react with indicators, with some metals and with some metal oxides and carbonates.

dilute acids   magnesium

You will need:

• some dilute acids which should be the same concentration (2 M) to make the comparison fair; ethanoic (acetic), hydrochloric and sulphuric are suggested
• metals such as magnesium, iron, zinc and copper
• copper(II) oxide
• sodium carbonate and calcium carbonate
• litmus paper
• test tubes, a glass rod, burner, dropper
• spill
• limewater
• sodium hydroxide solution.

1 Take a spot of each acid on a clean glass rod and touch some blue litmus paper. Note any colour change.

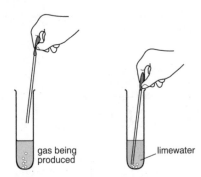

Fill the dropper with the gas (do not touch the liquid)

gas being produced

Squeeze the gas out into the limewater. If the limewater turns milky the gas is carbon dioxide.

limewater

■ **Figure 5.1** Testing for carbon dioxide.

Test for carbon dioxide

Bubble a sample of the gas through limewater. If the limewater turns milky, the gas is carbon dioxide.

The milkiness is caused by particles of insoluble calcium carbonate which are formed when the carbon dioxide reacts with the limewater (calcium hydroxide).

$$Ca(OH)_2(aq) + CO_2(g) \rightarrow CaCO_3(s) + H_2O(l)$$

2 Put a sample of each of the metals in a small quantity of each acid in a test tube. If you see bubbles, test the gas for hydrogen with a burning spill.

3 Put a sample of each of the carbonates in each of the acids and note what happens. If bubbles come off, collect a sample of the gas in the tube in a dropper and bubble it through a small quantity of limewater. Remember that if the limewater turns milky, the gas was carbon dioxide (see Figure 5.1).

4 Gently warm a **small** quantity of copper oxide with each acid and note what happens. Take particular note of any colour change. You may have to filter off any unused copper oxide before you can see the colour change clearly.

5 Take a small volume of acid and add to it a rather larger volume of sodium hydroxide solution. Note any changes. You may note a change in the temperature of the solution. Take a spot of the solution and touch some litmus paper with it. Note the colour of the litmus. Is it the same as when you put the acid on it?

Write the results down in a table.

You will see some patterns in your results. Acids seem to have some similar properties. These are summarised below.

- **Acids turn litmus red.**
- **Acids react with the more reactive metals to give hydrogen.**

A typical reaction is this:

Zinc + hydrochloric acid → zinc chloride + hydrogen

The hydrogen comes from the acid. The metal replaces the hydrogen in the acid. Only those metals in the upper half of the reactivity series will react in this way. Copper, for example, will not react with dilute acids like this.

$$Zn(s) + 2HCl(aq) \rightarrow ZnCl_2(aq) + H_2(g)$$

- **Acids react with carbonates to produce carbon dioxide.**

The reaction is this:

Hydrochloric acid + calcium carbonate → calcium chloride + water + carbon dioxide

$$2HCl(aq) + CaCO_3(s) \rightarrow CaCl_2(aq) + CO_2(g) + H_2O(l)$$

Any carbonate will react in this way with any acid. There is one interesting exception, however. If you add marble chips, calcium carbonate, to dilute sulphuric acid, you will see the reaction start but then it will stop. This is because the product of the reaction, calcium sulphate, is insoluble and coats the marble chips, preventing further attack by the sulphuric acid.

- **Acids react with metal oxides and hydroxides**.

We call these metal oxides and hydroxides **bases**. If they are soluble we call them **alkalis**. Acids will react with bases and alkalis. Two typical reactions are:

Sulphuric acid + copper oxide → copper sulphate + water

Sulphuric acid + sodium hydroxide → sodium sulphate + water

This reaction is called 'neutralisation' and you will study it in greater depth later. Note that water is always produced during neutralisation.

$$H_2SO_4(aq) + CuO(s) \rightarrow CuSO_4(aq) + H_2O(l)$$
$$H_2SO_4(aq) + 2NaOH(aq) \rightarrow Na_2SO_4(aq) + 2H_2O(l)$$

uestions

5.1 Write word equations for the following reactions:

a the action of hydrochloric acid on magnesium

b the action of nitric acid on sodium carbonate

c the action of ethanoic acid on calcium hydroxide.

5.2 *'Johnny, finding life a bore*

Drank some H_2SO_4

His father, an MD

Gave him $CaCO_3$

Now he's neutralised it's true

But he's full of CO_2'

The poet did not get his chemistry quite right. Explain why Johnny will not fill up with CO_2.

A pattern of acidity – pH

Investigation 5.1 showed that, when an acid is mixed with sodium hydroxide, a reaction takes place which destroys the acid. It no longer turns litmus paper red after the reaction. Sodium hydroxide is an example of an alkali. Alkalis are bases that are soluble in water and bases are oxides or hydroxides of metals.

Metal oxides are ionic and contain the oxide ion O^{2-}. Examples are calcium oxide, CaO and copper oxide, CuO.

Metal hydroxides contain the hydroxide ion, OH^-. Examples are sodium hydroxide, NaOH and calcium hydroxide, $Ca(OH)_2$.

The reaction between an acid and an alkali is called **neutralisation**. When sodium hydroxide was added to the acid in Investigation 5.1, the acid was neutralised by the alkali. More alkali was added than was used up by the acid and so some alkali was left over at the end.

There is a 14-point scale which is used to measure the acidity or

Figure 5.2 ■
The pH scale

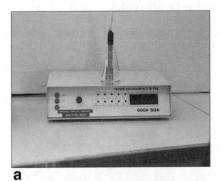

a

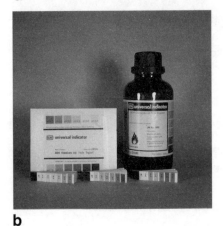

b

■ **Figure 5.3** pH can be measured (a) by a pH meter and (b) by universal indicator.

dilute acids
dilute sodium hydroxide solution

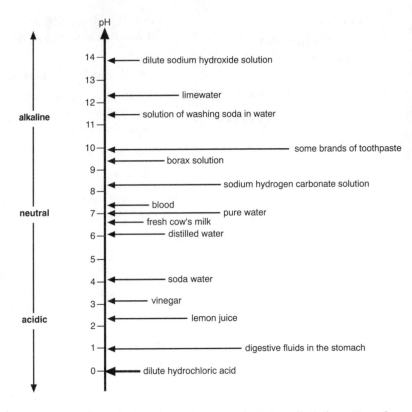

alkalinity of a solution (see Figure 5.2). It is called the pH scale. Strong acids have a low number on the pH scale and strong alkalis a high number. A solution that is exactly neutral, that is it is neither acidic nor alkaline, has a pH of 7. Pure water has a pH of 7.

We can measure the pH of any solution using universal indicator. This is a mixture of indicators which turns a different colour for every pH unit. We can also measure pH with a pH meter (see Figure 5.3). This is an electronic device with a special electrode that is placed in the liquid to give a voltage that depends on the pH of the liquid.

*I*nvestigation 5.2

Measuring the pH of some common solutions

You will need:
- test tubes
- glass rod
- strips of universal indicator paper
- samples of a number of common solutions such as the following:

pure water

vinegar

dilute hydrochloric acid

dilute sodium hydroxide solution

salt solution

rainwater

water from a pond or river

household liquids such as lavatory cleaner, window cleaner, floor cleaner, etc. (but not bleach as this will bleach the indicator paper)

baking soda solution

1 For each solution, take a small amount of it in a test tube. Dip into it a clean dry glass rod.

2 Cut the universal indicator into small pieces. Using the rod, put a small spot of liquid onto the universal indicator paper. Note the colour it changes to and find out the pH of the solution from the indicator colour chart.

3 Write the name of the solution on a pH chart.

This investigation shows that common solutions found around the house and in your neighbourhood have different pH values. Most are clustered at the middle of the scale around pH 7 and only a few, which we call strong acids or strong alkalis, are found at the ends.

Strong acids

On the pH scale, the acids with a low pH are called strong acids and those with a pH nearer 7 are called weak acids. Examples of strong acids are the common ones found in a laboratory such as hydrochloric acid (HCl), sulphuric acid (H_2SO_4) and nitric acid (HNO_3). These kinds of acids are called 'mineral acids' because they are made mainly from minerals that we dig out of the ground.

Weak acids

Weak acids have a pH between about 3 and 6. Examples are the acids we often eat such as vinegar (ethanoic acid), citric acid and tartaric acid. These are called 'organic acids' because they are found in living things or they are made from substances that we obtain from living things.

One example of a weak acid is rainwater. Rainwater is acidic because, as it falls, it dissolves some of the gases found in the air, such as carbon dioxide, which make it slightly acidic. Carbon dioxide is slightly soluble and it dissolves to form carbonic acid which has a pH of about 6. In Chapter 7 you will learn that some gases that are put into the air mainly by human activities can cause rainwater to be much more acidic than this and to be harmful to buildings and plants.

The difference between a **strong acid** and a **concentrated acid**

Concentration refers to the amount of water present in the acid. A concentrated acid has very little water in it. In a dilute acid, the acid is mixed with a lot of water.

Acid *strength* is a measure of the pH of the acid. This is caused mainly by the structure of the acid molecules, although mixing any acid with a lot of water will increase its pH. So we can have

Acids in the home

Name	Use
citric acid	fruit juice
ethanoic acid	vinegar
lactic acid	sour milk
phosphoric acid	rust remover
phenolic acids	TCP, Dettol
sulphuric acid	car batteries
carbonic acid	soda water, fizzy drinks

concentrated ethanoic acid which is a weak acid (pH 3) but dilute hydrochloric acid which is a strong acid (pH 1).

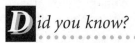id you know?

When you run upstairs quickly, you often feel a slight pain in your knees. This is due to lactic acid. The lactic acid is produced when the glucose in your muscles reacts to give you energy but cannot get enough oxygen to be converted completely into the usual products, carbon dioxide and water. Instead, it is turned into lactic acid. When you stop and rest, the lactic acid is turned back into glucose and the pain goes.

Some common acids

Acid	Formula
hydrochloric acid	HCl
sulphuric acid	H_2SO_4
nitric acid	HNO_3
ethanoic acid	CH_3COOH
carbonic acid	H_2CO_3

Some common alkalis

Name	Formula
sodium hydroxide	NaOH
potassium hydroxide	KOH
calcium hydroxide (lime)	$Ca(OH)_2$

Weak alkalis

Weak alkalis have a pH between about 8 and 11. Examples are alkalis we often use in cooking like baking soda (pH 9). Other examples are soap and toothpaste.

Strong alkalis

Strong alkalis have a pH greater than about 12. They must be treated with care as they are corrosive. They attack substances like wood and skin that are either living or once lived (**organic** substances). Substances that do this we call **caustic**. A good example is sodium hydroxide, often called caustic soda. Caustic soda is often used to clean blocked drains because it reacts easily with the kind of organic household waste that causes blockages.

The ions present in acids and alkalis

Look at the list of formulae for some common acids on the left.

There is one element common to all of them and that is hydrogen. All acids contain atoms of the element hydrogen. In fact, all acids contain hydrogen **ions**. All the acids in the box **ionise** in water. This means they split into hydrogen ions and a negative ion. Table 5.1 shows this.

Look at the list of common alkalis. The ion present in all these alkalis is the hydroxide ion, $(OH)^-$.

■ **Table 5.1 Ions in common acids.**

Acid	Ions present		Name of negative ion
Hydrochloric acid	H^+	Cl^-	Chloride
Sulphuric acid	H^+	SO_4^{2-}	Sulphate
Nitric acid	H^+	NO_3^-	Nitrate
Ethanoic acid	H^+	CH_3COO^-*	Ethanoate
Carbonic acid	H^+	CO_3^{2-}	Carbonate

*Note that only one of the four hydrogen atoms in ethanoic acid is ionised.

There is one compound that contains both hydrogen and the hydroxide group. This compound is water. If we write the formula of water as HOH you can see this clearly. However, you learnt in Chapter 2 that water was not ionic but covalent. This is mainly correct. Almost all the molecules present in water are covalent, but there are always just a few that have enough energy to break up into the hydrogen ion and the hydroxide ion.

This allows us to understand better what acids and alkalis are.

- **Acids are solutions that have more hydrogen ions per litre than water.**

- **Alkalis are solutions that have more hydroxide ions per litre than water.**

Indicators

Indicators are substances that change colour according to the pH of the solution they are in. Many of them are naturally occurring colours. Litmus is very useful because it changes colour at pH7, the point of neutrality between acids and alkalis. Other indicators change at different pH values. Universal indicators are mixtures of indicators made up to have a different colour for each pH unit. Table 5.2 shows the colours of the most common indicators.

■ **Table 5.2 Colour changes of some common indicators.**

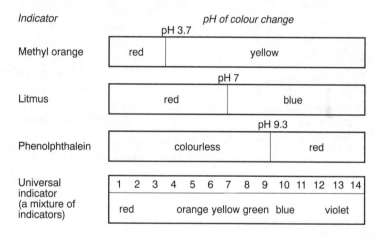

Neutralisation

Neutralisation is the reaction that takes place between an acid and a base and the products are a salt and water.

Salts

Salts are ionic compounds produced by the reaction between an acid and a base. They contain a metal ion and a non-metal ion.

Neutralisation

Neutralisation is the reaction that takes place when an acid reacts with an alkali or a base. The two reactions of acids you studied in Investigation 5.1 were with the base copper oxide and the alkali sodium hydroxide. In this reaction both the acid and the alkali are destroyed. One of the compounds formed in both cases is water. The other two compounds formed are what are called **salts**.

- **A salt is an ionic compound formed when an acid reacts with an alkali. It contains a metal ion and a non-metal ion.**

Look back at all the reactions of acids. You will see that salts are produced in every reaction. You will make some salts from acids later on in this chapter.

Protons and acidity

Acids contain hydrogen ions. You will remember from Chapter 2 that a hydrogen atom consists of a proton only in the nucleus with just one electron moving round it. A hydrogen ion therefore is just a proton because the electron has left it.

- Acids therefore are solutions which contain a high concentration of protons.

- The pH scale is a measure of the concentration of protons. The higher the concentration of protons, the lower the pH.

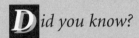 **D**id you know?

The pH of a solution is the negative logarithm (base 10) of the concentration of hydrogen ions in solution. This means that, if a solution has a concentration of hydrogen ions of 10^{-2} (1/100) moles per litre, it will have a pH of 2. Pure water, with a pH of 7, has a concentration of hydrogen ions of 10^{-7} or one ten–millionth of a mole of hydrogen ions per litre. (You will learn the meaning of a 'mole' in Chapter 10.)

Look again at the neutralisation reactions on page 95. Rewrite the equations showing all the ions. The acids contain ions. The copper oxide is ionic. The sodium hydroxide solution contains ions and both the salts formed are ionic. Only the water is covalent.

$$2H^+ + SO_4^{2-} + Cu^{2+} + O^{2-} \rightarrow Cu^{2+} + SO_4^{2-} + H_2O$$

$$2H^+ + SO_4^{2-} + 2Na^+ + 2OH^- \rightarrow 2Na^+ + SO_4^{2-} + 2H_2O$$

The only particles that have changed in these two reactions are the oxide and hydroxide ions and the hydrogen ions. They have joined together to form the covalent compound water.

$$2H^+ + O^{2-} \rightarrow H_2O$$

$$2H^+ + 2OH^- \rightarrow 2H_2O$$

Now we can clearly see what is happening during neutralisation. The hydrogen ion (or proton) in the acid is joining oxide or hydroxide ions to form water. This is called a **proton transfer reaction**. The proton is being transferred from the acid to the base to form water.

This idea can give us a better definition of an acid. The acids in the reactions all contain protons (hydrogen ions) which they donate to the alkali to form water. The alkalis in the reactions all receive the protons to form water. We can therefore define acids and alkalis like this:

- **an acid is a proton donor**
- **an alkali is a proton acceptor.**

pH in nature

Water is an extremely good solvent and, whenever something dissolves in water, the pH is likely to change. Because of this, if you measure the pH of your tap water, you will probably find it is not pH 7, the pH of pure water. If you live in an area where the rocks are made of limestone, your tap water may be slightly alkaline. In other areas the water may be slightly acidic.

pH in your body

There is a lot of water in your body. The pH varies according to where in the body the water is. Your blood is mainly water but has many substances dissolved or suspended in it. It has a pH slightly above 7.

Saliva contains a substance called an enzyme which helps to break down starch foods that you eat into the sugars that your body needs for energy. The enzyme only works well at a pH of about 8 so saliva should be slightly alkaline. The inside of your mouth is a nice, warm, wet place for bacteria to live, and they have plenty of food from the bits left between your teeth. These bacteria like to live in a slightly acid solution and they make acid as they feed. It is a good idea to clean your teeth regularly to remove the bacteria.

 nvestigation 5.3

Investigating the pH of toothpaste

You will need:
- universal indicator paper
- a number of different brands of toothpaste.

1 Using the universal indicator paper, find out the pH of each brand of toothpaste.

2 What is the range of pH of the brands of toothpaste? Why do you think that toothpaste is made to have a pH in this range?

When the food you eat reaches your stomach, it is mixed with juices that have a pH around 2. It is as low as this because your stomach contains the strong acid, hydrochloric acid. This helps to break down foods such as proteins.

The pH of soil

Most plants grow best in a soil that is slightly alkaline. Soil is a mixture of 'mineral' matter from the breaking down of rocks by rain and wind, and 'organic' matter formed from the breaking down of plant and animal remains. Fertile soils contain a great variety of organisms. All these are dependent on each other. Many of these organisms only survive well in slightly alkaline conditions. For the soil organisms to grow well, the soil must be 'open' which means that air and water should be able to get into it easily. If the mineral particles in the soil are too small, as in clay, the soil easily becomes waterlogged and this prevents air getting into it.

In order to improve their soils, farmers often spread lime on them to help the soil stay alkaline (see Figure 5.4). This is particularly

■ **Figure 5.4** Lime being spread on the soil.

important in areas where the soil is naturally acidic because of the rock from which it is made. It is also important where the soil is a heavy clay that easily gets waterlogged. Adding lime also helps to break down heavy clay soils.

The 'lime' that is put on the soil can be either one of two chemicals. It is sometimes crushed limestone, calcium carbonate, and sometimes 'slaked lime', calcium hydroxide. The calcium hydroxide is made from limestone (see page 118) which occurs naturally. The limestone acts slowly, being broken down slowly in the soil to calcium hydroxide. The calcium hydroxide acts quickly; it is the hydroxide of the metal calcium and is therefore a base. It is slightly soluble, giving an alkaline solution.

 **Questions**

5.3 Explain the difference between a weak acid and a dilute acid.

5.4 Pure distilled water has a pH of 7. Rainwater often has a pH of between 5 and 6. Explain this.

5.5 Explain why toothpastes are usually alkaline.

5.6 Why do farmers in some regions spread lime on their soil?

Another pattern–acidic and basic oxides

phosphous pentoxide
sodium hydroxide
calcium oxide

I **nvestigation 5.4**

The pH of solutions of oxides

You will need:

• test tubes

• glass rod

• combustion spoon

• universal indicator paper

• small samples of some oxides or hydroxides of a number of metals or non-metals such as:

sodium hydroxide

calcium oxide

magnesium oxide

iron oxide

copper oxide

sulphur (to make sulphur dioxide)

soda water (solution of carbon dioxide in water)

silicon dioxide (clean sand)

phosphorus pentoxide.

1 Mix a **very** small quantity of each oxide or hydroxide with a little water in a test tube. Shake it to see if it dissolves.

2 Test the resulting solution with universal indicator paper in the usual way. Note the pH of the solution.

3 In the case of sulphur, make the oxide, sulphur dioxide, by burning a small quantity on a combustion spoon and when it is well alight lower it into a test tube which has a little water in the bottom. Withdraw the spoon and shake the tube to dissolve the gas.

4 Write the results in a table which gives some idea of the solubility of the oxide and also the pH of the resulting solution. Do you see any pattern in the results?

A base has already been defined (page 95) as the oxide or hydroxide of a metal. You have learnt that bases react with acids to form salts and that this process is called neutralisation. Investigation 5.4 shows that bases, if they are soluble in the water, produce an alkaline solution. The bases that are insoluble (iron oxide and copper oxide) do not affect the pH of the water. We call these metal oxides **basic oxides**.

The other oxides you tested were oxides of non-metals – carbon dioxide, silicon dioxide, sulphur dioxide and phosphorus pentoxide. All these are soluble except silicon dioxide and all those that dissolved produced acidic solutions. We call these oxides of non-metals **acidic oxides**.

You now know another difference, a chemical difference, between metals and non-metals. **Metals form basic oxides, non-metals form acidic oxides**.

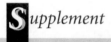*upplement*

Neutral oxides

There are some oxides of elements which are neither acidic nor basic. If these oxides dissolve in water, they do not affect the pH. These are called neutral oxides. The most common one is water itself. Others that are well known are carbon monoxide and two oxides of nitrogen, nitrogen monoxide (NO) and dinitrogen monoxide (N_2O) which is used as an anaesthetic, particularly by dentists.

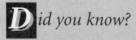*id you know?*

Dinitrogen monoxide is known as 'laughing gas' because sometimes patients that come round after being anaesthetised with it burst into uncontrollable laughter (despite the toothache!).

Amphoteric oxides

When sodium hydroxide (or hydroxide ions) is added to solutions containing the ions of aluminium or calcium, the hydroxides of the metals form because these hydroxides are insoluble. This reaction is shown in the following equations.

The third equation is an ionic equation showing the *general reaction* for the formation of the hydroxide of a metal (symbol M). This reaction only works if the metal hydroxide is insoluble:

Aluminium chloride + sodium hydroxide → aluminium hydroxide + sodium chloride

$$AlCl_3(aq) + 3NaOH(aq) \rightarrow Al(OH)_3(s) + 3NaCl(aq)$$

Calcium chloride + sodium hydroxide → calcium hydroxide + sodium chloride

$$CaCl_2(aq) + 2NaOH(aq) \rightarrow Ca(OH)_2(s) + 2NaCl(aq)$$

The general ionic equation for the reaction is:

$$M^{2+}(aq) + 2(OH)^-(aq) \rightarrow M(OH)_2(s)$$

When acid is added, it reacts with the metal hydroxides, neutralising them. This reaction can also be shown as a general reaction. The hydroxide reacts with the hydrogen ions and water is formed. The metal ions are left in solution. They are the metal ions in the solution of the salt that is formed.

Aluminium hydroxide + hydrochloric acid → aluminium chloride + water

$$Al(OH)_3(s) + 3HCl(aq) \rightarrow AlCl_3(aq) + 3H_2O(l)$$

Calcium hydroxide + hydrochloric acid → calcium chloride + water

$$Ca(OH)_2(s) + 2HCl(aq) \rightarrow CaCl_2(aq) + 2H_2O(l)$$

The general ionic equation is:

$$M(OH)_2(s) + 2H^+(aq) \rightarrow M^{2+}(aq) + 2H_2O(l)$$

When alkali is added to the metal hydroxides, there is a difference between the two metals.

Nothing happens to the calcium hydroxide when alkali is added. This is expected; calcium hydroxide is a base and bases do not react with other bases or alkalis, they react with acids.

With aluminium hydroxide, however, there is a reaction. The aluminium hydroxide is behaving like an acid and it is reacting with the alkali sodium hydroxide. In the reaction, a salt is formed, as in any neutralisation, but in this case the aluminium appears in the anion, not as the cation. The equation for the reaction is as follows:

Acid + alkali → salt + water

Aluminium hydroxide + sodium hydroxide → sodium aluminate + water

$$Al(OH)_3(s) + NaOH(aq) \rightarrow NaAlO_2(aq) + 2H_2O(l)$$

Aluminium hydroxide is behaving like both a basic oxide and an acidic oxide. We call oxides like these **amphoteric** oxides (another more recent name is amphiprotic oxides). The metals that form amphoteric oxides are those that are near to the border between metals and non-metals in the Periodic Table. Lead and zinc are other metals that form amphoteric oxides.

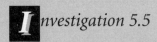

What is an amphoteric oxide or hydroxide?

You will need:

dilute acids and alkalis

- test tubes
- dilute acid
- dilute sodium hydroxide solution
- aluminium chloride
- calcium chloride.

1 Make solutions of aluminium chloride and calcium chloride (the nitrates are also suitable) by taking half a small spatula full of the salt and dissolving it in about 2 cm of water in a test tube.

2 Carefully add a small amount of the dilute sodium hydroxide solution. In both cases a white precipitate will appear. This is the hydroxide of the metal which in both cases is only slightly soluble in water.

3 In each case, divide the precipitate in two.

4 To the first half in each case, add some acid and note that the precipitate disappears.

5 To the second half in each case add more sodium hydroxide solution. This time note the difference between the two. The calcium hydroxide stays as a precipitate but the aluminium hydroxide reacts with the sodium hydroxide and a clear solution is formed.

You can now see that the move from metal to non-metal as you go from left to right across the Periodic Table does not happen suddenly but is gradual. Metals such as aluminium, lead and zinc show some characteristics of non-metals by forming oxides that behave like acidic oxides, and some non-metals on the other side of the line show some metallic properties such as a shiny appearance.

Questions

5.7 Classify the following oxides or hydroxides as acidic, amphoteric or basic. The Periodic Table on page 27 will help.

Rubidium oxide

Manganese(III) oxide

Selenium dioxide

Lead(II) hydroxide.

5.8 Make a table showing the trends in the properties of the oxides across Period 3 of the Periodic Table (Na–Ar). In your table, consider state, solubility and reaction with acids and alkalis.

Salts

Look back at Investigation 5.1. This investigation demonstrated some of the properties of acids. Acids react with bases, with most metals and with carbonates. One of the products in every case is a salt. A salt is an ionic crystalline compound. The positive ion is a metal ion. The negative ion is either a non-metal or an ion made of a group of non-metal atoms joined together but with an overall charge.

Table salt, sodium chloride, is a typical salt and has given its name to this big class of compounds, salts.

We can write general equations for the reactions you looked at in Investigation 5.1:

Acid + base → salt + water

Acid + metal → salt + hydrogen

Acid + carbonate → salt + carbon dioxide + water

*I*nvestigation 5.6

Making salts

In this investigation you will repeat what you did in Investigation 5.1 but you will go on to obtain a sample of the salt produced in the reaction. You will use a number of the methods of purification you met in Chapter 1.

dilute acids

You will need:
- test tubes or beakers
- granulated zinc
- calcium carbonate (marble chips)
- copper oxide
- two acids, dilute sulphuric and dilute hydrochloric
- burner, evaporating basin, stirring rod, filter funnel and filter paper

1 Put a sample of zinc in a small quantity of acid in a test tube or beaker. Allow it to react. If the zinc is used up, add more. When all the acid is used up, filter off the zinc.

2 The solution will contain the zinc salt of the acid you used (zinc chloride if you used hydrochloric acid and zinc sulphate if you used sulphuric acid). Evaporate off the water until you see signs of solid around the edge.

3 Leave it to cool. Crystals of the salt will appear. Filter them off.

4 Put some marble chips in hydrochloric acid (do not use sulphuric acid, the reaction will not work). They will react and carbon dioxide will be given off. If all the marble is used up, add more.

5 When all the acid has been used up, filter off the unused marble chips. Evaporate the solution, leave to cool and filter as in steps 2 and 3. The product is the salt calcium chloride.

6 Gently warm a **small** quantity of copper oxide with sulphuric acid in a beaker. The copper oxide will be used up leaving a clear blue solution. Add more copper oxide. Repeat this until there is unused copper oxide in the beaker all the time. This happens when all the sulphuric acid has been used up.

7 Repeat steps 2 and 3 to get crystals of copper sulphate.

Figure 5.5 shows the general way of preparing salts like zinc and copper sulphate.

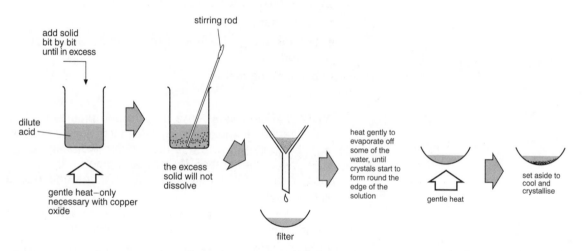

■ **Figure 5.5** Sequence for preparing soluble salts from an insoluble starting material.

In this investigation you have used an insoluble substance to react with the acid. When all the acid was used up, you filtered off the unused insoluble substance. In this way you could be sure that the liquid contained only the salt and water. It was then easy to obtain the pure salt by evaporation and crystallisation.

The reactions are shown by the equations:

Zinc + sulphuric acid → zinc sulphate + hydrogen

Calcium carbonate + hydrochloric acid → calcium chloride + carbon dioxide + water

Copper oxide + sulphuric acid → copper sulphate + water

$$Zn(s) + H_2SO_4(aq) \rightarrow ZnSO_4(aq) + H_2(g)$$

$$CaCO_3(s) + 2HCl(aq) \rightarrow CaCl_2(aq) + CO_2(g) + H_2O(l)$$

$$CuO(s) + H_2SO_4(aq) \rightarrow CuSO_4(aq) + H_2O(l)$$

In the next example, an acid is used to neutralise an alkali to give a salt and water. Both of the reactants are soluble. You must therefore add just the right amount of the acid to neutralise the alkali. You cannot filter off any unused alkali after the reaction. In this case you will use an indicator to tell you when you have added just the right amount of acid. At this point the indicator will change from its alkali colour to its acid colour. We call this point the **end-point**.

Investigation 5.7

dilute hydrochloric acid
dilute sodium hydroxide solution

Making sodium chloride

You will need:

- beaker or conical flask
- dilute hydrochloric acid
- dilute sodium hydroxide solution (both solutions the same approximate concentration – about 1M)
- litmus paper
- two dropping pipettes, a measuring cylinder and a glass rod
- evaporating dish
- burner.

[**NOTE** You can also use a burette and pipette for this investigation. It makes the work much easier but you must be taught how to use them before you can do the experiment. Remember, if you use a pipette, it is not a good idea to fill it using your mouth; instead use a pipette filler.]

1 Take a beaker or (preferably) a conical flask and put into it 10 cm³ of the sodium hydroxide solution.

2 Using a clean measuring cylinder, add to the alkali about 8 cm³ of the acid. Stir or shake the liquid. With the glass rod, put a spot of the liquid on the litmus paper. If the concentrations of the two solutions were approximately the same, the paper will turn blue as not all the alkali has been neutralised. If the paper is red, go straight to Step 4.

3 With the dropping pipette add more acid carefully and regularly stir and test as before with litmus. You will reach a point when you have added a little too much acid and the litmus paper turns red.

4 With a clean dropping pipette, add, very carefully, drops of alkali. Stir and test with litmus after each drop. Try and stop just when the litmus is in between blue and red. It will be a purple colour. This is called the **end-point**. If you go too far, add drops of acid again until you get back to the end–point.

5 Evaporate the water. The white solid left at the end is sodium chloride.

Hydrochloric acid + sodium hydroxide → sodium chloride + water

$$HCl(aq) + NaOH(aq) \rightarrow NaCl(aq) + H_2O(l)$$

The process you have just carried out is called a **titration**. It is a process widely used in industrial laboratories, not for making a chemical as you did but for **analysis**. You carry out an analysis of something when you want to find out what it is made of or how much of a particular chemical is present in it.

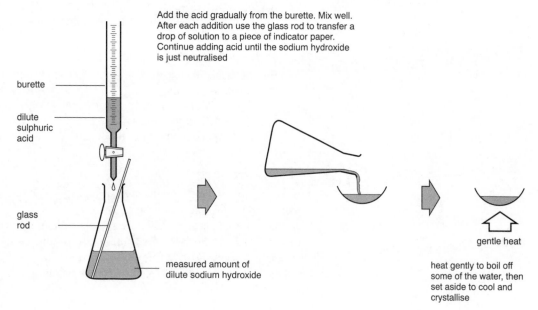

Add the acid gradually from the burette. Mix well. After each addition use the glass rod to transfer a drop of solution to a piece of indicator paper. Continue adding acid until the sodium hydroxide is just neutralised

burette

dilute sulphuric acid

glass rod

measured amount of dilute sodium hydroxide

gentle heat

heat gently to boil off some of the water, then set aside to cool and crystallise

■ **Figure 5.6** Preparing a salt using titration.

A better piece of equipment for measuring out the acid than the measuring cylinder is a burette. A burette allows you to add the acid very accurately by allowing one drop at a time through the tap. Figure 5.6 shows this method of preparing a salt if you have a burette .

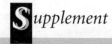
Supplement

Making an insoluble salt

In all the methods of making salts that have been studied so far, the product has been a solution of the salt in water. The salt is then obtained by evaporation or crystallisation. A different method is used if the salt you want to make is insoluble.

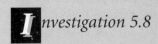

Investigation 5.8

lead nitrate

lead iodide

Making an insoluble salt, lead iodide

You will need:

- test tube
- filter funnel and filter paper
- solutions of lead nitrate (or ethanoate) and potassium iodide.

1 Put the lead nitrate solution in a test tube to a depth of about 1 cm. Add a similar amount of the potassium iodide solution. Note the yellow precipitate. This is lead iodide.

2 Filter the precipitate.

3 Wash the precipitate by pouring a little water through it before you take the filter paper out of the funnel.

4 Allow the residue on the filter paper to dry.

5 (Optional) You can make attractive crystals of lead iodide by dissolving a little in warm water. Filter it while it is hot to remove any lead iodide that has not dissolved. Allow the filtrate to cool. As it cools you will see the lead iodide crystals form.

Any insoluble salt can be prepared in this way. The salt is made of the two ions, the anion and the cation. To prepare an insoluble salt, all that is needed is a solution of a soluble compound that contains the cation and another of a soluble compound containing the anion. In this case the two solutions were lead nitrate and potassium iodide. Lead ethanoate and sodium iodide would have been just as good.

When the two solutions are mixed, the insoluble salt immediately appears as a precipitate. This is filtered and washed to remove traces of the soluble salt left in the solution.

Lead nitrate + potassium iodide → lead iodide + potassium nitrate

$$Pb(NO_3)_2(aq) + 2KI(aq) \rightarrow PbI_2(s) + 2KNO_3(aq)$$

The equation for the reaction is shown above. However, nothing happens to the nitrate or the potassium ions in this reaction. In the original solutions they are present as ions in solution and at the end they are still there as ions in solution in the filtrate. So we can write a much simpler ionic equation for the reaction by leaving them out:

$$Pb^{2+}(aq) + 2I^-(aq) \rightarrow PbI_2(s)$$

This is a general equation. It would also apply, for example, if lead ethanoate and sodium iodide were used.

Identifying ions in salts

You learnt above that **analysis** was what chemists did when they wanted to find out what chemicals there were in a substance. **Qualitative analysis** is what chemists do if they want to find out just what is present. **Quantitative analysis** is what chemists do when they want to know *how much* of a substance is present. The titration you did is an example of quantitative analysis. The rest of this section is about qualitative analysis. When you do the next investigation you are doing qualitative analysis.

*I*nvestigation 5.9

Identifying some unknown chemicals

You will need:

- unlabelled bottles that contain the following chemicals:

aluminium sulphate ($Al_2(SO_4)_3$)

copper sulphate ($CuSO_4$)

iron(II) nitrate ($Fe(NO_3)_2$)

iron(III) chloride ($FeCl_3$)

sodium carbonate (Na_2CO_3)

sodium iodide (NaI)

ammonium chloride (NH_4Cl)

calcium chloride ($CaCl_2$)

- the following reagents:

sodium hydroxide solution

ammonium hydroxide solution

limewater

silver nitrate solution

lead nitrate solution

aluminium powder

dilute hydrochloric acid

dilute nitric acid

barium chloride solution

The reagents should preferably be in dropping bottles. If they are not, you will need one dropper for each reagent

- red litmus paper
- micro test tubes
- small burner.

Your task is to identify the chemicals you were given. To do this, use the analysis tables on page 112.

copper sulphate
dilute acids and
alkalis

lead nitrate
silver nitrate
barium chloride

Tables 5.3 and 5.4 give details of tests to identify some cations and anions. For the anion table (Table 5.4), the order in which you carry out the work is important. For example, you should always test for the sulphate ion before the chloride ion because sulphates can also

■ **Table 5.3 Qualitative analysis: cations.**

Cation	Test	Result
Aluminium	Add two drops of sodium hydroxide solution	A white precipitate will form
	Add excess sodium hydroxide solution	The precipitate will disappear
Zinc	Add two drops of sodium hydroxide solution	A white precipitate will form
	Add excess sodium hydroxide solution	The precipitate will disappear
	Add two drops of ammonium hydroxide solution	A white precipitate will form
	Add excess ammonium hydroxide solution	The precipitate will disappear
Calcium	Add two drops of sodium hydroxide solution	A white precipitate will form
	Add excess sodium hydroxide solution	The precipitate will remain
Copper	Add two drops of sodium hydroxide solution	A blue precipitate will form
	Add two drops of ammonium hydroxide solution	A blue precipitate will form
	Add excess ammonium hydroxide solution	The precipitate will disappear and a deep blue clear solution will form
Iron(II)	Add two drops of sodium hydroxide solution	A green precipitate will form. This will gradually turn brown on the surface
Iron(III)	Add two drops of sodium hydroxide solution	A brown precipitate will form
Ammonium	Add four drops of sodium hydroxide solution and warm. Hold a piece of moist red litmus paper in the mouth of the tube	Ammonia gas will be given off which will turn the litmus paper blue
Sodium		No reaction will be seen when any of these tests are tried

■ **Table 5.4 Qualitative analysis: anions.**

Anion	Test	Result
Carbonate	Add dilute acid. Test the gas evolved with limewater (page 94)	Limewater turns milky
Sulphate	Add two drops of dilute hydrochloric acid followed by two drops of barium chloride solution	White precipitate
Chloride	Add two drops of dilute nitric acid followed by two drops of silver nitrate solution	White precipitate
Iodide	Add two drops of dilute nitric acid followed by two drops of silver nitrate solution	Yellow precipitate
	Confirm by adding two drops of lead nitrate solution to another sample	Yellow precipitate
Nitrate	Add a few particles of aluminium and four drops of sodium hydroxide solution. Warm and place a piece of moist red litmus paper in the mouth of the tube. (Note, an ammonium salt will give a positive result for this test. Test for the ammonium ion first.)	Ammonia gas will be given off which will turn litmus paper blue

give a positive result in the chloride test. A carbonate will give a positive result with both the chloride test and the sulphate test so the carbonate test should be done first.

When carrying out these tests, always use small quantities. About 5 mm depth of the original solution in a micro test tube is a good guide. When you heat anything, use the smallest flame you can get with your burner and move the tube continuously in and out of the flame. Small quantities will heat up very quickly and boil over suddenly.

The chemistry behind the tests – cations

When you carry out the tests for the cations, you make the metal hydroxide. Most metal hydroxides are insoluble and those of transition metals are coloured. The colour of the precipitate therefore tells you which metal is present. Copper forms a blue hydroxide $(Cu(OH)_2)$ whereas iron forms two hydroxides, one brown $(Fe(OH)_3)$ and one green $(Fe(OH)_2)$

Iron(II) ion + hydroxide ion → iron(II) hydroxide

Iron(III) ion + hydroxide ion → iron(III) hydroxide

Copper ion + hydroxide ion → copper hydroxide

$$Fe^{2+}(aq) + 2OH^-(aq) \rightarrow Fe(OH)_2(s) \text{ (green)}$$
$$Fe^{3+}(aq) + 3OH^-(aq) \rightarrow Fe(OH)_3(s) \text{ (brown)}$$
$$Cu^{2+}(aq) + 2OH^-(aq) \rightarrow Cu(OH)_2(s) \text{ (blue)}$$

Iron, like many transition metals, shows variable valency. It can form two ions, the iron(II) ion and the iron(III) ion. The iron(II) ion, which is sometimes called the ferrous ion, forms a series of salts which are green in colour. The iron(III) ion (sometimes called the ferric ion) is much more common and it forms a series of salts which are brown in colour (see Table 5.5).

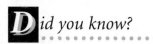 id you know?

The brown colour of sand and of most rocks is due to the presence of the brown iron(III) ion. Without it, sand would be colourless and look like sugar.

■ Table 5.5 Iron compounds.

Iron(II) compounds			Iron(III) compounds		
Compound	Formula	Colour	Compound	Formula	Colour
Iron(II) sulphate	$FeSO_4$	Green	Iron(III) sulphate	$Fe_2(SO_4)_3$	Brown
Iron(II) hydroxide	$Fe(OH)_2$	Green	Iron(III) hydroxide	$Fe(OH)_3$	Brown
Iron(II) carbonate	$FeCO_3$	Pale green	Iron(III) chloride	$FeCl_3$	Orange
			Iron(III) oxide	Fe_2O_3	Brown

Copper hydroxide has the additional property that it will react with excess ammonia to form a clear deep blue solution. This solution contains a coloured ion which has a complex formula involving the copper and molecules of ammonia.

Aluminium hydroxide and zinc hydroxides are both white in colour and, being amphoteric, they both react with excess strong alkali such as sodium hydroxide solution (see above). Calcium hydroxide is also white but because it is not amphoteric, the hydroxide does not react with excess alkali. Zinc hydroxide will react with excess ammonium hydroxide to give a clear solution. In doing this it is unlike calcium and aluminium hydroxides, but similar to its fellow transition metal copper.

The ammonium ion is identified by heating it with an alkali such as sodium hydroxide solution. Ammonia gas is evolved which has a very distinctive smell. The gas can easily be identified as it turns moist red litmus paper blue.

Ammonium chloride + sodium hydroxide → sodium chloride + water + ammonia

$$NH_4Cl(aq) + NaOH(aq) \rightarrow NaCl(aq) + H_2O(l) + NH_3(g)$$

This can be seen more easily as an ionic equation:

$$NH_4^+(aq) + OH^-(aq) \rightarrow H_2O(l) + NH_3(g)$$

Test for ammonia

Heat the liquid containing ammonia and test the vapour evolved with moist red litmus paper. Ammonia gas also has the characteristic smell of ammonia.

The chemistry behind the tests – anions

The test for a carbonate is well known. A carbonate will give carbon dioxide when hydrochloric acid is added and this turns limewater milky. This is the first anion test that should be done because the carbonate anion will give a positive result in all the other tests as well.

Carbonate ion + hydrochloric acid → chloride ion + carbon dioxide + water

$$CO_3^{2-}(aq) + 2HCl(aq) \rightarrow 2Cl^-(aq) + CO_2(g) + H_2O(l)$$

To identify the other anions, a precipitate of an insoluble salt of the anion is made. The insoluble sulphate is barium sulphate and it is made by adding barium chloride to any sulphate.

sulphate ion + barium chloride → barium sulphate + chloride ion

$$SO_4^{2-}(aq) + BaCl_2(aq) \rightarrow BaSO_4(s) + 2Cl^-(aq)$$

The insoluble chloride is silver chloride. This is made when silver nitrate solution is added to any chloride. Silver sulphate is also insoluble and so a sulphate will also produce a precipitate. This is why the sulphate test must be done before the chloride test.

Chloride ion + silver nitrate → silver chloride + nitrate ion

$$Cl^-(aq) + AgNO_3(aq) \rightarrow AgCl(s) + NO_3^-(aq)$$

The iodide test is similar. A yellow precipitate of lead iodide is produced when lead nitrate solution is added to an iodide.

Iodide ion + lead nitrate → lead iodide + nitrate ion

$$2I^-(aq) + Pb(NO_3)_2(aq) \rightarrow PbI_2(s) + 2NO_3^-(aq)$$

All nitrates are soluble and so it is not possible to identify a nitrate by making a precipitate of an insoluble one. Instead, the nitrate ion is changed into an ammonium ion by warming it with aluminium powder. The ammonium ion is then identified by warming with alkali as described above.

Industrial processes

Apart from industry based on oil, the chemical industry based on acids and alkalis is the most important economically. These are the industries which produce the basic chemicals on which all the other chemical industries depend. There are three important ones to be considered, the manufacture of sulphuric acid, the industry based on lime and the alkali industry.

The sulphuric acid industry

The manufacture of sulphuric acid is one of the biggest of the world's chemical industries. 122 million tonnes of the acid were made in 1990. Sulphuric acid is a chemical from which many other useful materials are made. It is a heavy, extremely corrosive, liquid which causes burns almost immediately if a spot comes into contact with the skin.

The reason why it is so dangerous to living tissue is not because it is an acid but because it is a **dehydrating agent**. This means that it will remove water from anything which contains it. If it comes into contact with the skin, it removes water from it just like a fire does. The result is a burn just like a burn caused by fire. The acid should be handled with great care and eye protection should be worn. Any splashes of the acid should be washed off immediately with a large quantity of water.

Sulphuric acid is made from sulphur dioxide gas. Most of the sulphur dioxide gas is produced by burning sulphur and the sulphur is obtained from large deposits found in a number of places in the world.

Sulphur + oxygen → sulphur dioxide

$$S(s) + O_2(g) \rightarrow SO_2(g)$$

In countries that have no sulphur deposits, sulphur dioxide is sometimes made from calcium sulphate by heating it with coke.

This produces carbon dioxide and calcium oxide as well as sulphur dioxide. The calcium oxide, a basic oxide, can be used to remove unwanted sulphur dioxide, an acidic oxide, from power station chimney gases. This process turns the calcium oxide back into calcium sulphate which can be used again to make sulphur dioxide. This is a good example of a pollutant from one industry being used as an important chemical in another.

The sulphur dioxide is first converted into sulphur trioxide by mixing it with oxygen and passing it over a catalyst at about 450 °C. The catalyst is the oxide of the transition metal vanadium. This process is called the **Contact Process** (see Figure 5.7).

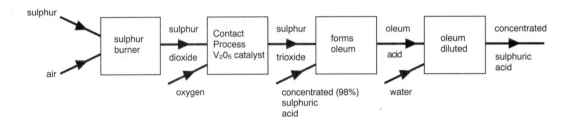

■ **Figure 5.7** Flow diagram of the Contact Process.

Sulphur dioxide + oxygen ⇌ sulphur trioxide

$$2SO_2(g) + O_2(g) \underset{V_2O_5 \text{ catalyst}}{\rightleftharpoons} 2SO_3(g)$$

This reaction will go both ways and that is why the double arrow is used. Reactions which do this are quite common and you will learn more about them in Chapter 11.

The sulphur trioxide produced in this way must be added to water to make sulphuric acid. However, this process produces much heat and it is easier to dissolve it first in concentrated sulphuric acid. The product is a substance called **oleum** which has a formula $H_2S_2O_7$. This can be converted into sulphuric acid later by adding water.

Sulphur trioxide + sulphuric acid → oleum

Oleum + water → sulphuric acid

$$SO_3(g) + H_2SO_4(l) \rightarrow H_2S_2O_7(l)$$
$$H_2S_2O_7(l) + H_2O(l) \rightarrow 2H_2SO_4(aq)$$

Since water need only be added at a later stage, transporting oleum is cheaper than transporting concentrated sulphuric acid (a tanker lorry full of oleum gives more than a tankerful of concentrated sulphuric acid when water is added).

Figure 5.8 shows a sulphuric acid plant.

■ **Figure 5.8** Sulphuric acid plant.

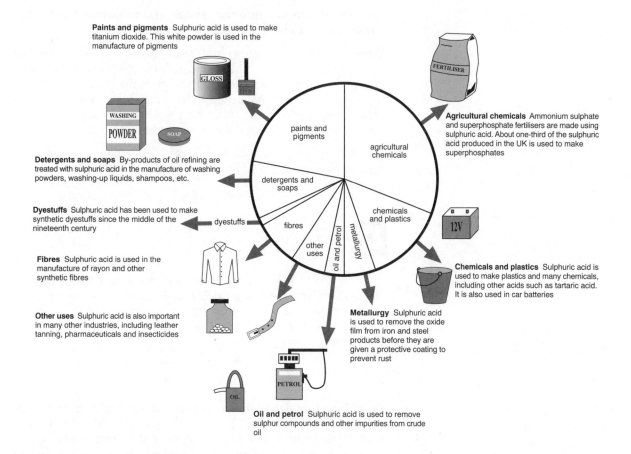

Paints and pigments Sulphuric acid is used to make titanium dioxide. This white powder is used in the manufacture of pigments

Detergents and soaps By-products of oil refining are treated with sulphuric acid in the manufacture of washing powders, washing-up liquids, shampoos, etc.

Dyestuffs Sulphuric acid has been used to make synthetic dyestuffs since the middle of the nineteenth century

Fibres Sulphuric acid is used in the manufacture of rayon and other synthetic fibres

Other uses Sulphuric acid is also important in many other industries, including leather tanning, pharmaceuticals and insecticides

Agricultural chemicals Ammonium sulphate and superphosphate fertilisers are made using sulphuric acid. About one-third of the sulphuric acid produced in the UK is used to make superphosphates

Chemicals and plastics Sulphuric acid is used to make plastics and many chemicals, including other acids such as tartaric acid. It is also used in car batteries

Metallurgy Sulphuric acid is used to remove the oxide film from iron and steel products before they are given a protective coating to prevent rust

Oil and petrol Sulphuric acid is used to remove sulphur compounds and other impurities from crude oil

■ **Figure 5.9** Uses of sulphuric acid.

■ **Figure 5.10** Limestone quarry.

The pie chart (Figure 5.9) shows some of the main uses of sulphuric acid.

Industries based on lime

Limestone rock (calcium carbonate) occurs widely throughout the world. It was formed many millions of years ago when shellfish and other sea creatures died and their remains fell to the bottom of the sea. Their shells were made from calcium carbonate. Over millions of years these shells became compressed into layers of limestone. Rock that is made in layers like this is called **sedimentary rock**.

Marble and chalk are also forms of calcium carbonate. Marble is produced when limestone is subjected to high temperatures and pressures in the earth's crust which cause it to melt and then solidify again. We call this kind of rock **metamorphic rock**.

Limestone is widely quarried (see Figure 5.10). One of its main uses is as a building material; because it is sedimentary and has a layer structure it is easily cut into regular shaped stones which make particularly good buildings.

Another major use for limestone is making cement. It is heated with clay in a furnace at about 1400 °C and the product is a mixture of calcium and aluminium silicates. These are in a powder form when they come out of the furnace. When water is added to the mixture the two silicates form long crystals which lock around each other as they grow. If sand is added to the cement, the particles of sand are also locked into the crystals and the whole mass is very strong. This is called concrete.

When concrete sets, it does not dry out, the water in it becomes part of the silicate crystals which are formed. We call water that is part of crystals 'water of crystallisation'. The slower the crystals are allowed to form, the bigger and stronger they are. This is why it is a good idea to keep the concrete moist for a week as it sets, particularly in warm climates. Concrete will even set under water!

Another use for limestone is as a 'flux' in furnaces for extracting metals. This use was described more fully in Chapter 4.

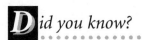

Did you know?

The world production of cement has increased from 103 million tonnes in 1950 to 1200 million tonnes in 1990 just 40 years later. This is a measure of the huge amount of building that has happened in the last half century.

Quicklime and slaked lime (calcium oxide and calcium hydroxide) are made from limestone. This is a very large chemical industry. To make quicklime the limestone is heated to over 1000 °C in a furnace. At this temperature it decomposes, losing carbon dioxide. What is left is calcium oxide which is given the name **quicklime**.

Calcium carbonate → calcium oxide + carbon dioxide

$$CaCO_3(s) \rightarrow CaO(s) + CO_2(g)$$

The quicklime is then 'slaked' with water to form slaked lime, calcium hydroxide. In this process water is added and much heat is evolved.

Calcium oxide + water → calcium hydroxide

$$CaO(s) + H_2O(l) \rightarrow Ca(OH)_2(s)$$

Calcium oxide, quicklime, does not have many uses because it reacts with water so easily that it reacts with the moisture of the air. This means that it is difficult to store as it must be kept in sealed bags or bottles. Once these have been opened, the quicklime soon reacts to give slaked lime. Quicklime has the unpleasant property that it reacts rapidly with any living or dead animal matter. It must therefore always be handled with great care. Because of this property, it is used to destroy diseased animal carcasses such as cattle that have been slaughtered because they have foot and mouth disease.

The three main uses for slaked lime are as a fertiliser, for making sodium hydroxide from salt in the alkali industry (page 120) and for neutralising acidic industrial waste products. One waste product is sulphur dioxide. This is produced when coal that contains sulphur is burnt or when sulphide ores are smelted (Chapter 4). The sulphur dioxide goes into the atmosphere and in some parts of the world has become a serious pollutant. As you found out when you read about the sulphuric acid industry, the sulphur dioxide can be absorbed by calcium oxide and put to good use making sulphuric acid.

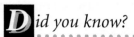id you know?

When limestone is heated to form calcium oxide, it glows with a greenish–white light. In the days before electrical stage lighting in theatres, a gas flame was used to heat limestone to provide the light for the actors and actresses on stage. This light was called 'limelight'. The word has now gone into the English language. When somebody is the focus of attention, we say he or she is 'in the limelight'.

The many uses for limestone are summarised in Figure 5.11.

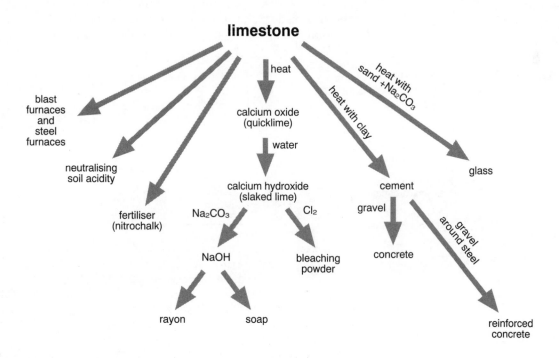

■ **Figure 5.11** Uses of limestone.

■ **Figure 5.12** A salt pan being exploited.

The alkali industry

This is the industry which uses salt, sodium chloride, as its raw material. It also requires a source of energy, usually coal, and a supply of calcium hydroxide. The industry has therefore become established where these three are plentiful. Salt is found in large quantities where ancient oceans have dried up and the rock salt formed can be mined or quarried. Alternatively, salt can be obtained from salt pans by evaporation (see Figure 5.12).

The sodium chloride is converted into sodium carbonate or sodium hydroxide, both of which are alkalis. These alkalis are then used to make other materials which we use in large quantities, such as soap and detergents. There are two processes that are used to make alkali from salt. One is called electrolysis and the other is a process invented over a century ago called the Solvay process. Figure 5.13 shows the products and starting materials for these processes.

The cheapest alkali is produced by the Solvay process but unfortunately this process does not make chlorine. In recent years the demand for chlorine for making chemicals such as the useful plastic, PVC, has risen. This means that more alkali is now being made by the more expensive process, electrolysis.

In the electrolysis process an electric current is passed through a solution of sodium chloride. In the solution there are four ions, the positive ions, hydrogen (H^+) and sodium (Na^+) and the negative ions, chloride (Cl^-) and hydroxide (OH^-). The sodium and chloride ions come from the salt and the others from the water. The electricity causes two of the ions to form elements, hydrogen and chlorine (see Chapter 6). These two gases escape from the solution and are collected. The ions left behind in the solution are sodium and hydroxide. Solid sodium hydroxide can be obtained from this solution.

■ **Figure 5.13** Inputs and outputs of the alkali industry: (a) the Solvay process and (b) electrolysis of brine.

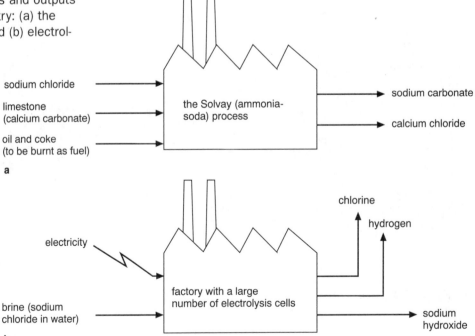

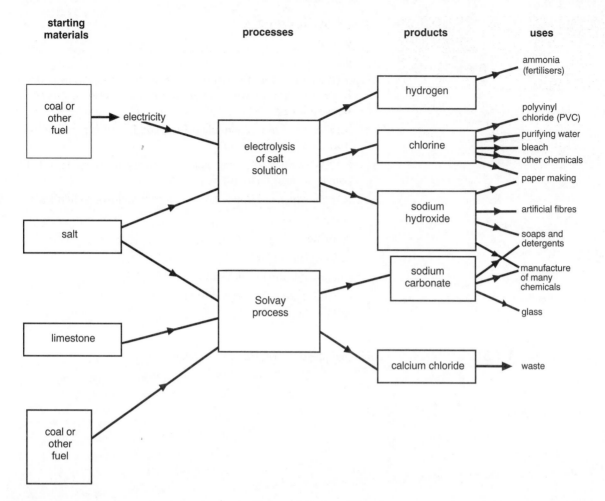

starting materials | processes | products | uses

■ **Figure 5.14** Schematic diagram of the alkali industry.

■ **Figure 5.15** To make paper, wood pulp is purified by soaking it in concentrated sodium hydroxide solution. The bleach used to make the paper white is made from chlorine.

Sodium chloride is also the main source of the element chlorine and so the alkali industry produces this as well. Chlorine is used in several other industries. The main industry which uses chlorine is the plastics industry because one of the most useful plastics is polyvinyl chloride or PVC which is a strong but flexible plastic which has many uses, from clothing to electrical insulation. The world currently produces about 50 million tonnes of chlorine each year.

Figure 5.14 summarises the main uses for the products of the alkali industry. Almost all the major industrial chemistry processes use products from the alkali industry (e.g. Figure 5.15). It is not surprising therefore, that the world centres of the chemical industry have grown up in areas where there are good supplies of salt, limestone and coal.

uestions

5.9 Draw schematic diagrams showing starting materials, processes and products for the manufacture of the following substances:

sulphuric acid

sodium hydroxide

calcium hydroxide

cement

glass.

5.10 Explain why the major centres of the chemical industry in the world have arisen where there is a plentiful supply of salt and limestone.

5.11 What is concrete made of? Explain how it is possible for it to set hard under water.

5.12 Why does sulphuric acid cause very nasty blisters if it comes into contact with skin?

5.13 List the most important uses for the following chemicals:

sulphuric acid

chlorine

sodium carbonate

calcium carbonate (limestone)

calcium hydroxide (slaked lime)

sodium hydroxide.

Review questions on this chapter can be found on pages 239–40.

Energy and chemistry

Driving a car, riding a bicycle, keeping warm, cooking food, listening to a radio; all these activities need energy from chemical reactions to keep them going. So do you. Without energy from the food you eat, you could not use your muscles and indeed your heart could not beat. Electricity is a particularly useful form of energy that we can obtain directly from chemical reactions. We can also use electricity to make chemical reactions happen. This chapter helps you understand what chemical energy is and where it comes from.

Conservation of energy

You will have learned in your physics that we cannot create energy and we do not use energy up. All we can do is to change it from one form to another. This is known as the Law of Conservation of Energy. This chapter is about chemical energy and how we can make use of it by converting it into other forms of energy.

Figures 6.1 and 6.2 show everyday chemical reactions that we use to provide us with energy.

Energy changes during chemical reactions

dilute acids
dilute alkali

magnesium ribbon

*I*nvestigation 6.1

Some energy changes

You will need:

- magnesium ribbon
- dilute acid
- dilute alkali such as sodium hydroxide solution
- potassium hydrogencarbonate
- tongs
- test tubes
- burner
- thermometer (optional).

Carry out the following reactions and note all the energy changes you can detect.

1 Take approximately 5 cm of magnesium ribbon in a pair of tongs and set fire to it. Do not look directly at

■ **Figure 6.1** We rely on chemical energy to keep us warm.

■ **Figure 6.2** Some chemical reactions give off a lot of energy in a very short space of time. These buildings are being demolished using a controlled explosion.

the flame, as it is very bright and can damage your eyes.

2 Take approximately 2 cm of dilute acid in a test tube. Add a small piece of magnesium. Note what happens. Do you detect any energy changes? Use a thermometer if you wish.

3 Take approximately 2 cm of dilute acid in a test tube. Add to it a similar volume of dilute alkali. Do you notice any energy changes? Use a thermometer if you wish.

4 Take approximately 1 cm depth of dilute acid in a test tube. Carefully add some crystals of potassium hydrogen carbonate. Do you detect any energy changes? Use a thermometer if you wish. If no potassium hydrogen carbonate is available, sodium hydrogen carbonate (baking soda) can be used but the temperature change is quite small and a thermometer will be needed to detect it.

In the first three reactions, energy was given off. In the first, it was in the form of heat energy and light energy. In the second and third reaction, the solution got warm because heat energy was given off. In the third reaction, the heat that was produced was the only thing that told you that a reaction was taking place.

We call a reaction like these that gives off energy an **exothermic** reaction.

In the fourth reaction, the test tube and the solution got colder. Heat was taken in during the reaction, not given off. We call a reaction like this that takes in energy an **endothermic** reaction.

A change in energy, either an endothermic change or an exothermic one, is the sign that a chemical reaction has taken place. Whenever a chemical reaction happens, there is an energy change.

Most chemical reactions are exothermic.

Chemical energy is stored in the electrons that make up the bonds between atoms. When a chemical reaction occurs, these electrons move to make more stable bonds which have less energy stored in them. This stored energy is rather like the stored energy – called potential energy – of an object on a table. The object can fall to the floor. When it falls, it loses some of its potential energy which is changed into energy of movement (kinetic energy). Electrons in an atom can move to a position of lower potential energy during a chemical reaction. When they do, the potential energy that is lost appears as other forms of energy such as heat.

We can show this in a graphical form for a reaction (Figure 6.3). Think about the first reaction in the investigation when magnesium is burnt in air to form magnesium oxide.

The reaction is:

Magnesium + oxygen → magnesium oxide

$$2Mg(s) + O_2(g) \rightarrow 2MgO(s)$$

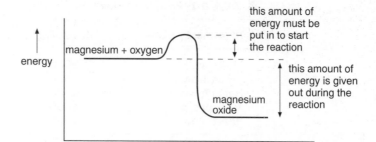

The amount of energy stored in the magnesium and oxygen before the reaction is shown by the line on the left. This is higher than the line on the right which shows the energy stored in the magnesium oxide. The difference between the two lines shows the energy given out when the magnesium burns. Magnesium does not burn by itself, a small amount of energy from a flame has to be given to it to start it off. This amount is shown by the hump between the two lines.

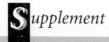

Energy changes when bonds break and form

Think more about this reaction between magnesium and oxygen.

$$2Mg(s) + O_2(g) \rightarrow 2MgO(s)$$

What must happen to the bonds in the magnesium and the oxygen when the reaction happens?

• The metallic bonds holding the two magnesium atoms to other magnesium atoms must break.

• The covalent bond between the two oxygen atoms in the molecule must break.

• The ions of magnesium and oxide must form.

• The ions come together in the form of a crystal lattice.

The first two of these processes involves the breaking of bonds. The second two of these processes involve the formation of an ionic bond in a crystal.

When bonds are broken and atoms are pulled apart, energy is needed. This is happening in the first two processes. When bonds are formed and atoms come together, energy is given out. This is what is happening in the second two processes. In this reaction, the amount of energy given out in the second two steps is greater than the amount needed to make the first two steps happen. This means that, over all four steps, energy is given out.

Energy in food

We get our energy from the food we eat. In our bodies, chemical reactions break this food down and the energy is released. Food is made out of molecules that contain carbon, like the wood in a fire. The energy in the food is not released all at once like the energy in the firewood; if it was we would all explode into flames after a meal! The energy is given out in a number of small steps in amounts small enough for the muscles to use.

High-energy foods	kJ/100 g	Low-energy foods	kJ/100 g
Most fats	>3000	Most raw vegetables	<100
Sweet biscuits	2000	Most fresh fruit	<200
Hard cheeses	1500	Boiled rice	500
Most pasta	1500	Eggs	650
Roast meat	>1000	Most bread	<1000

Important note: These are *approximate* figures only. Different ways of cooking and different amounts of sugar make a big difference.

Some foods contain much more useful energy in the chemical bonds than others. This is shown in Table 6.1. The unit of energy is the joule but this is rather small so we usually measure food energy in kilojoules (kJ).

The energy used by our muscles comes from glucose. The glucose is produced when the food we eat is digested. It is taken to the muscles by the blood and there it reacts with oxygen. The products are carbon dioxide and water and the reaction produces a lot of energy.

Glucose + oxygen → carbon dioxide + water + *energy*

This energy originally came from the sun. The green plants which we eat to obtain the glucose made the glucose originally from carbon dioxide in the air and water in the ground. This reaction is called **photosynthesis**. The reaction is the reverse of the reaction in our muscles. It is endothermic, taking in light energy from the sun.

Carbon dioxide + water + *energy* → glucose + oxygen

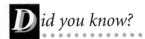

Did you know?

The process of breaking down food starts with the cooking. This means that energy is given out during cooking; cooking is exothermic. This may surprise you because you usually put energy into cooking. However, if you start off cooking a stew in a pot and then you take it off the stove and put it into a well-insulated box, it will continue to cook with no extra heat. In the past, a box like this was used quite often. It was called a 'haybox' because the insulating material was hay.

In the reactions studied in Investigation 6.1, chemical energy was converted into heat energy and also, in the first reaction, into light energy (see Figure 6.4). These are not the only energy forms that chemical energy can be changed into during a reaction. We can also get mechanical and electrical energy and these are studied in the next sections.

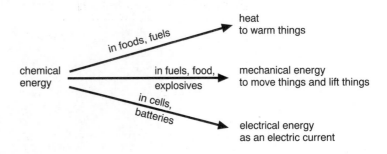

chemical energy

in foods, fuels → heat to warm things

in fuels, food, explosives → mechanical energy to move things and lift things

in cells, batteries → electrical energy as an electric current

■ **Figure 6.4** Conversions of chemical energy.

Questions

6.1 We get our energy from glucose. In our muscles it reacts with oxygen and is converted into water and carbon dioxide. Explain where the energy comes from.

6.2 Explain, giving examples, what is meant by endothermic and exothermic reactions.

6.3 Calcium carbonate → calcium oxide + carbon dioxide

This decomposition reaction of calcium carbonate is endothermic. Explain what you must do to calcium carbonate to make it decompose. Draw an energy diagram (similar to Figure 6.3) for the reaction.

6.4 Explain why the reactions that take place during cooking food are usually exothermic.

6.5 Reactions that produce gases are often endothermic. Can you explain why this is so?

Fuels

All our common fuels contain the element carbon. We can classify them into two groups, **renewable fuels** and **non-renewable fuels**.

The renewable fuels come from living material and after we have used them we can replace them by growing more. The non-renewable fuels were made millions of years ago when living things that were around then died and their remains decayed in the absence of air.

In the Carboniferous period around 200–300 million years ago, the world was a very different place from what we see today. There were no humans, of course; we have only existed for a few million years. The plants then were not the kinds we see around today, they were more like giant ferns. Much of the land was swampy, the climate was hot and the air was damp. The ferns were huge, much bigger than most of the trees we have today (see Figure 6.5).

When this vegetation died, it fell into the swampy water where there was very little oxygen. The lack of oxygen prevented the vegetation from decomposing completely. Instead it was gradually compressed at the bottom of the swamps. Later, more soils were deposited on top of the vegetation layer, and under the great pressures of the layers above it gradually turned into coal.

■ **Figure 6.5** Carboniferous period environment.

At the same time, in the warm seas, small shellfish lived and died and their remains fell to the bottom. The same thing happened to their remains but instead of forming coal they changed into oil and gas. Oil and gas can often escape through rocks as many rocks are porous (which means that they have small holes in them that liquids and gases can get through). One rock that is not porous, however, is rock salt and this is formed when ancient seas dry up. If the rock salt formed on top of the oil and gas deposits, it traps them and we can now use them (see Figure 6.6).

We call these fuels **fossil fuels** because, like fossils, they are the remains of once-living things. This kind of decay is not happening to living things today and so these fuels are non-renewable. Once we have used them, they are gone for ever.

Table 6.2 lists some of our fuels. The two fuels alcohol and hydrogen are not widely used at present. They have been included as examples of possible fuels of the future when the fossil fuels have been used up.

■ **Table 6.2 Fuels.**

State	Renewable fuels	Non-renewable fuels
Solid fuel	Wood	Coal
Liquid fuel	Alcohol	Oil
Gaseous fuel	Hydrogen	Natural gas

Figure 6.7 on page 130 shows how the use of different fuels has increased over the last 40 years. The renewable solid fuel, wood, on the graph accounts for a only a very small proportion of solid fuel used. We have become very dependent on the non-renewable fuels coal, oil and gas and these are now beginning to run out.

Note the units in which the fuels on the graph are compared. The unit is 'tonnes coal equivalent'. This is the amount of a particular

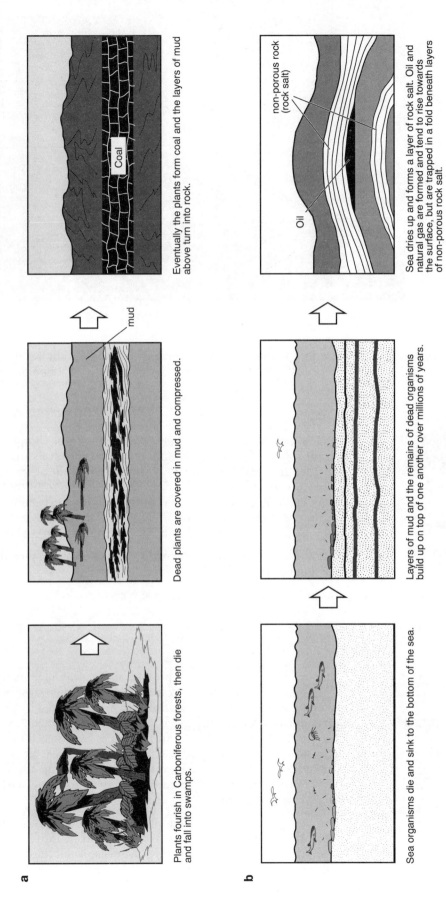

Figure 6.6 Formation of (a) coal and (b) oil and natural gas.

a

Plants flourish in Carboniferous forests, then die and fall into swamps.

Dead plants are covered in mud and compressed.

mud

Eventually the plants form coal and the layers of mud above turn into rock.

Coal

b

Sea organisms die and sink to the bottom of the sea.

Layers of mud and the remains of dead organisms build up on top of one another over millions of years.

Sea dries up and forms a layer of rock salt. Oil and natural gas are formed and tend to rise towards the surface, but are trapped in a fold beneath layers of non-porous rock salt.

non-porous rock (rock salt)

Oil

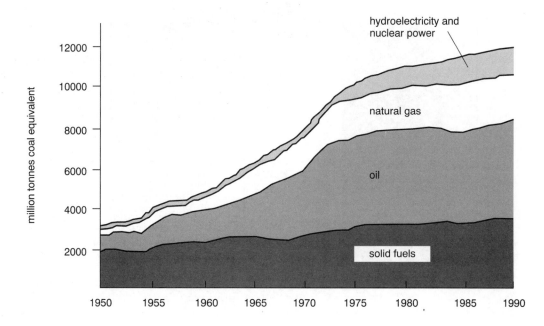

fuel that is equivalent to a tonne of coal. So 0.6 tonnes of oil and 700 cubic metres of gas are each equivalent to 1 tonne of coal (see Figure 6.8).

Coal

Coal is mainly carbon but it also contains a lot of compounds of carbon. Many of these compounds are useful chemicals and so they are often removed from the coal by heating it in the absence of air. When this happens, the chemicals distil off. The solid that is left behind is coke. Coke, unlike coal, burns without much smoke and it burns at a higher temperature than coal. This means that coke is more useful to industry and causes less pollution than coal.

When coke and coal burn, the main product is carbon dioxide. The reaction is very exothermic.

Carbon + oxygen → carbon dioxide + *energy*

$$C(s) + O_2(g) \rightarrow CO_2(g)$$

Although coal is quite cheap to produce and is plentiful in many parts of the world, it is expensive to use. Coal cannot be transported by pumping it along pipes. Instead it has to be transported by train and lorry which is very expensive. It is also much more difficult to control in a furnace than oil and gas which can be easily switched on and off using taps. It is therefore used mainly in very large-scale furnaces such as large power stations and blast furnaces. These large furnaces are made to run continuously because it is very difficult and wasteful to relight coal furnaces often.

Coal can quite easily be turned into a gas fuel and, in some parts of the world, such as South Africa, coal is also made into liquid fuels. As the world gradually uses up its supplies of oil, these processes will become more important.

1 tonne of coal

is equivalent to

0.6 tonnes of oil

or

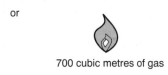

700 cubic metres of gas

or

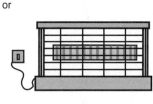

a single-bar electric fire producing heat for 7450 hours

■ **Figure 6.8** Tonnes coal equivalent.

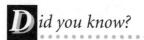

*D*id you know?

Scientists are working on ways to convert coal into gas underground so that it will not have to be mined. This will allow us to use small seams of coal or seams that are dangerous to mine because of weaknesses in the surrounding rocks.

Crude oil

Crude oil – its correct name is petroleum which means 'liquid stone' – is a mixture of **hydrocarbons**. Hydrocarbons are compounds made from the two elements hydrogen and carbon.

Crude oil is refined to give us many very useful substances. This process will be described in Chapter 8. The fuels we get from oil are particularly useful for transport as they can easily be carried around and, being liquid, are easily carried through pipes and burnt in different types of engines. Coal cannot be used in this way as easily.

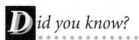

*D*id you know?

You can find a process similar to the formation of oil happening today. Poke around with a stick in the muddy bottom of a pond or marsh. You may see bubbles coming up out of the mud. These bubbles are the hydrocarbon gas methane, which is sometimes called 'marsh gas'. If you collect the gas in a jam jar you can set fire to it.

Gas

When we talk of coal, oil and gas as the three fossil fuels by 'gas' we mean methane gas. Methane was formed in the same way as oil, between 150 million and 300 million years ago. It is the simplest hydrocarbon, having only one atom of carbon in its molecule, CH_4. It is present in gas fields in a number of places in the world. In many countries it is pumped directly to industry and to houses through a long network of pipes in the same way as water is delivered to homes.

*I*nvestigation 6.2

methylated spirits
paraffin

What are the products when fuels burn?

You will need:

• fuels such as methylated spirits, paraffin, a candle, wood (do **NOT** use petrol for this investigation)

• burner

• test tubes

- polythene bags
- limewater
- cobalt chloride paper or anhydrous copper sulphate.

1 Put the fuel in the burner and light the wick.

2 Hold a cold test tube above the burner to catch some of the gases produced as the fuel burns. Look carefully at the sides of the tube.

3 Put a small quantity of limewater in the tube with the gases and shake. Note any changes in the limewater.

4 Test any condensation you see with blue cobalt chloride paper or with anhydrous copper sulphate.

5 Repeat the investigation with other fuels and with the candle and a small piece of wood.

6 Repeat the experiment collecting the gases from a car exhaust pipe. This can be done by holding the tube containing the limewater briefly near the exhaust pipe. You could also collect a sample of the exhaust gases in a polythene bag. This will allow you to look more carefully at it.

CARE Car exhaust gases contain carbon monoxide, which is poisonous. Do not breathe in the gases.

You are looking for evidence of carbon dioxide and of water vapour and of any other possible products that you might see.

Tests for water

1 Warm a piece of cobalt chloride paper until it is blue. Touch the liquid with it. If the liquid is water the cobalt chloride paper will turn pink.

2 Touch the liquid with a crystal of white anhydrous copper sulphate. If the liquid is water the crystal will turn blue.

When hydrocarbons burn, the products are carbon dioxide and water. The water is produced by the hydrogen atoms combining with the oxygen during burning. The carbon dioxide comes from the carbon.

Hydrocarbon + oxygen → carbon dioxide + hydrogen + *energy*

The equation shows the burning of the gas butane, which is a hydrocarbon.

Butane + oxygen → carbon dioxide + water vapour

$$2C_4H_{10}(g) + 13O_2(g) \rightarrow 8CO_2(g) + 10H_2O(g)$$

You should have detected both carbon dioxide and water when you burnt all the fuels. Even wood contains hydrogen; the main molecule that it is made out of is cellulose which is a carbohydrate. Carbohydrates are compounds made of carbon, hydrogen and oxygen.

Very often, however, not enough oxygen can get to the flame to burn the hydrocarbon completely. When this happens, carbon monoxide (CO) is one of the products and sometimes unburned carbon (C) is produced. You will probably have seen this with diesel-engined lorries, particularly if they are old (see Figure 6.9). The unburned carbon appears as a black smoke.

Carbon monoxide is a dangerous gas because it has no colour or smell and it is poisonous. Whenever you see a yellow flame when fuels are burnt you can be sure that some carbon monoxide is being

■ **Figure 6.9** Not enough oxygen is mixing with the diesel fuel in the engine of this lorry. Unburnt carbon is present in the exhaust fumes.

Figure 6.10 Wood is only a renewable fuel if we plant more trees to replace the ones we burn. In the picture above taken in Malaysia we can see the devastating result of excessive logging.

produced because when fuels burn completely the flame is blue. Sometimes, when people light a heater inside at night, the carbon monoxide cannot escape and it can kill people. Heaters that burn fuels should only be used where there is good ventilation.

Sustainable fuel supplies

Our supplies of coal, oil and gas will eventually be used up. This is predicted to happen within the next few decades for oil and gas. It is important that we use, more and more, sources of energy that are renewable. Something that is sustainable is something that can be kept going indefinitely. If we use renewable energy resources, it means that our supply of fuel is sustainable.

Renewable energy sources are those which come indirectly from the sun. We can generate electricity from hydro-electric schemes which use the potential energy of water. The water was given this energy by the sun. We can also use plant matter as a source of energy. The energy in the plants originally came from the sun and was converted into chemical energy in the plant during the process of photosynthesis.

Wood is a renewable source of energy. In most parts of the world it is the main source of energy in the home. It is only renewable, however, if new trees are allowed to grow, or are planted, to replace the ones used. In many places this is not happening. In these places the people will gradually run short of the energy they need to live (see Figure 6.10).

Ethanol (alcohol) is another renewable energy source. It is commonly available throughout the world as methylated spirits. It can be made from plant matter by fermentation. This is a process that uses the micro-organism yeast to convert sugars into ethanol. Sugars are available naturally in many plants and can be made from cellulose, the material that all plants are made of. You will study this further in Chapter 9.

Ethanol has the formula C_2H_5OH. When it burns, carbon dioxide and water vapour are produced.

Ethanol + oxygen → carbon dioxide + water + *energy*

$$C_2H_5OH(l) + 3O_2(g) \rightarrow 2CO_2(g) + 3H_2O(g)$$

Hydrogen is a possible fuel of the future. It can be made from water using electricity (page 146). When it burns, the only product is water vapour and so it does not pollute.

Hydrogen + oxygen → water + *energy*

$$2H_2(g) + O_2(g) \rightarrow 2H_2O(g)$$

Figure 6.11 The airship Hindenburg showed how explosive hydrogen is. It was filled with hydrogen and caught fire from a static electricity spark when it earthed itself on its mooring mast.

Hydrogen can be used by car engines without a major modification in the design. Hydrogen is the lightest gas and was once widely used to fill large airships before the days of large passenger aircraft. The main problem with hydrogen is that it is dangerously explosive as Figure 6.11 shows.

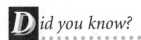

Questions

6.6 A Bunsen burner burns methane or propane as a fuel. What are the products of the burning? The burner gives a different flame according to whether the air hole is open or closed. In which flame is the combustion of the gas more complete? What evidence is there for incomplete burning in the other flame?

6.7 Explain why coal is used mainly in large power stations, whereas oil is burnt in small ones that are used to increase the supply of electricity at peak times.

6.8 Hydrogen is a fuel that can easily be made from water and causes hardly any pollution when it is burnt. Give two reasons why it is not widely used.

6.9 Study the graph of world fuel use on page 130 . Our supplies of oil will begin to run out in the next few decades, gas a little after that, but there are known coal reserves to last another century at present rates of production. Predict how you think the graph will change in the next 30 years. Give reasons for your predictions.

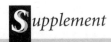

Supplement

Cells and batteries

To find out how the potato clock (Figure 6.12) works try this investigation.

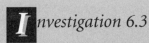

Investigation 6.3

Electricity from chemicals

You will need:

- strips of a number of different metals about 10 cm long. Suggested ones are copper, zinc, iron and magnesium
- sodium chloride
- beaker
- voltmeter

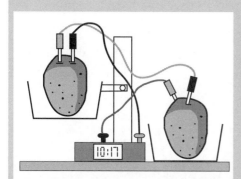

Figure 6.12 This electric clock seems to be powered by a potato. How does it work?

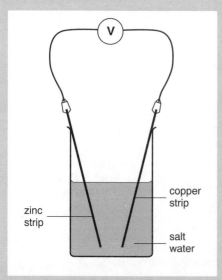

zinc strip

copper strip

salt water

Figure 6.13 Cell with two metals and voltmeter.

• two leads fitted with crocodile clips.

1 Dissolve some salt in water and put the solution in a beaker.

2 Put two different metals in the solution and connect them to the voltmeter as shown in Figure 6.13.

3 Measure the voltage and note which metal is the positive pole.

4 Repeat the experiment with all possible combinations of metals.

5 Look at the results. Which metal was always positive in all the experiments you did with it? Can you arrange the metals in a list so that the positive one in every experiment comes lower in the list than the negative one?

In this investigation you have made some cells. All that is needed to make a cell is two different metals and an ionic solution. In the potato clock in Figure 6.12, the two metals are probably copper and zinc and the solution is the liquid in the potato which, being slightly salty, contains ions.

You will have noticed in the investigation that the voltage depended on the metals you used. If the metals are far apart in the reactivity series, the voltage is large; if they are close together the voltage is smaller. The order of reactivity of the four metals used is:

magnesium zinc iron copper.

This is the same order as you should have obtained in step 5 of the investigation.

To summarise:

• the less reactive metal is always the positive pole of the cell

• the voltage of the cell depends on the difference in reactivity of the two metals.

If you look at the metals used in the investigation, you will notice that the most reactive one, which is always the negative pole, is eaten away while the current flows through the voltmeter. When any metal is put into the salt solution, it will start to corrode. Metals react by losing one or two electrons and some (those high on the reactivity series) lose them more easily than others.

If the two metals are placed in a solution containing ions and connected together with a wire, a circuit is formed. When the metals react and form ions the electrons which the atoms lose can flow back round the circuit. This will mean that one metal is pushing electrons one way and the second is pushing them the other way.

The more reactive one pushes harder (we say it has a greater potential) and so the current is set up flowing from the more reactive metal to the less reactive one.

This is shown in Figure 6.14 with the metals copper and zinc.

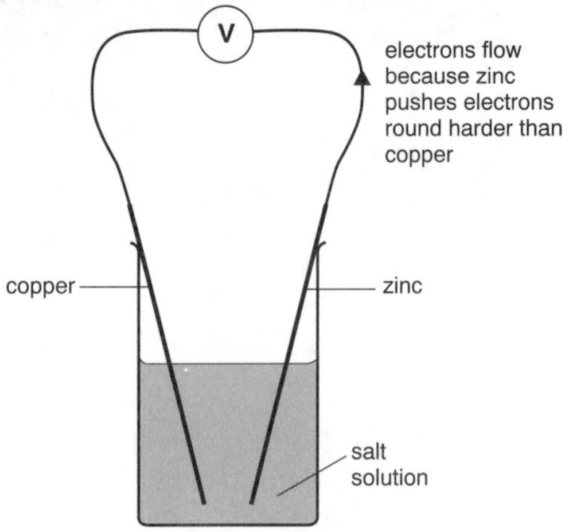

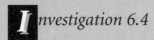

reaction at the copper

$2H^+ + 2e^- \rightarrow H_2$

Electrons in the copper are given up to positive ions in the solution (usually H^+)
The copper becomes coated in bubbles of hydrogen

reaction at the zinc

$Zn \rightarrow Zn^{2+} + 2e^-$

Electrons given up by the zinc are pushed round the wire

■ **Figure 6.14** Why the copper–zinc cell works.

Commercial cells

Cells are a convenient portable source of electrical energy. All of them work in the same way as the one made in the investigation. Two poles made out of different conducting materials (usually metals) dip into a solution containing ions. In 'dry' cells, the solution is a paste so that it does not spill out. The voltage of cells depends, as shown in the investigation, on the difference in reactivity between the materials of the two poles.

Some cells are rechargeable. This means that the chemical reactions that happen when the cell gives electricity can be reversed if an electric current is passed through the cell. The current is passed through the cell in the opposite direction from the current that it produces when it is used.

A very useful rechargeable cell is the lead–acid cell used in cars. You can easily make and test one as follows.

*I*nvestigation 6.4

Making a lead–acid cell

You will need:

- two strips of lead
- dilute sulphuric acid
- beaker
- d.c. supply
- torch bulb and holder
- leads with crocodile clips.

dilute sulphuric acid

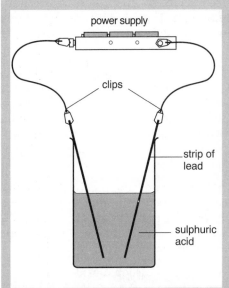

■ **Figure 6.15** Experimental lead–acid cell.

1 The apparatus in Figure 6.15 is a simple lead–acid cell. Set it up and charge it with a low voltage d.c. supply.

2 Disconnect the charging supply and connect instead a torch bulb. Note that the time it will stay lit will depend on how long the cell was charged.

When this cell is charged, lead oxide is formed on one of the lead strips. When it is discharged, this reaction goes the opposite way and a stream of electrons is produced. Figures 6.16 and 6.17 show the reactions that happen at the lead strips and the way the electrons flow.

Batteries are sets of cells connected in series. A car battery has six cells, each giving a little over 2 volts connected in series. This gives an overall voltage of a little over 12 volts.

uestions

6.10 Describe how you would use an orange to light a 1.5 amp bulb. What else will you need besides an orange and a bulb? Explain how your idea will work.

6.11 A cell has two electrodes dipping into salt water. The electrodes are made out of iron and copper. Which metal is the positive pole of the cell? How would you make the cell produce a higher voltage? Explain your answer.

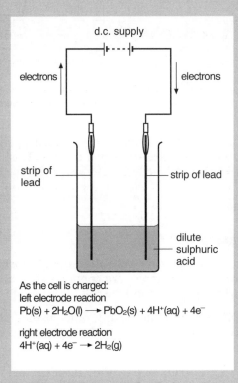

As the cell is charged:
left electrode reaction
$Pb(s) + 2H_2O(l) \longrightarrow PbO_2(s) + 4H^+(aq) + 4e^-$

right electrode reaction
$4H^+(aq) + 4e^- \longrightarrow 2H_2(g)$

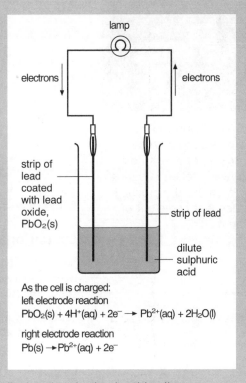

As the cell is charged:
left electrode reaction
$PbO_2(s) + 4H^+(aq) + 2e^- \longrightarrow Pb^{2+}(aq) + 2H_2O(l)$

right electrode reaction
$Pb(s) \longrightarrow Pb^{2+}(aq) + 2e^-$

■ **Figures 6.16 and 6.17** Charging and discharging the lead–acid cell.

Redox reactions

For centuries, chemists have referred to the process of obtaining metals from their ores as **reduction**. This word was used because a large amount of ore is always needed to get a small quantity of metal.

English is a living language, however, and the exact meanings of words are changing all the time. This is particularly true of scientific words. These words often take on extra meanings as our understanding of nature gets deeper. So we still use the word reduction to mean the extraction of metals from their ores but, as you will learn in the next sections, the word has other definitions as well which have been added as our knowledge of chemistry has improved.

In Chapter 4 you studied the reduction of iron ore. In the reaction, the ore, iron oxide, was changed to the metal, iron. In the process, oxygen was removed from the ore. The **reducing agent** (the chemical that was put in the furnace to remove the oxygen) was carbon monoxide. The equation shows what happened.

Iron oxide   +   carbon   →   iron   +   carbon dioxide
    ore   *reducing*   *metal*
                  agent

$$Fe_2O_3(s) + 3CO(g) \rightarrow 2Fe(l) + 3CO_2(g)$$

In Chapter 4 you also studied the corrosion of metals. Most metals react with oxygen to form the metal oxide. Some metals, such as magnesium, react readily in a spectacular way by burning. The reaction below shows what happens when iron wool burns in oxygen. The name we give to this kind of reaction is **oxidation**.

Iron + oxygen → iron oxide

$$4Fe(s) + 3O_2(g) \rightarrow 2Fe_2O_3(s)$$

Oxidation is the reverse of reduction. The reactions we have been discussing are called reduction–oxidation reactions or **redox** reactions for short.

Look again at the reduction of iron oxide. What is happening to the carbon? The carbon is oxidised to carbon dioxide. This is why the two reactions, oxidation and reduction, are always grouped together. Whenever there is a reduction, there is also an oxidation. Consider Figure 6.18.

Oxidation state

Some elements, particularly the transition metals, form not one oxide but two or more. Examples are copper and iron. Table 6.3 shows the two oxides of copper and the two sulphates of iron.

The roman number in the modern name of the oxides refers to the **oxidation state** of the metal. In these simple compounds the oxidation state is the same as the valency of the metal.

One of the typical properties of transition metals is that they show variable valency. It is more accurate to describe them as showing

■ **Figure 6.18** This racing car engine works by the oxidation of fuel. The air needed to oxidise the fuel is taken in through the top. What are the products of oxidation that come out of the exhaust pipe?

Oxidation is the addition of oxygen.
Reduction is the removal of oxygen.

variable oxidation states. For example, the oxidation state of manganese in potassium permanganate is 7. For this reason, the correct modern name for potassium permanganate is potassium manganate(VII). The oxidation states of iron in the two sulphates shown in Table 6.3 are 2 and 3 respectively.

■ **Table 6.3 The two oxides of copper and the sulphates of iron.**

	Formula	Colour	Oxidation state of metal	Old name
Copper(I) oxide	Cu_2O	Brown	1	Cuprous oxide
Copper(II) oxide	CuO	Black	2	Cupric oxide
Iron(II) sulphate	$FeSO_4$	Green	2	Ferrous sulphate
Iron(III) sulphate	$Fe_2(SO_4)_3$	Orange	3	Ferric sulphate

Supplement

Let us return to the **reduction** of iron oxide.

$$Fe_2O_3(s) + 3CO(g) \rightarrow 2Fe(l) + 3CO_2(g)$$

What has happened to the iron in this reaction? It has changed from iron ions in the oxide into iron atoms in the pure metal. In order to do this, it has gained electrons:

$$Fe^{3+} + 3e^- \rightarrow Fe$$

Think also about the opposite reaction, the burning of steel wool in oxygen:

$$2Fe(s) + 3O_2(g) \rightarrow 2Fe_2O_3(s)$$

In this **oxidation** the iron has changed from atoms into ions. The atoms of iron have lost electrons:

$$Fe \rightarrow Fe^{3+} + 3e^-$$

This leads us to a better definition of oxidation and reduction.

- **Reduction is gain of electrons.**
- **Oxidation is loss of electrons.**

This is a much more useful definition because it is not limited only to reactions involving oxygen. In Chapter 3 you studied the reaction of iron and chlorine. If you lower hot iron wool into a gas jar of chlorine, it will burn and iron(III) chloride will form. If you lower the hot iron into a gas jar of oxygen, it will burn and iron(III) oxide will form.

$$2Fe(s) + 3Cl_2(g) \rightarrow 2FeCl_3(s)$$
$$4Fe(s) + 3O_2(g) \rightarrow 2Fe_2O_3(s)$$

The same thing has happened to the iron in both cases. The iron atoms have lost electrons to form iron ions.

$$Fe \rightarrow Fe^{3+} + 3e^-$$

Reduction is gain of electrons.
Oxidation is loss of electrons.

The iron has been oxidised. In one case the oxidising agent is chlorine, in the other case it is oxygen.

In these reactions the chlorine and the oxygen have both gained the electrons that have been lost by the iron.

$$O_2 + 4e^- \rightarrow 2O^{2-}$$

$$Cl_2 + 2e^- \rightarrow 2Cl^-$$

The chlorine and the oxygen have been reduced to chloride and oxide ions.

In Chapter 4 you studied how metals could displace less reactive metals from solutions of their compounds. For example, if zinc is put in a solution of copper sulphate, copper and zinc sulphate are formed:

$$Zn(s) + CuSO_4(aq) \rightarrow Cu(s) + ZnSO_4(aq)$$

In this reaction, the zinc forms zinc ions and the copper ions are changed into copper atoms.

$$Zn \rightarrow Zn^{2+} + 2e^-$$

$$Cu^{2+} + 2e^- \rightarrow Cu$$

These equations show that the zinc has been oxidised and the copper ions have been reduced.

Questions

6.12 Iron ore is reduced in the blast furnace. Explain what is meant by the word 'reduced'. In the blast furnace, what is the reducing agent?

6.13 Explain what is meant by the word 'oxidation'. Give some examples of oxidation from everyday life.

6.14 In the following reactions, name the substance that is oxidised and the substance that is reduced.

Carbon + carbon dioxide $\rightarrow$ carbon monoxide

Magnesium + copper oxide $\rightarrow$ magnesium oxide + copper

Calcium + water $\rightarrow$ calcium hydroxide + hydrogen

6.15 In the following reactions, write equations showing which particles have gained electrons and which have lost them.

$$2AgNO_3(aq) + Pb(s) \rightarrow Pb(NO_3)_2(aq) + 2Ag(s)$$

$$Zn(s) + CuO(s) \rightarrow ZnO(s) + Cu(s)$$

$$Mg(s) + I_2(s) \rightarrow MgI_2(s)$$

In each case state what is the oxidising agent and what is the reducing agent.

Electrolysis

Earlier in this chapter you studied how electricity can be produced from a chemical reaction. In Chapter 4 you saw how electricity could be used to make a reaction take place. In this section you will study this further.

concentrated hyrochloric acid

dilute sulphuric acid

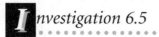

*I*nvestigation 6.5

What is the effect of electricity on a number of solutions?

You will need:

- the following solutions (2 M):

sodium chloride

potassium bromide

copper sulphate

copper chloride

zinc sulphate

- concentrated hydrochloric acid (optional)
- dilute sulphuric acid
- small beakers
- two test tubes
- wires with crocodile clips
- a source of about 4 V d.c.
- graphite rods about 10 cm long
- litmus paper.

1 Set up the apparatus as shown in Figure 6.19. This is called an electrolysis cell. The process you are going to study is called electrolysis.

2 Put some sodium chloride solution in the cell and switch on the current. Note any evidence of changes (colour change, smell, bubbles) on or near the graphite rods. Test any gases that are produced for hydrogen, oxygen and chlorine.

3 Repeat the experiment with all the other solutions except for the acids.

4 Repeat it also with the concentrated hydrochloric acid solution (**CARE**, this should be done by a teacher).

5 Repeat the experiment with pure water. Add a little dilute sulphuric acid to the water. Do you notice any changes?

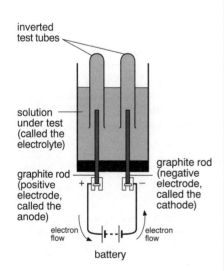

■ **Figure 6.19** Electrolysis cell.

The electrolysis cell you set up consisted of a number of different parts which have special names. These are shown in Figure 6.19. The liquid is known as the **electrolyte**; the rods that dip into the liquid are called **electrodes**. The electrode connected to the positive terminal of the supply is called the **anode**. The negative electrode is called the **cathode**.

Electricity, everyone is taught, flows from positive to negative. However, we now know that an electric current is actually a stream of electrons. These are negatively charged and so they actually flow from the negative pole of the battery to the positive one. This is the opposite direction from the direction we are all taught. When you learn about electrolysis it is important to understand this. It means that:

- electrons flow into the solution from the cathode
- electrons flow away from the solution along the anode.

This electron flow is shown in Figure 6.19.

You will have noticed some gas produced at some of the electrodes. Chlorine gas is easy to identify; it has a well known smell and it bleaches litmus paper. Other gases have to be collected and then tested. This is rather difficult as quite small quantities of the gases are produced. It is difficult to collect and identify oxygen because it reacts with the carbon of the electrode and carbon dioxide is also produced.

Table 6.4 shows some of the products of electrolysis of a number of solutions.

The table shows two important patterns.

- Metals or hydrogen are formed at the cathode.
- Non-metals (except hydrogen) are formed at the anode.

The solutions that are electrolysed all contain an ionic compound and water. Sometimes the product of the electrolysis comes from the water (hydrogen at the cathode and oxygen at the anode) and sometimes it comes from the ionic substance.

■ **Table 6.4 The products of electrolysis of a number of solutions.**

Electrolyte	At the cathode	At the anode
Copper(II) chloride solution	A salmon pink solid collects around the carbon rod. It is **copper**	A yellow–green gas collects. It bleaches indicator paper. It is **chlorine**
Sodium chloride solution	A clear, colourless gas collects. The gas burns with a squeaky pop. It is **hydrogen**	**Chlorine** is produced.
Potassium bromide solution	**Hydrogen** is produced	A dark red colour forms around the carbon rod. It is due to **bromine**
Copper(II) sulphate solution	**Copper** is produced	A clear, colourless gas collects. It relights a glowing splint. It is **oxygen**
Zinc sulphate solution	**Hydrogen** is produced. Also, there is some grey solid around the rod. It is **zinc**	**Oxygen** is produced

Patterns such as these can be seen from the table:

At the cathode

• The product is the metal when it is near the bottom of the reactivity series.

• The more reactive metals are not produced; instead hydrogen from the water is the product.

At the anode

• If the solution contains halide ions, these elements are liberated at the anode.

• When the electrolyte is a sulphate or nitrate, electrolysis liberates oxygen from the water.

Pure water will not conduct electricity and so it cannot be electrolysed. When the electrodes are put into the water, no gases can be seen. However, when a small amount of a solution containing ions, such as dilute sulphuric acid, is added, the electrolysis starts. The water is split up by the electric current and oxygen is produced at the anode and hydrogen at the cathode.

For electrolysis to take place, ions have to be present in the liquid and be able to move. This happens in a solution. It also can happen in a molten ionic compound. Most ionic substances will melt between about 300 and 1000 °C and so it is possible to electrolyse molten compounds heated by gas. In Chapter 4 you studied the electrolysis of aluminium oxide to make aluminium. Many metals, particularly those in Groups I and II, are obtained in this way.

It is possible to obtain lead in the school laboratory by electrolysis of molten lead bromide in a crucible. It is not a very pleasant reaction to do as bromine vapour is produced at the anode and this has an acrid smell and is rather poisonous. Figure 6.20 shows how it can be done. The lead falls to the bottom and can be recovered after the crucible has cooled.

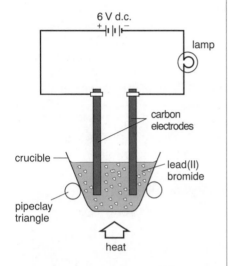

■ **Figure 6.20** Electrolysis of molten lead bromide.

Supplement

Explaining electrolysis

Ionic solutions will conduct electricity because the charge is carried by the ions moving through the solution.

*I*nvestigation 6.6

Studying the movement of ions

You will need:

potassium
permanganate

• d.c. power supply of 20 volts or more
• filter paper
• microscope slide
• leads with crocodile clips
• potassium permanganate.

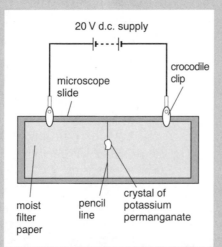

Figure 6.22 Ion movement in electrolysis.

Figure 6.21 Michael Faraday, 1791–1867, was a Scottish scientist who is best known for his work on electromagnetism and his invention of the electric motor. However, he was a professor of chemistry and was the first to explain electrolysis. In the 1830s he introduced the word 'ion' to mean an electrically charged atom.

1 Cut a piece of filter paper the size of a microscope slide and moisten it with water.

2 Place a single potassium permanganate crystal on the centre as shown (see Figure 6.22). Some colour from the crystal will sink into the paper.

3 Connect the power supply and switch on. After a few minutes, note what has happened to the coloured spot on the paper.

After a few minutes, the purple stain on the filter paper will have moved towards the positive crocodile clip. This illustrates that the purple ion is negatively charged. The purple ion is the permanganate ion, MnO_4^-.

In an electrolysis circuit, the power supply is a source of electrons and also a pump to make them go along the wire. In the electrolyte the positive ions (cations) are attracted towards the negative electrode (cathode) and the negative ions (anions) are attracted towards the positive electrode (anode) (see Figure 6.23).

When a cation reaches the cathode, an electron (or two electrons if the cation has two charges) joins the ion and forms a neutral atom. This then appears as the element at the electrode. In the cell shown, the cations are copper ions and so we see a deposit of copper forming on the cathode.

When anions reach the anode, they give up electrons, also forming neutral atoms. This element then appears at the anode. In the electrolysis of copper chloride, for example, these reactions happen at the electrodes.

At the cathode:

$Cu^{2+} + 2e^- \rightarrow Cu$

At the anode:

$2Cl^- \rightarrow Cl_2 + 2e^-$

The cathode will become coated in copper and there will be the smell of chlorine at the anode.

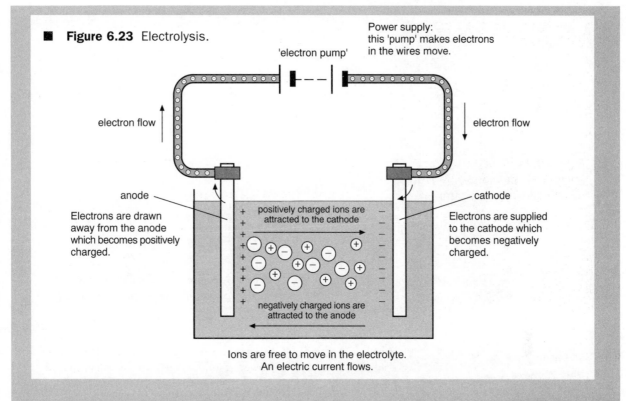

■ **Figure 6.23** Electrolysis.

Ions are free to move in the electrolyte.
An electric current flows.

The products observed at the electrodes will depend on the ions present in the solution. Most of the ionic compounds we have studied in this chapter are called salts. A salt is any ionic compound of a metal, other than its oxide or hydroxide. In any solution of a salt the following products could be produced at the electrodes:

At the cathode
Metal (from the salt)
Hydrogen (from the water)
At the anode
Non-metal (from the salt)
Oxygen (from the water)

Which product we see depends upon two factors:

- the ease with which the ions are discharged
- the concentration of the salt.

Some ions are discharged more readily than others. Metal ions near the bottom of the reactivity series are discharged easily. Those at the top are not easily discharged. This is to be expected. The metals at the top of the series form compounds readily and cannot easily be obtained from their compounds.

We can draw a line in the reactivity series. Below the line, metals will be discharged from their solutions. Above the line, metals will not be discharged; hydrogen from the water will be discharged instead. The line occurs as shown just above zinc (see Figure 6.24).

If the solution of the salt is very dilute, however, some hydrogen will be discharged even from solutions of salts of metals near the bottom

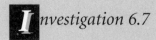

potassium	
sodium	
calcium	
magnesium	These metals are not discharged from their solutions
- -	
zinc	
iron	
copper	These metals are discharged from their solutions
silver	
gold	

Figure 6.24 Reactivity series showing which metal ions are discharged during electrolysis.

of the series. This is because there are not enough metal ions near the electrodes in the very dilute solution and so some hydrogen will be produced as well.

At the anode we find that the usual product is oxygen except where the salt is a halide. In this case the halogen is liberated. If the halide solution is very dilute, however, some oxygen will also be produced.

Very pure water does not conduct electricity because it is covalent and does not contain ions. If the water contains just a tiny amount of an ionic impurity (such as salt or sulphuric acid) it will conduct electricity and be electrolysed. The products are hydrogen at the cathode and oxygen at the anode.

*I*nvestigation 6.7

Electrolysis of copper sulphate between copper electrodes

You will need:
- small beaker
- two strips of copper
- d.c power supply, about 6 V
- copper sulphate solution.

1 Repeat Investigation 6.5 using copper sulphate solution (see Figure 6.25) but this time use strips of copper as electrodes. Allow the experiment to run for at least 15 minutes or so. Watch for signs of activity at the electrodes.

2 At the end of the experiment, examine the electrodes carefully.

copper sulphate

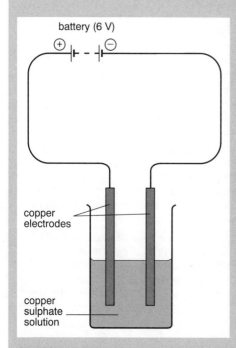

battery (6 V)

copper electrodes

copper sulphate solution

■ **Figure 6.25** Electrolysis of copper sulphate between copper electrodes.

In this investigation you will not have seen any signs of a gas at either electrode. At the end of the investigation you will find a deposit of copper as expected on the cathode. At the anode, however, a different reaction has taken place from that you observed with carbon electrodes. When you used carbon electrodes, oxygen gas, from the water, was liberated. In this case, no anion was discharged at all. Instead, copper atoms in the electrode gave up electrons and they became ions. These ions replaced the ones that were discharged at the cathode.

You can see from the equation box that when copper electrodes are used, the action at the anode is the reverse of the action at the cathode.

At the cathode:

$$Cu^{2+} + 2e^- \rightarrow Cu$$

At the anode:

$$Cu \rightarrow Cu^{2+} + 2e^-$$

This reaction is used in industry to purify the crude copper produced by smelting. The crude copper is made the anode and the cathode is a piece of pure copper. As the electrolysis proceeds, the cathode gets bigger and the anode gets smaller. The impurities fall to the bottom of the cell underneath the anode.

Applications of electrolysis

There are two important applications of electrolysis. One is the manufacture of useful elements from their compounds and the other is electroplating.

We make many elements by electrolysis. The manufacture of chlorine is described in Chapter 5 and the production of copper and aluminium is covered in Chapter 4.

Electroplating is used widely to coat one metal with another one. When you electrolysed the copper salts in Investigation 6.4, you will have noticed that the cathode became coated in copper. The copper coat was probably rather soft and could be scraped off easily. It is possible, however, to make a very hard-wearing coating if the right conditions are used.

Chromium, nickel, silver and gold are often plated onto less expensive metals. Table 6.5 gives some examples of these.

The articles to be plated are made the cathode of an electrolysis cell. The electrolyte contains a solution of the ion of the metal to be deposited.

■ **Figure 6.26** These silver plated objects look like solid silver but cost a lot less.

■ Table 6.5 Uses of electroplating.

Metal electroplated	Uses
Chromium and nickel	Steel objects are chromium or nickel plated to prevent them from corroding. Examples are bicycle wheels, taps, kettles, watches and other household metal items used under conditions where paint would wear off
Silver	Ornaments or cutlery made out of copper or an alloy of copper and silver or copper and nickel are plated with silver to give an attractive and corrosion resistant finish. The objects are much cheaper than they would be if they were made of solid silver
Gold	Ornamental items are also finished with gold plating. The metal parts of electronic components are often gold plated. This ensures that the surface is free from corrosion and makes good electrical contacts

uestions

6.16 What are the products of electrolysis of the following solutions?

potassium iodide

nickel sulphate (nickel is just above copper on the reactivity series)

magnesium chloride

6.17 Draw a diagram to show how you would electroplate a copper ring with silver. Show which is the anode and which the cathode. Show which electrolyte you would use.

6.18 Sodium is manufactured commercially by electrolysis of molten sodium chloride. Explain why it is not possible to use sodium chloride solution for this.

Review questions on this chapter can be found on pages 240–1.

7 Chemistry and our environment

We all live on a rather small blue–green planet which just happens to have the right average temperature and atmosphere to allow life to thrive (Figure 7.1). These conditions are controlled by a complicated web of chemical reactions. These reactions control the composition of the atmosphere and of the rivers and seas. They also control what happens to the energy from the sun when it reaches us. They ensure that dangerous radiation from the sun is filtered out before it gets to us and that the planet does not heat up or cool down too much. It is important that we try and understand something of this chemical balance so that we do not accidentally upset it.

Our atmosphere

The atmosphere forms a thin layer around the surface of the planet. Without it, most life could not exist. Pure dry air is a mixture of nine gases but is mainly nitrogen and oxygen. Oxygen is a very important gas for us because it is the reaction of a wide variety of substances with oxygen that gives us the energy we need to survive. We burn fuels in oxygen to keep us warm, to power our vehicles and to generate most of our electricity. It is the reaction between oxygen and sugars in our body that provides us with the energy that keeps us alive.

id you know?

Oxygen is a poisonous gas. We could not survive for long if we had to breathe pure oxygen. Air is safe because the oxygen is 'diluted' with nitrogen.

xperiment

We can use gas syringes to measure accurately the percentage of oxygen in the air (see Figure 7.2). Gas syringes are accurately made glass syringes with tightly fitting airtight plungers. They are calibrated and can hold 100 cm³ of gas. 100 cm³ of air is passed slowly

Figure 7.1 Earthrise on the moon. This photograph of our small planet was taken by American astronauts.

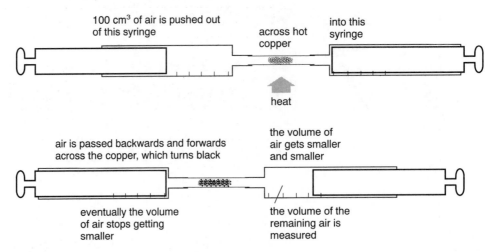

100 cm³ of air is pushed out of this syringe

across hot copper

into this syringe

heat

air is passed backwards and forwards across the copper, which turns black

the volume of air gets smaller and smaller

eventually the volume of air stops getting smaller

the volume of the remaining air is measured

■ **Figure 7.2** Apparatus to measure the oxygen content of the air.

■ **Table 7.1 Composition of air by volume.**

Gas	Volume percentage in dry air
Nitrogen	78.03
Oxygen	20.99
Argon	0.93
Carbon dioxide	0.03
Neon	0.001 5
Hydrogen	0.001 0
Helium	0.000 5
Krypton	0.000 1
Xenon	0.000 008

backwards and forwards across granules of heated copper as shown in Figure 7.2.

In the experiment, the oxygen combines with the hot copper as it is passed slowly over it. Eventually all the oxygen has combined with the copper. The remaining air is allowed to cool to the original temperature and the new volume is read. Subtracting this from the original 100 cm³ gives the volume of oxygen. Because the original volume of air was 100 cm³, this number is also the percentage of oxygen in air.

Table 7.1 shows the main constituents of dry air. It shows that a little under four-fifths of the air is nitrogen and a little over one-fifth is oxygen. The remaining seven gases account for only around 1%. One substance is not included in the table and that is water vapour. The amount of this in the atmosphere is variable and depends on the weather.

*D*id you know?

You breathe in and out approximately 15 000 litres of air each day. When you are doing vigorous exercise, you need up to 40 litres every minute.

Oxygen and nitrogen

Table 7.2 shows the properties of the two main gases, nitrogen and oxygen.

Oxygen	Nitrogen
Boiling point −183 °C	Boiling point −196 °C
Molecular formula O_2	Molecular formula N_2
Colourless gas	Colourless gas
Has no smell	Has no smell
Slightly soluble in water	Less soluble than oxygen
Solution is neutral	Solution is neutral
Does not burn	Does not burn
Necessary for other substances to burn	Does not help other substances burn
Relights a glowing spill	

Test for oxygen
Light a spill. Blow it out so that it is glowing. Put it in the gas. If the spill relights, the gas is oxygen.

Oxygen and nitrogen are physically very similar but chemically very different. Oxygen is very reactive. When elements burn in air they are combining with oxygen. Substances that burn in air burn very brightly in pure oxygen. A glowing wooden spill will burst into flame if it is put into pure oxygen. This is the chemical test for oxygen. Nitrogen, however, is very unreactive. It will not allow substances to burn in it and if a glowing spill is put into it, the spill is extinguished.

The proportion of oxygen in the air stays constant even though it is continually being used up when substances burn and when living things respire. This is because another process, photosynthesis, produces oxygen. The chemical reaction that happens when living things respire converts carbohydrates to carbon dioxide and water. The chemical reaction that happens during photosynthesis is the opposite; carbon dioxide and water are converted into carbohydrates. Because of these processes, oxygen is continuously recycled. This is shown in Figure 7.3.

■ **Figure 7.3** Oxygen and carbon cycles showing respiration and photosynthesis.

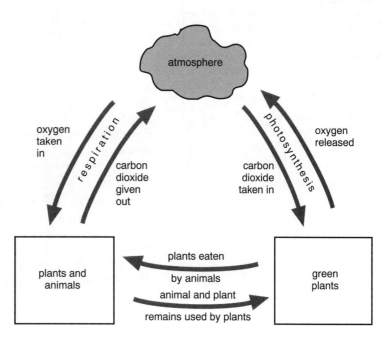

Respiration

Glucose + oxygen → carbon dioxide + water

$$C_6H_{12}O_6(aq) + 6O_2(g) \rightarrow 6CO_2(g) + 6H_2O(g)$$

Photosynthesis

Carbon dioxide + water → glucose + oxygen

$$6CO_2(g) + 6H_2O(g) \rightarrow C_6H_{12}O_6(aq) + 6O_2(g)$$

Carbon dioxide

Carbon dioxide makes up only 0.03% of the atmosphere. This means that, when we take a deep breath, we only breathe in about a tenth of a cubic centimetre of it. However, it is a very important gas in the atmosphere (see Figure 7.4). It is given off when materials that contain carbon combine with oxygen in processes such as burning and respiration. It is absorbed from the air during photosynthesis. Carbon, like oxygen, is continuously recycled in these processes. The same process recycles both elements.

The proportion of carbon dioxide in the atmosphere in 1890 was about 15% less than it is today. This has increased because we are burning an increasingly large amount of fossil fuels. This increase is worrying scientists and this is studied further later (page 161).

Inert gases

Argon makes up about 1% of the atmosphere. This means that an average classroom will contain 3–4 cubic metres of it. It is quite a common gas! The other inert gases are rarer as Table 7.3 shows.

The discovery of the inert gases is an interesting story. As long ago as 1785, only ten years after the discovery of oxygen in the air, a British scientist called Cavendish was working on the problem of the composition of air. He carried out some difficult experiments in which he absorbed all the oxygen and nitrogen from the air. Every time he did the experiment he was surprised to find that a little bit of the air was left over. 'Not more than one hundred and twentieth of the whole' he wrote at the time. Nobody could explain it then and the work was forgotten for 100 years.

In 1895 the chemist Rayleigh made some nitrogen from dry air by removing oxygen and carbon dioxide from it. He noticed that this nitrogen was slightly more dense than nitrogen prepared chemically. It was only then that scientists realised how important was the work of Cavendish a century earlier. They realised that Cavendish had discovered another gas in the air and this was named argon.

Carbon dioxide
Sublimes −78 °C
Molecular formula CO_2
Colourless gas
Has no smell
Slightly soluble in water
Solution is weakly acidic
Does not burn
Extinguishes burning materials
Turns limewater milky

■ **Figure 7.4** The properties of carbon dioxide.

■ **Table 7.3** Some properties of inert gases.

Gas	% in dry air	Boiling point (°C)
Helium	0.0005	−269
Neon	0.002	−246
Argon	1	−186
Krypton	0.000 1	−152
Xenon	0.000 01	−107

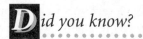

*D*id you know?

There is no hydrogen in air mainly because the hydrogen molecules are moving so fast that they can escape from the atmosphere into space.

*Q*uestions

7.1 Draw a pie chart showing the composition of air. Include the four most common gases by name but include all the others in a single segment.

7.2 Devise an experiment which you could do to find the percentage of oxygen in the air you breathe out. Describe the measurements you would make and the calculations you would do.

7.3 When we breathe and when we burn things we are continually using up oxygen from the air. Yet the percentage of oxygen in the air stays constant. Explain why this is so.

7.4 Respiration is a chemical reaction. Explain what happens during the reaction. What similarities are there between this reaction and photosynthesis?

■ **Table 7.4 Uses of gases of the air.**

Gas	Use
Oxygen	• Breathing apparatus in hospitals to help patients with breathing difficulties. Mountaineers and divers also use oxygen mixed with other gases to breathe in places where air is not available. • For welding and cutting steel. The hydrocarbon gas acetylene is burnt with oxygen to give a flame hot enough to melt steel. • Making steel from cast iron (see Chapter 4, page 82).
Argon	• Filling filament light bulbs.
Nitrogen	• For making ammonia which is then used mainly to make fertilisers.
Carbon dioxide	• Added to drinks to make them fizzy. Much of the carbon dioxide used for this purpose is a by-product of the fermentation process used to make beer. The carbon dioxide is dissolved under pressure. When the can is opened the pressure falls and the gas can escape from the liquid causing the fizz. • For refrigeration. Lumps of solid carbon dioxide (called 'dry ice') are placed inside some refrigerators to keep the contents cold. • In fire extinguishers. The gas is heavy and smothers the fire, preventing air getting to it.

Making use of the gases of the air

Air is a very important raw material in the chemical industry. Hot air is blown into many furnaces – such as the blast furnace – as a convenient source of oxygen. Air is also used as a cooling fluid for many processes. The cooling towers in large power stations are familiar sites all over the world. Air is also separated into the gases that it is made from. All of these gases have their uses.

Table 7.4 summarises the use we make of the gases of the air.

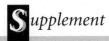

Separating the gases in the air

The gases that make up the air are separated by fractional distillation. The air is first cooled until it liquefies. This process makes use of the common observation that, when a gas is compressed it gets hot and when a compressed gas expands it cools. (Let a tyre down and feel the gas that comes out!) Air is compressed and it gets warm. The compressed gas is then cooled by cold nitrogen and then allowed to expand. As it expands it cools sufficiently for some to liquefy. The air that has turned to liquid is tapped off and the rest goes back into the compressor. Figure 7.5 shows this.

The liquid air is then separated into pure gases by fractional distillation (Figure 7.6). The top of the column is the coldest part and nitrogen distils off here. Oxygen has the highest boiling point of the three main gases of the air and so is tapped off near the bottom of the column.

■ **Figure 7.5** Flow chart showing liquefaction of air.

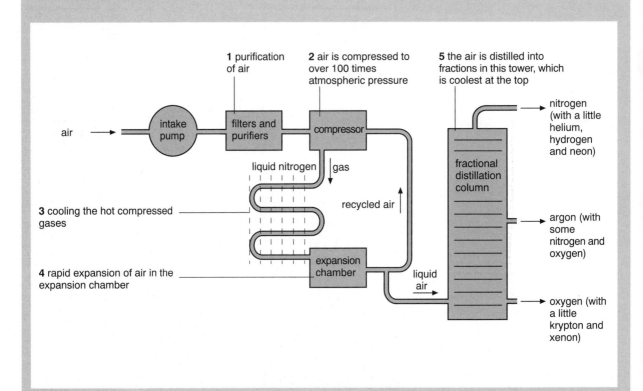

■ **Figure 7.6** Air is distilled in the tower in this picture.

■ **Figure 7.7** The huge BASF plant at Ludwigshaven opened in 1913 to make nitrate fertilisers from nitrogen. (b) The plant used the process Fritz Haber had invented only five years before. His original apparatus is shown in (a).

a

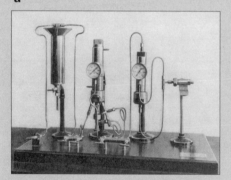

b

Using nitrogen to make fertilisers

All plants need nitrogen to grow. They need the nitrogen in the form of nitrates or ammonia which are ionic and soluble and so can be taken up easily by the plant. Most plants cannot make use of the huge supply of nitrogen gas all around them in the air because nitrogen is very unreactive and the plants have not evolved a way of absorbing it and converting it into nitrates.

There are two natural ways, however, in which nitrogen in the air is converted to nitrates that can be used by plants. We call this process 'fixing' nitrogen. When lightning discharges through the air, it causes nitrogen to combine with oxygen to form nitrogen dioxide which reacts with water to form the nitrate ion. The second natural way is carried out by tiny bacteria found on the roots of some plants such as acacia trees and peas and beans. These 'nitrogen-fixing' bacteria can convert nitrogen gas into nitrates which can then be used by the plant they are living on.

D id you know?

The soils of the plains of southern and eastern Africa are not very rich in nitrates because nitrates are very soluble and are easily washed out in the heavy rains that fall there from time to time. Much of the nitrogen in the soil there is 'fixed' by bacteria on the roots of the acacia trees ('thorn trees') that are very common there. When these trees are cut down for firewood or to clear the land for agriculture, the main supply of nitrates is lost. The wise farmers leave many of their acacia trees in the ground.

The expanding populations of industrial countries towards the end of the nineteenth century needed feeding. The food crops needed nitrate fertiliser and, at that time, the only source of nitrates were deposits in India and Argentina and these were running out. These fertilisers had to be brought to Europe by boat. The Germans realised that, if they were ever to be at war with a country that could cut off their supply of fertiliser coming in by sea, they would not be able to feed their people.

It became very important for Germany to invent a process for making nitrate fertiliser from nitrogen in the air like the bacteria on the roots of peas were able to do. It was a chemical engineer called Fritz Haber who invented the process.

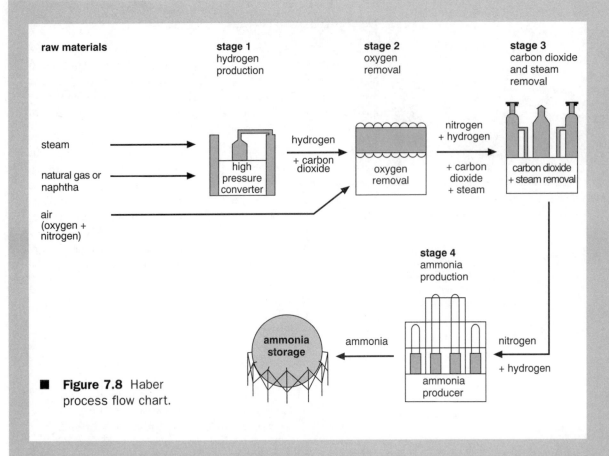

raw materials

stage 1
hydrogen
production

stage 2
oxygen
removal

stage 3
carbon dioxide
and steam
removal

steam

natural gas or
naphtha

air
(oxygen +
nitrogen)

high
pressure
converter

hydrogen
+ carbon
dioxide

oxygen
removal

nitrogen
+ hydrogen

+ carbon
dioxide
+ steam

carbon dioxide
+ steam removal

stage 4
ammonia
production

ammonia
storage

ammonia

ammonia
producer

nitrogen

+ hydrogen

■ **Figure 7.8** Haber
process flow chart.

He invented it in 1908 and by 1913 a giant industrial plant had been built in Ludwigshaven in Germany to manufacture nitrates using the Haber process (see Figures 7.7 and 7.8). (Only a few months later, war in Europe cut off Germany's supply of nitrates from across the seas.)

The flow chart shows the process invented by Haber. The first stage is the manufacture of hydrogen from methane or naphtha (a similar gas obtained from coal). In this stage the methane reacts with steam giving a mixture of hydrogen and carbon dioxide.

At the second stage, air is added to provide the nitrogen. Unfortunately, air also contains oxygen which is not needed and has to be removed. To do this, some of the hydrogen is burnt, combining with the oxygen to form water (steam). The mixture now contains nitrogen, hydrogen, steam and carbon dioxide.

In the third stage, the mixture is bubbled through alkali, such as potassium hydroxide solution. This removes the water and the carbon dioxide leaving nitrogen and hydrogen.

In the fourth stage the two gases are made to combine by passing them over a catalyst made of iron at a pressure of about 200 atmospheres (200 times the pressure of the atmosphere) and a temperature of 450 °C. The hot gases are cooled to liquefy the ammonia and unchanged hydrogen and nitrogen are recycled.

Reactions of the Haber process

Stage 1

$$CH_4(g) + 2H_2O(g) \rightarrow CO_2(g) + 4H_2(g)$$

Stage 2

$$2H_2(g) + O_2(g) \rightarrow 2H_2O(g)$$

Stage 3

$$CO_2(g) + 2KOH(aq) \rightarrow K_2CO_3(aq) + H_2O(l)$$

Stage 4

$$N_2(g) + 3H_2(g) \rightleftharpoons 2NH_3(g)$$

This is another example of a reversible reaction. You will return to this in Chapter 11.

The Haber process converts nitrogen from the air into ammonia. To make ammonia into useful fertilisers, it is converted either into ammonium salts or into nitrates.

To convert ammonia gas into ammonium salts, it is bubbled through an acid. It will react, for example, with sulphuric acid to form ammonium sulphate (the fertiliser 'sulphate of ammonia').

Making ammonium sulphate from ammonia

$$2NH_3(g) + H_2SO_4(aq) \rightarrow (NH_4)_2SO_4(aq)$$

To convert ammonia into nitrates, it must first be converted into nitric acid. To do this, air is mixed with the ammonia and the mixture is passed through a platinum gauze heated to red heat. The ammonia is oxidised to nitrogen dioxide and this is dissolved in water to form nitric acid. The nitric acid is then neutralised with alkali to make nitrates.

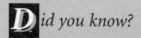

Did you know?

On fertiliser bags you can often see some letters and numbers like *N:P:K 2:3:2*. Have you ever thought what they mean? The letters refer to the three elements nitrogen, phosphorus and potassium, which are essential for the good growth of plants. The numbers refer to the ratio of these elements in the fertilisers.

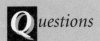
7.5 Plants need nitrogen, in the form of nitrates, to grow. They cannot make use of the nitrogen in the air because they cannot convert the nitrogen into the nitrates. There are two natural ways in which this can happen. What are they?

7.6 Haber invented a process to make nitrate fertiliser from the nitrogen in the air.

a What other materials are needed for this process?

b What are the conditions used in the main reaction between nitrogen and hydrogen?

c How is the ammonia made by the Haber process converted into useful fertiliser?

7.7 Describe the process we use to obtain oxygen and nitrogen from the air.

Pollution of the atmosphere

Some of the planets and moons in our solar system have atmospheres, others do not. The ones that have no atmosphere are all either very cold if they are far from the sun or very hot if they are near the sun. Mercury is the nearest planet to the sun and it has no atmosphere. The temperature of the side facing the sun is very hot, about 425 °C, and the temperature of the side facing away from the sun is very cold, about −180 °C. Venus, the next planet from the sun, has a thick atmosphere and it has a temperature all over its surface of about 460 °C. It is the atmosphere on Venus that keeps it warm, even on the night side. The atmosphere traps the heat of the sun.

Our atmosphere contains just the right amount of gases to keep the temperature of the surface of the earth at an average of about 25 °C. This is very important because life on earth depends on the existence of liquid water, and water is only a liquid between 0 °C and 100 °C. Life could not have evolved if the temperature was either too high or too low for water to exist as a liquid.

**D**id you know?

The body temperature of all warm-blooded animals is about the same, 37 °C. This is because the important molecules called enzymes which catalyse the chemical reactions in the body work best at this temperature. This means that there can only be life similar to life on earth on planets that have a similar constant temperature to earth.

If life is to continue on earth, it is important that the temperature of the surface does not change much. This temperature is kept at a temperature suitable for life by our atmosphere. It is very important, therefore, that we should look after our atmosphere.

■ **Table 7.5 Common air pollutants.**

Pollutant	Source	Effect
Carbon monoxide	Incomplete burning of fuels	Poisonous. It combines with the haemoglobin in the blood and so prevents the blood carrying oxygen around the body
Carbon dioxide	Combustion of fuels	Too much carbon dioxide in the air causes the temperature of the surface of the earth to rise. This is called the 'greenhouse effect' and it is described on page 161
Sulphur dioxide	Burning of fuels that contain sulphur as an impurity and the smelting of sulphide ores	Dissolves in rain making the rain acidic. This causes damage to limestone and concrete buildings. It also makes some soils very acidic, killing the vegetation. This is a particular problem in the eastern parts of Europe where large areas of evergreen forests are dying. Sulphur dioxide also prevents the proper growth of plants by stopping photosynthesis
Oxides of nitrogen	Formed in car engines when oxygen and nitrogen in the air combine under the high pressures and temperatures of the engine	Cause acidic rain like sulphur dioxide
Lead compounds	From car exhausts. Much petrol contains lead compounds. These are added to prevent the petrol from burning in the engine before it is ignited by the spark	Lead causes damage to brain cells, particularly in young children
Chlorofluorocarbons (CFCs)	From aerosol sprays and refrigerators	Destroy the layer of a gas called ozone in the upper atmosphere. This is described on page 162

■ **Figure 7.9** This natural gas plant in Australia uses the atmosphere as a dustbin to get rid of unwanted gases through the high chimneys.

a

b

■ **Figure 7.10** Some effects of acid rain: (a) damage to carved stonework and (b) dead pine trees.

Unfortunately, we often use it as a huge dustbin for any gas or smoke that we want to get rid of (see Figure 7.9).

We cause pollution of the atmosphere whenever we put into it any waste gases that are not normally there. We also put into the air many gases (such as carbon dioxide or sulphur dioxide) that are there naturally. If we cause the concentration of these gases to increase much above their natural concentrations then we cause pollution. Table 7.5 and Figure 7.10 show some of the ways we pollute the air and the problems the pollution can cause.

Supplement

The car engine causes a lot of air pollution. The list in Table 7.6 below shows some of the compounds present in exhaust gases and the problems they cause.

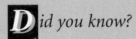

Did you know?

The catalyst in catalytic converters is platinum which is a rare metal mined mainly in South Africa. Because the ore is low grade, much waste and pollution is caused by the mining process. The platinum is used to help clean up a first-world pollution problem but is creating a third-world one.

Scientists have only recently begun to understand all the different chemical reactions that go on in the different layers of the atmosphere. These reactions all help to keep the gases in the atmosphere at the correct concentration. We are learning now how some of the

Table 7.6 Problems caused by compounds present in exhaust gases.

Compound	Problems caused
Carbon dioxide	See the greenhouse effect opposite.
Carbon monoxide	This is poisonous. It prevents the blood carrying oxygen around the body and the victim dies of suffocation.
Partly burnt hydrocarbons including soot	These are often carcinogenic (cancer forming). They also cause deposits on buildings which are dirty and often acidic.
Lead compounds	In many countries a lead compound is added to the petrol to improve its performance. Lead compounds destroy brain cells and this is particularly serious for young children.
Nitrogen oxides	These are formed when nitrogen combines with oxygen in the engine. They cause acid rain. In sunlight they also catalyse the formation of ozone in the lower atmosphere. Ozone causes eyes to water and can damage the inside of the lungs, particularly in old people.
	In many countries now, petrol is lead-free but unfortunately lead-free petrol is more expensive to make than leaded petrol. Also many new cars are fitted with **catalytic converters** in the exhaust pipes. These remove the carbon monoxide, the unburnt hydrocarbons and the oxides of nitrogen. The catalyst is made of platinum which is easily 'poisoned' by lead in petrol and so catalytic converters cannot be introduced until lead-free petrol is available.

pollutants can interfere with these reactions and cause changes in the natural balance of the gases. Two ways in which pollutants can interfere with the balance of gases are by causing the atmosphere to heat up and by destroying the ozone layer.

The greenhouse effect

Everything gives off heat. Heat, you will learn in your physics, is a form of electromagnetic radiation like light. Substances that are very hot give off heat radiation that has a higher frequency than substances that are cool. This is well known; a very hot fire is yellowish white and a cooler one is red. Red light is radiation with a lower frequency than yellow light. The sun is very hot; its surface is about 6000 °C. Much of the radiation it gives off has a high frequency. This radiation comes through the atmosphere and warms the earth.

The earth is only around 25 °C and so it emits heat radiation of a lower frequency than the sun. This heat radiation can be absorbed by certain molecules in the atmosphere. Compounds which can absorb this energy are water vapour, methane and carbon dioxide. This is why a cloudy night in winter is usually warmer than a clear night; the water in the cloud stops the heat escaping.

So it is the presence of gases such as methane, water vapour and carbon dioxide in the air that keeps our planet warm. This is called the 'greenhouse effect' and these gases are sometimes called 'greenhouse gases' (see Figure 7.11). If the concentration of these gases increases, there is a possibility that the planet might heat up too much. We do not yet know much about what might happen if the planet were to heat up, but we can guess that it will cause the water in the oceans to expand and so the sea level will get higher and could flood low lying cities and some of the Pacific island countries could even disappear.

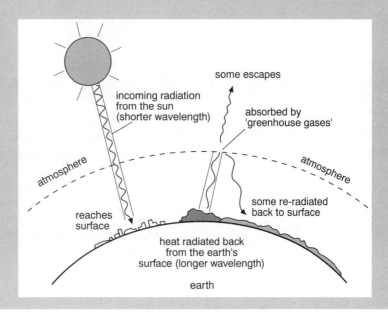

■ **Figure 7.11** The greenhouse effect.

Radar maps of the surface of our sister planet Venus show that there were once rivers and oceans on Venus. The 'runaway' greenhouse effect on Venus has caused the rivers and seas to evaporate. Other elements such as sulphur have also evaporated and now that planet's atmosphere contains dense clouds of sulphuric acid vapour (see Figure 7.12). Could earth become like Venus in the future?

■ Figure 7.12 Venus showing thick cloud.

The United Nations Organisation has recently held a number of important meetings at which nations have tried to plan for a gradual reduction in the amounts of greenhouse gases they put into the atmosphere. So far, there has been very little agreement on what action to take.

The ozone layer

Ozone is a form of oxygen. Instead of two atoms in the molecule as in oxygen, ozone has three. It is formed in the upper atmosphere when high frequency radiation (called cosmic radiation) from the sun causes oxygen molecules to form ozone. Ozone is a very important gas to us as it forms a shield in the upper atmosphere that prevents cosmic radiation and ultra-violet radiation, which are harmful to living things, from reaching us.

Did you know?

Ozone is quite a well-known gas. Photocopiers, and any other source of static electricity, can cause it to form from oxygen. You may have noticed a strange bitter smell near photocopiers; this is ozone. It is a poisonous gas and is formed on hot days in badly polluted cities when the sun causes products from car exhausts to react with each other.

Substances called CFCs from refrigerators and aerosol sprays are very unreactive substances and therefore they stay in the atmosphere a long time. Gradually they diffuse up to the upper levels of the atmosphere. Here they break down when cosmic radiation hits them and produce chlorine atoms. Chlorine atoms react with ozone. One chlorine atom can destroy many molecules of ozone because it acts as a catalyst and is not used up itself. In recent years the ozone layer has been getting thinner because of this. This has been most noticeable over the south pole where the CFCs diffuse to during the quiet winter months of night-time when there is not much wind. In the spring when radiation from the sun first hits the atmosphere over the south pole, chlorine atoms are formed and the ozone is destroyed.

The ozone 'hole' in the southern spring allows harmful radiation to reach the earth's surface and this has caused damage to eyes of farm animals in the south of South America. It is predicted that there will be an increase in skin cancer amongst people who sunbathe in spring in countries like Australia and South Africa. This skin cancer is caused by an increase in the amount of harmful radiation getting through the atmosphere.

Most of the nations have now agreed to reduce the amount of CFCs they produce, but many scientists studying the ozone 'holes' which appear now above both poles in spring believe that more must be done. One point that particularly worries the scientists is that the CFCs stay in the atmosphere so long that, even if all use were stopped now, it would be over ten years before the ozone layer stopped getting thinner.

The three chemists who discovered how CFCs destroyed ozone in the upper atmosphere, Paul Crutzen, Mario Molina and Sherwood Rowland, were awarded the Nobel Prize for Chemistry in 1995.

Water

The water we use in our homes comes from rivers, lakes and boreholes and even in some cases, the sea. Before it can be used for drinking, it must be purified as water is the most common carrier of disease. Water is a very good solvent and so the water we drink always contains dissolved substances. Water without any dissolved material in it tastes very dull and bland.

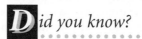
Did you know?

One of the substances that is dissolved in the water we drink is oxygen gas. In fact, the concentration of oxygen dissolved in water that is saturated with oxygen is about one and a half times greater than the concentration of oxygen in air.

The water cycle

Because water is such a good solvent, most of the water on the planet is salty. Rain has dissolved the salt out of the rocks on the earth's surface and washed it down into the sea. However, the water that we drink does not come directly from the sea. It first evaporates from the sea and then condenses as rain. This process is called the water cycle (see Figure 7.13).

The water in the lakes and the rivers that we drink is therefore not very salty. It may, however, contain suspended solids. These are particles of solids which are insoluble but which the river water is

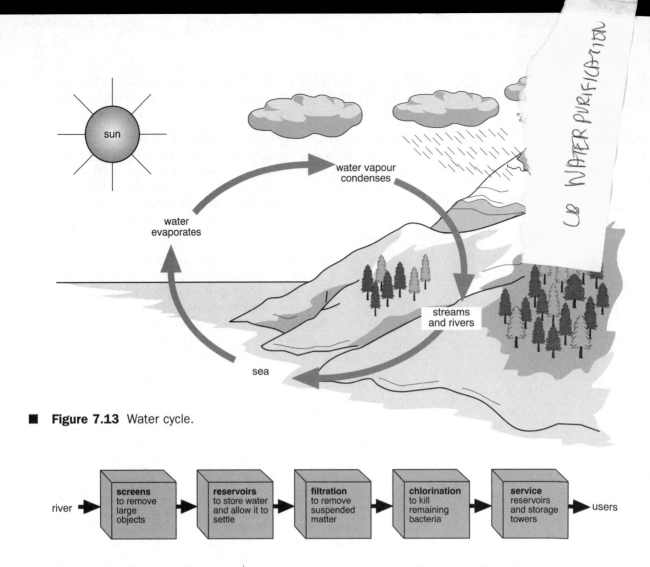

CB WATER PURIFICATION

■ **Figure 7.13** Water cycle.

river →	**screens** to remove large objects	**reservoirs** to store water and allow it to settle	**filtration** to remove suspended matter	**chlorination** to kill remaining bacteria	**service** reservoirs and storage towers	→ users

■ **Figure 7.14** Water purification.

carrying along as it flows. These are filtered out of the water by filtering it through a bed of sand. Bacteria in the water will pass through the sand filter and therefore these have to be killed before the water is suitable for drinking. To do this, some chlorine gas is bubbled through the water. You can often smell the chlorine in drinking water (see Figure 7.14).

Sewage is 98–99% water and it is sensible to recover the pure water from it. To do this, it is first filtered to remove large solids. It is then held in tanks to allow more solids to settle out. The liquid is then passed through gravel beds containing bacteria which decompose the organic substances in the water (see Figure 7.15). This water is good enough to be put into a purification plant to make drinking water. It is often said that the water drunk in a city such as London has been drunk ten times before on its way down the river!

Uses of water

We often think that the main use of water is in our homes but in many parts of the world this is not the case. Water is used industrially for cleaning and cooling. Slaughterhouses, for example, use a lot of water to ensure that the meat they produce is clean. A particularly important use for water is in cooling. Many power stations use water to cool the steam that has been used to drive the turbines. In

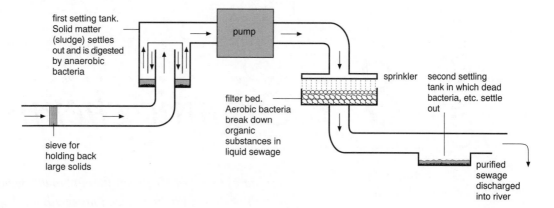

first setting tank. Solid matter (sludge) settles out and is digested by anaerobic bacteria

pump

sprinkler

second settling tank in which dead bacteria, etc. settle out

filter bed. Aerobic bacteria break down organic substances in liquid sewage

sieve for holding back large solids

purified sewage discharged into river

■ **Figure 7.15** Sewage treatment.

fact, some power stations use so much water for cooling that when we are asked to save water in times of drought, we could save a lot by just turning off the lights!

Pollution of water

When we use water, we make it dirty. Very often after it has been used, it is returned to rivers and lakes without being properly treated to clean it. This causes water pollution.

A serious form of pollution occurs when the soluble impurities in the water are phosphates or nitrates. These are plant nutrients and cause the growth of a lot of algae in the water. When these algae eventually die, they rot. When rotting takes place, bacteria are involved which need oxygen. If there is too much algae rotting, all the dissolved oxygen in the water is used up. This means that all the other life in the water that needs oxygen dies. This process is called **eutrophication**.

The nitrates and phosphates that cause pollution often come from fertilisers and therefore badly polluted rivers can often be found in open county far away from industry.

uestions

7.8 Look at Table 7.5 showing the causes of air pollution. For each gas, think of at least one way of reducing the pollution.

7.9 Design an experiment to show that gases from the burning of fuels are acidic.

7.10 Sometimes farmers have to throw away supplies of milk that are accidentally contaminated or which go sour before they reach the dairy. Some of them throw the milk away in a river. Explain how this can cause serious water pollution.

7.11 Draw a flow chart to show how sewage can be converted into water that can be safely drunk.

7.12 Explain how air pollution can cause **a** the greenhouse effect and **b** the thinning of the ozone layer. Suggest ways that this pollution can be reduced.

Review questions on this chapter can be found on pages 241–2.

8 Organic chemistry

All around us today we see things that are made by people. Many of these things could not have been made without the fossil fuels coal, oil and gas. These fuels provide us with the energy to drive the machines we use to make things. The fuels are also the raw materials for many industries, particularly the plastics industry. All these fuels contain a rather special element, carbon, and this chapter introduces you to the chemistry of carbon. This branch of chemistry has a special name, organic chemistry, because it was once thought that the kinds of carbon compounds you will study could only be made by living (organic) things.

Fossil fuels

As you discovered in Chapter 6, coal, oil and gas were formed in the past from living things and, like fossils, are now trapped under layers of rock. Because of this we call them fossil fuels. They are very important to us. We make use of them all the time as fuels and as raw materials from which we make many useful chemicals and materials, such as plastics, that are now part of our everyday lives.

Fuels are either **renewable** or **non-renewable**. Wood is an example of a renewable fuel because we can grow more to replace what we use. Fossil fuels, however, are non-renewable. This means that once we have used them they are gone. Figure 6.7 on page 130 shows the increase in the use of fuels in recent years. We know the approximate amount of these fuels still left in the ground (what we call the reserves of fuel). It is quite easy to calculate how long these fuels are likely to last us if we keep on using them as we are at present. Figure 8.1 shows this. As you can see, we will run short of oil and gas in a generation or so. It is difficult to imagine life without fossil fuels; we should use them carefully and not waste them.

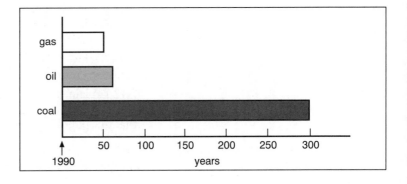

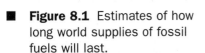

■ **Figure 8.1** Estimates of how long world supplies of fossil fuels will last.

■ **Figure 8.2** Common things we make from fossil fuels.

petroleum

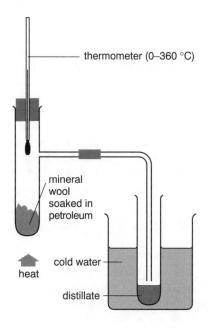

thermometer (0–360 °C)

mineral
wool
soaked in
petroleum

cold water

heat

distillate

■ **Figure 8.3** Petroleum distillation apparatus.

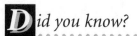

*D*id you know?

About 60% of all the known oil reserves are under one country – Saudi Arabia.

What can we make from fossil fuels?

We make many useful materials from fossil fuels. Figure 8.2 shows some of these. To make these materials we must first of all extract useful pure chemicals from the fuel. This is done by heating it and distilling it. We can even distil coal! When coal is heated (in the absence of air so that it does not burn) we get a liquid from it that contains a number of useful chemicals from which some of the items in Figure 8.2 can be made. Detergents and aspirin are two examples of materials that we can make from chemicals that we get from coal.

The correct name for crude oil is 'petroleum' which means 'liquid rock'. We can refine petroleum by fractional distillation.

*I*nvestigation 8.1

Distilling petroleum

Warning – this investigation must be done under the close supervision of a teacher because of the fire hazard. A fire extinguisher (not water) or a sand bucket should be within easy reach.

You will need:

- petroleum
- test tube (Pyrex), bung and delivery tube
- thermometer (0–360 °C)
- beaker and collecting tubes
- burner
- mineral wool
- tin lid.

1 Put some petroleum in the test tube together with some mineral wool to help it boil smoothly (see Figure 8.3).

2 Adjust the flame of the burner so that it is very small and can heat gently. Heat the petroleum and distil it. Collect the distillate in a tube cooled by water.

3 The temperature of the vapour that distils over can be read on the thermometer. Control the flame so that this rises slowly. When the temperature reaches 70 °C, use a new collecting tube. Change the collecting tube again at 120 °C and 170 °C. Continue heating until the temperature reaches 240 °C.

4 You have separated the petroleum into several fractions (don't forget the fraction left in the heating tube). Look at each fraction and describe its appearance and viscosity (how runny it is). Test each fraction by pouring a small quantity onto a tin lid and setting fire to it. Describe how well it burns and what the flame looks like. If it does not set fire put a piece of mineral wool in it to act as a wick. Write all the results down.

Table 8.1 shows a summary of the properties of the fractions you have prepared in Investigation 8.1. The table also gives the name that the chemists give to each of the fractions. Each fraction is a mixture of **hydrocarbons** which are compounds of hydrogen and carbon. The higher the melting point of a hydrocarbon, the greater the number of carbon atoms each molecule contains. Table 8.1 also gives an idea of the number of carbon atoms in the hydrocarbon molecules in each fraction.

■ **Table 8.1 Petroleum fractions.** (The properties of fractions obtained by the small-scale fractional distillation of crude oil.)

Boiling range	20–70 °C	70–120 °C	120–170 °C	170–240 °C
Name of fraction	Petrol	Naphtha	Paraffin	Diesel oil
Colour	Pale yellow	Yellow	Dark yellow	Brown
Viscosity	Runny	Fairly runny	Fairly viscous	Viscous
How does it burn?	Easily, with clean yellow flame	Quite easily, yellow flame, some smoke	Harder to burn, quite smoky flame	Hard to burn, smoky flame
Number of carbon atoms in the molecules	5–10	8–12	9–16	15–30

The uses of the different fractions from petroleum depend on the properties of the fraction. The 'light' fractions that vaporise and burn easily are useful for fuel in cars. The 'heavier' fractions are more viscous and are useful as lubricating oils. (A liquid that is viscous is one which does not flow easily, such as treacle.) Candle wax is made from the lubricating oil fraction and is a mixture of hydrocarbons with about 20 atoms in the molecule. Table 8.2 summarises the uses made of the different fractions from the distillation of petroleum.

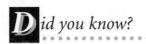

id you know?

The diesel fuel sold in winter is a different mixture of hydrocarbons from the mixture sold in summer. This is because diesel sets rather like vaseline at a little below 0 °C and will not work as a fuel. More of the lighter fractions are added in winter to prevent this.

Figure 8.4 This photograph of the oil refinery at Salt Lake City, USA shows the tall fractionating column and the storage tanks for the petroleum and the purified fractions.

 **Table 8.2** Uses of petroleum fractions.

Fraction	Boiling range	Uses
Fuel gas	–160–20 °C	Fuels for gas ovens, LPG, chemicals
Petrol (gasoline)	20–70 °C	Fuel for vehicles, chemicals
Naphtha	70–120 °C	Chemicals
Paraffin (kerosine)	120–240 °C	Fuel for central heating and jet engines, chemicals
Diesel oils and lubricating oils	240–350 °C	Fuel for diesel engines, trains and central heating, chemicals, lubricants
Bitumen	Above 350 °C	Roofing, waterproofing, asphalting on roads

Industrially, the distillation of crude oil takes place on a very large scale and is a continuous process. The crude oil is continuously fed into the heated vessel at the bottom and the oil is vaporised. The fractionating column varies in temperature from about 360 °C at the bottom near the heater to about 20 °C at the top. The different fractions are tapped off up the column as shown in Figures 8.4 and 8.5 (overleaf).

Questions

8.1 Why is crude oil so important to us? What could be done to ensure that it is used more economically?

8.2 How is crude oil separated into different fractions? List the boiling range and main uses of each fraction.

8.3 Why is the chemistry of carbon called 'organic chemistry'?

8.4 Why are coal, oil and gas sometimes called 'fossil fuels'?

8.5 When oil is burned, the energy that is released originally came from the sun. Explain this statement.

Carbon, a special element

The fractions from crude oil contain mixtures of hydrocarbons, compounds made of hydrogen and carbon only. Carbon is the only element that can form molecules like these. It is an amazing element; it forms well over a million different compounds and new ones are being made or discovered every day. There are more compounds of carbon than there are of all the other elements put together.

Without the element carbon, this book you are reading would not exist and you would not be here to read it. Both the book and you are made mainly out of carbon compounds. Life itself exists because of the special properties of carbon, because the molecules, called DNA, which control all the processes of life are based on carbon.

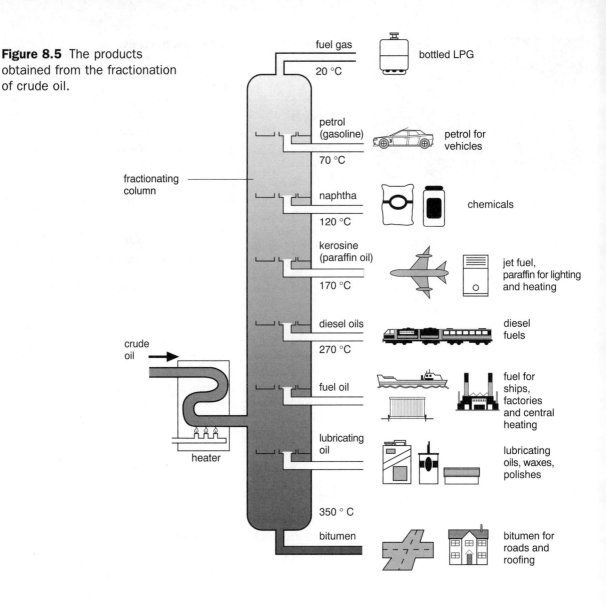

Figure 8.5 The products obtained from the fractionation of crude oil.

fractionating column

crude oil

heater

fuel gas — bottled LPG

20 °C

petrol (gasoline) — petrol for vehicles

70 °C

naphtha — chemicals

120 °C

kerosine (paraffin oil) — jet fuel, paraffin for lighting and heating

170 °C

diesel oils — diesel fuels

270 °C

fuel oil — fuel for ships, factories and central heating

lubricating oil — lubricating oils, waxes, polishes

350 ° C

bitumen — bitumen for roads and roofing

Carbon is at the top of Group IV in the centre of the Periodic Table. It forms four covalent bonds by sharing its four electrons with other elements. What makes it different from other elements is that it can form long chains of carbon atoms joined strongly together by covalent bonds. These chains can be straight or branched and other elements can join onto them.

Table 8.3 shows some of the molecules of well-known compounds. Note that the bonds formed by carbon point away from the atom towards the corner of a tetrahedron (look at the structure of methane, natural gas, in the table). This means that a chain of carbon atoms is not actually straight but crooked. The 'space-filling' model of the atoms gives us a better idea of what the molecule really looks like as it shows the space around the atoms that is taken up by the electrons. Table 8.3 also shows the compound water, for comparison.

Table 8.3 shows a number of different carbon compounds. We can classify these compounds into groups. Compounds within a group

■ Table 8.3 Structure of water, methane, butane, octane, polythene and ethanol

Name	Molecular formula	Structural formula	Ball and spring model	Space-filling model
Water	H_2O			
Methane	CH_4			
Butane	C_4H_{10}			
Octane	C_8H_{18}			
Polythene	C_nH_{2n}			
Ethanol	C_2H_5OH			

■ Table 8.4 Structure of the first four alkanes.

Name	Methane	Ethane	Propane	Butane
Formula	CH_4	C_2H_6	C_3H_8	C_4H_{10}
Structural formula	H | H—C—H | H	H H | | H—C—C—H | | H H	H H H | | | H—C—C—C—H | | | H H H	H H H H | | | | H—C—C—C—C—H | | | | H H H H

will have a similar structure and properties. In the rest of this chapter you will study a few of these groups.

Alkanes

Table 8.4 shows the structure of four hydrocarbons called methane, ethane, propane and butane. All of them are gases. Methane is natural gas that is obtained from gas fields found in many parts of the world. Methane is also produced in the stomachs of animals that feed on grass and excreted from time to time as a (dangerously flammable!) waste product. Propane and butane are commonly used throughout the world as a fuel for cooking.

The four compounds in Table 8.4 are the first four of a series of hydrocarbons with similar structures that we call the **alkanes**. Notice that, as you go along the series, the next compound contains one more carbon atom and two more hydrogen atoms than the previous one.

You can also see that, if an alkane contains n carbon atoms, it will have $2n + 2$ hydrogen atoms. We can write the general formula for the alkanes as $C_nH_{(2n+2)}$.

There are many alkanes. As the number of carbon atoms gets larger and the molecule gets bigger, the boiling points of the alkanes rise. This means that the smallest, such as the ones in Table 8.4, are gases but larger ones, such as octane shown in Table 8.3, are liquids. Petrol is a mixture of hydrocarbons, one of which is octane. Candle wax is a mixture of alkanes that are solids. The main alkane in candle wax is called eicosane and contains 20 carbon atoms ($C_{20}H_{42}$).

The most important property of the alkanes is that they burn. The next experiment, which is very similar to Investigation 6.2, tells you something about this reaction.

Investigation 8.2

Burning alkanes

You will need:

alkanes

- several alkanes such as a gas burner (cigarette lighter), paraffin burner, candle (do **NOT** use petrol)
- test tube

- limewater (freshly made)
- beaker
- cobalt chloride paper or anhydrous copper sulphate.

1 Burn the alkane. Hold a beaker containing cold water briefly in the flame. What do you notice on the outside of the beaker? If you have any cobalt chloride paper, warm it gently until it turns blue and then touch the outside of the beaker with it. Remember that blue cobalt chloride paper turns pink when water touches it.

2 Hold a test tube briefly upside down over the flame and then put a small quantity of freshly made limewater in the tube and shake. Note any change.

3 Repeat the experiments with the other alkanes.

This experiment tells you that alkanes burn to give water and carbon dioxide. The carbon dioxide is produced by the carbon in the alkane and the water comes from the hydrogen. We can write equations showing this. The second equation is a general one for all alkanes.

Methane + oxygen → carbon dioxide + water

Alkane + oxygen → carbon dioxide + water

$$CH_4(g) + 2O_2(g) \rightarrow CO_2(g) + 2H_2O(g)$$

The alkanes are a series of compounds with a similar structure and similar properties. They have similar properties, of course, because they have similar structures. We call a series of compounds like this a **homologous series**.

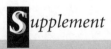

upplement

The reaction of alkanes with halogens

The only reaction of alkanes of importance other than burning is the reaction with halogens. In this reaction, one of the hydrogens is replaced by a halogen. Light energy is required to make the reaction happen. Any of the hydrogens can be replaced. The reaction can continue until all the hydrogens have been replaced by the halogen and so a mixture of products is often obtained. This reaction is quite vigorous with most alkanes and with methane it is dangerously explosive.

$$CH_4(g) + Cl_2(g) \rightarrow CH_3Cl(g) + HCl(g)$$

Other products can be CH_2Cl_2, $CHCl_3$ (which is the anaesthetic chloroform) and CCl_4.

This is an important reaction commercially as these 'halocarbons' are useful as solvents, anaesthetics and refrigerants. Tetrachloromethane (CCl_4) is useful for putting out fires. Fire extinguishers in vehicles often contain this because it is useful for electrical fires as it does not conduct electricity.

■ **Table 8.5 Three isomers of pentane, C_5H_{12}.**

Structural formula			
	(pentane structure)	(2-methylbutane structure)	(2,2-dimethylpropane structure)
Name	Pentane	2-methylbutane	2,2–dimethylpropane
boiling point (°C)	37	29	9

Branched chains

In all the hydrocarbons you have studied so far the carbon atoms have been arranged in a single chain. Many alkanes, however, are branched chain compounds. Consider the alkane C_5H_{12}. How many structures can you draw for this if you also draw all the possible branched structures? The answer is three and they are shown in Table 8.5.

These molecules, which have the same molecular formula but different structures, are called **structural isomers**. Structural isomerism is very common in organic chemistry. The three isomers in the table all have different names and different properties. (You may be able to see a pattern in the names; the basic name is that of the longest carbon chain in the molecule and each of these carbons is numbered). You can see that the third isomer, 2,2 dimethylpropane, has the lowest boiling point. This is because it has the most compact structure of the three, rather like a ball, and needs least energy to make the molecules escape from the liquid.

Questions

8.6 What do the names of the alkanes have in common? What is the general formula of the alkanes? Draw the structure of the straight chain alkane with seven carbon atoms.

Number of carbon atoms	Formula	Name	State at room temperature	Boiling point (°C)
1	CH_4	Methane	gas	−161
2	C_2H_6	Ethane	gas	−89
3	C_3H_8	Propane	gas	−42
4	C_4H_{10}	Butane	gas	0
5	C_5H_{12}	Pentane	liquid	37
6	C_6H_{14}	Hexane	liquid	70
7	C_7H_{16}	Heptane	liquid	99
8	C_8H_{18}	Octane	liquid	127
9	C_9H_{20}	Nonane	liquid	152
10	$C_{10}H_{22}$	Decane	liquid	174

8.7 Table 8.6 shows the boiling points of the first ten alkanes. Plot a graph of the boiling point against the number of carbon atoms in the molecule and use it to predict the boiling point of $C_{12}H_{26}$. Why do you think the boiling points get higher as the molecule gets longer?

8.8 Draw all the possible structural isomers of C_6H_{14}.

8.9 How many possible products are there when chlorine reacts with ethane? Draw them all.

Alkenes

Another homologous series of compounds is the alkenes. Table 8.7 shows the structure of some members of this series.

■ **Table 8.7 Structure of the three alkenes.**

Name	Molecular formula	Structural formula	Ball and spring model	Space-filling model
Ethene	C_2H_4			
Propene	C_3H_6			
Butene	C_4H_8			

You can see that these three, ethene, propene and butene, are very similar to the alkanes ethane, propane and butane. The only difference is that the alkenes contain a **double bond**. This is a bond that is made by sharing not two, but four electrons. This difference between the structure of alkenes and alkanes makes an important difference between the properties of the two series of compounds. Alkenes are not as readily available as alkanes and so before we can study the properties of an alkene we must make one.

Investigation 8.3

Making ethene

You will need:

- liquid paraffin
- bits of broken pot
- test tube, bung and delivery tube
- test tubes and bungs to collect gas
- mineral wool
- burner
- beaker.

1 Soak the mineral wool in the paraffin. Use the heavy medicinal paraffin. Set up the apparatus as shown in Figure 8.6.

2 Heat the paraffin gently and the porous pot strongly. With a bit of practice you can do this with one burner. Just move the burner onto the paraffin now and then. You should notice some bubbles of a gas entering the collecting tube. Collect several tubes of the gas.

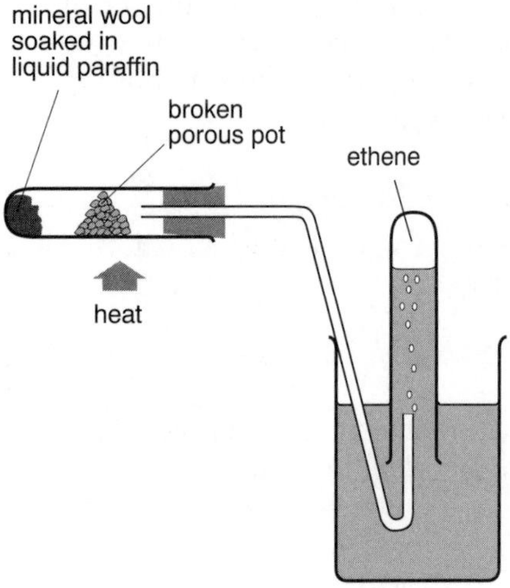

The gas you have collected is ethene. The process for making ethene that you have used is called **cracking**. It is the way ethene and other small hydrocarbon molecules are made industrially from larger alkane molecules.

The next investigation shows some of the properties of ethene.

Investigation 8.4

The properties of ethene

You will need:

- tubes of ethene from Investigation 8.3
- bromine water
- potassium permanganate solution acidified with a little dilute sulphuric acid
- limewater and cobalt chloride paper
- test tubes
- droppers
- an alkane such as paraffin or camping gas.

paraffin

ethene
camping gas
paraffin

potassium
permanganate
bromine
water

■ **Figure 8.6** Apparatus for the preparation of ethene.

mineral wool soaked in liquid paraffin

broken porous pot

ethene

heat

1 Smell the gas you have produced. It has a sweetish smell. You could compare this with the paraffin you used to make it; alkanes have very little smell.

2 Set fire to a tube of ethene. Note that it burns with a yellow flame. Look carefully at the inside of the test tube. If you see any condensation you could test it with cobalt chloride paper. Put a little limewater in the tube and shake. Note what happens.

3 Add a few drops of bromine water to a tube of ethene. Note any colour change. Do the same with potassium permanganate solution.

4 Repeat Step 2 using a tube containing an alkane such as camping gas or paraffin. Compare the results with Step 2.

This investigation shows some similarities and some differences between alkanes and alkenes. These are summarised in Table 8.8.

■ **Table 8.8 Differences and similarities between alkanes and alkenes.**

	Alkane	Alkene
Colour	Colourless	Colourless
Smell	No smell	Sweetish smell
Does it burn?	Burns easily	Burns easily with a yellow flame
Reaction with aqueous bromine, which is orange	No reaction	The bromine solution becomes colourless on shaking
Reaction with an acid solution of potassium permanganate, which is purple	No reaction	The purple solution becomes colourless on shaking

The alkene reacted with both bromine and potassium permanganate, decolorising them because of the presence of the double bond. Alkanes have no double bonds and are therefore unreactive. We can use these two simple reactions to test for the presence of a double bond in some organic substances, as the next investigation shows.

*I*nvestigation 8.5

Testing for double bonds

You will need:
- cooking oil
- margarine

potassium permanganate
bromine water

- lard
- potassium permanganate solution acidified with a little diluite sulphuric acid
- test tube
- burner.

1 Take a small amount of cooking oil in a test tube. Add a few drops of potassium permanganate solution. Shake the two together. Look at the colour in the aqueous layer.

2 Repeat the procedure with the two solids. You may have to warm them gently until they melt.

Cooking oil and margarine both contain carbon–carbon double bonds whereas lard does not. The double bonds will cause the decolourisation of the potassium permanganate solutions.

We have a special name for compounds such as the margarine and the cooking oil that contain double bonds. We say they have in them **unsaturated** hydrocarbon chains. Compounds such as the lard that do not have double bonds in them are called **saturated**.

Supplement

Addition of bromine to double bonds

The reason why potassium permanganate and bromine water are decolorised when they are added to alkenes is that they react with the double bond. The bromine breaks the double bond, forming two extra single bonds to bromine atoms as shown in Figure 8.7.

This kind of reaction, in which a reagent like bromine adds on to double bond, is called an **addition reaction** to a double bond. It is a very important reaction because it allows a great many useful substances to be made from alkenes. In the next chapter you will study useful substances called polymers. One polymer, a very well-known substance called polyethene or polythene, is made when molecules of ethene are made to add onto each other.

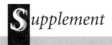

■ **Figure 8.7** Bromine adding to a double bond.

Addition of hydrogen to a double bond

One important addition reaction of alkenes is the addition of hydrogen. If you compare the structure of alkenes and alkanes that have the same number of carbon atoms, the difference is in the number of hydrogen atoms. It is possible to change an alkene to an alkane by adding hydrogen as in Figure 8.8. This is an important process in the food industry. Vegetable oils such as sunflower oil are easily obtained from plants. These can be used unchanged for cooking. However, if the double bonds in them are made to combine with hydrogen they become solids. These solids are margarines.

The terms 'saturated' and 'unsaturated' refer to the way that margarine is made. The hydrogen is passed through the heated oil which contains a catalyst of powdered nickel. At the end of the

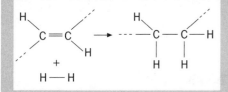

■ **Figure 8.8** Addition of hydrogen to a double bond.

alcohol

■ **Figure 8.9** Addition of steam to a double bond.

reaction the nickel is filtered off and can be used again. Some margarines are soft and some are hard. The soft ones still have some double bonds in them but the hard ones do not. We say that the hard ones are 'saturated' with hydrogen whereas the soft ones are 'unsaturated'.

Addition of water to a double bond

Another important addition reaction of alkenes is the reaction with steam. Like the reaction with hydrogen, a catalyst is used to speed this reaction up. It is important because, as Figure 8.9 shows, the product has the group of atoms – OH attached to one of the carbons that was part of the double bond. This group of atoms is called the **hydroxyl group** and organic compounds that contain this group are called **alcohols**.

This process is used in industry as one way of making the common alcohol called ethanol. It is described in the next section.

Questions

8.10 You are given two flammable liquid hydrocarbons. One of them is an alkene and another is an alkane. How would you find out which was which?

8.11 Propene has a formula C_3H_6. Draw its structure. Describe how it reacts with **a** bromine and **b** steam. Draw the formula for the product of the reaction with bromine.

8.12 Explain, giving examples, what is meant by 'addition reaction'.

8.13 Explain how margarine is made from vegetable oils. A margarine is advertised as 'high in polyunsaturates'. What do you think the makers mean by this?

A renewable fuel – ethanol

Ethanol is the scientific name for the liquid commonly known as alcohol. It is the substance produced by the fermentation of sugar in fruits. It is the chemical in wines and beers that causes drunkenness.

Ethanol has the structure shown in Figure 8.10. The figure also shows the structure of ethane. The difference between the two is that in ethanol, one of the hydrogen atoms has been replaced by an oxygen and a hydrogen. This -OH group is called the hydroxyl group. Ethanol is one example of a homologous series of compounds called the **alcohols**. Table 8.9 shows three typical alcohols.

Methylated spirits, fuel and solvent

Methylated spirits is a well-known fuel. It is mainly ethanol but also contains some methanol which is poisonous, causing blindness and death if it is drunk in sufficient quantity. The methylated spirits that is used industrially is colourless but when it is sold to the

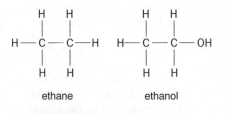

ethane   ethanol

■ **Figure 8.10** Structures of ethane and ethanol.

■ Table 8.9 Structure of methanol, ethanol and propanol.

Name	Molecular formula	Structural formula	Ball and spring model	Space-filling model
Methanol	CH₃OH	H—C—OH with H above and H below (H bonded to O)		
Ethanol	C₂H₅OH	H—C—C—OH with H atoms on carbons		
Propanol	C₃H₇OH	H—C—C—C—OH with H atoms on carbons		

public as a fuel, a purple dye is added to it so that people always know what it is and do not accidentally drink it.

When ethanol burns, it produces carbon dioxide and water. You can easily show this by repeating Investigation 8.2 using ethanol as the fuel.

Ethanol + oxygen → carbon dioxide + water

$$C_2H_5OH(l) + 3O_2(g) \rightarrow 2CO_2(g) + 3H_2O(g)$$

Methylated spirits is also widely used as a solvent in industry for paints, soaps and dyes.

Making ethanol

Ethanol is made in two ways. One way uses oil as the raw material. Ethene is made from the oil by cracking as you did in Investigation 8.3. The ethene is then heated to 300 °C under pressure with steam and phosphoric acid. The phosphoric acid is a catalyst in the reaction. Most of the ethanol used in industry is made this way. Because this method starts from oil, this ethanol is non-renewable. However, it is possible to make ethanol by a method which starts from a renewable resource, plant material.

Ethanol in wines and beers is made from sugars by a process called fermentation. This is a natural process carried out by organisms called yeasts. They convert sugar into alcohol and carbon dioxide. In the process they are able to obtain, and make use of, some of the energy in the sugars. The process can be represented by the equation:

Sugar → ethanol + carbon dioxide

$$C_6H_{12}O_6(aq) \rightarrow 2C_2H_5OH(l) + 2CO_2(g)$$

In Investigation 8.6 you can try producing your own ethanol by fermenting sugar and then distilling ethanol out of the solution that is produced.

ethanol

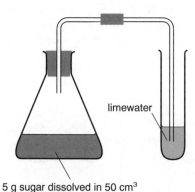

5 g sugar dissolved in 50 cm³ water + 1 spatula measure of yeast

■ **Figure 8.11** Fermentation of sugar.

*I*nvestigation 8.6

Making ethanol by fermentation

You will need:

- sugar
- limewater
- conical flask and test tube
- bung and delivery tube
- distillation flask
- fractionating column
- Liebig condenser
- thermometer
- filter funnel and paper
- boiling chips (bits of broken pot)
- yeast.

1 Add about a teaspoonful of sugar to water in a flask with a little yeast as shown in Figure 8.11. Allow any gas produced to bubble out through fresh limewater.

2 After a few days, when the bubbles have stopped,

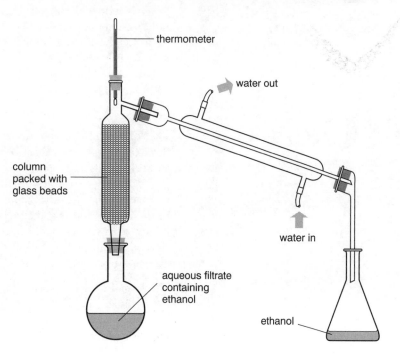

■ **Figure 8.12** Distillation of alcohol.

filter the solution to get rid of much of the yeast. Put the filtrate in the distillation flask together with a few pot chips to help smooth boiling. Set up the fractionating column and condenser as shown in Figure 8.12. Distil the mixture and collect the liquid that comes over at around 78°C.

The limewater in the initial fermentation step will turn milky showing that the process of fermentation produces carbon dioxide. You should be able to collect a small amount of alcohol when you distil the fermentation liquid. However, do not expect much, the yeast can only make alcohol up to a concentration of about 12% before it dies, poisoned by its own alcohol!

A wide variety of plant material can be fermented in this way to produce ethanol. The plant material is renewable and so this process is a way of making a useful fuel that is renewable. It is possible to adapt car engines to run on ethanol and some countries, such as Brazil, which have no oil reserves of their own make ethanol which they add to petrol sold at the pumps.

 uestions

8.14 Describe two ways of making ethanol, one starting from plant matter and the other from crude oil. Explain which of these methods is sustainable.

8.15 List the uses of ethanol. Ethanol is the main constituent of methylated spirits. What else is present in methylated spirits? Why is a purple dye added to methylated spirits?

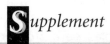 upplement

Organic acids

When an alcoholic drink is left around open to the air, it turns rather unpleasant and acidic. This is a natural process caused by bacteria. The alcohol is oxidised by the oxygen in the air and the product is an acid. The acid produced when ethanol is oxidised is called ethanoic acid. Its old name is acetic acid and its common name is vinegar.

Ethanol + oxygen → ethanoic acid

The oxidation of ethanol which bacteria are able to do using air as the oxidising agent can also be done in the laboratory using a suitable oxidising agent such as potassium permanganate or potassium dichromate. Both these reagents are well-known inorganic substances that can give up oxygen to other compounds. In the process they are themselves reduced. The reaction is easy to follow because there is a colour change; potassium permanganate changes from purple to light pink and potassium dichromate changes from orange to green.

The ethanol is heated for some time with the oxidising agent. The mixture is then distilled and the fraction distilling around 118 °C, the boiling point of ethanoic acid, is collected. It is a liquid at room temperature and has a very strong vinegary smell. Vinegar is a dilute solution of ethanoic acid.

Organic acids react in two characteristic ways. They react with alkalis like all acids and they also react with alcohols. You will recall from Chapter 5 that alkalis are solutions that contain the hydroxide ion, OH⁻. Alcohols are organic compounds which contain the covalently bonded -OH group. We will look at these two reactions in turn and compare them.

Ethanoic acid as a typical acid

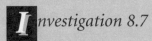 nvestigation 8.7

dilute
sodium hydroxide

Reactions of ethanoic acid as an acid

You will need:
- dilute ethanoic acid
- zinc
- sodium hydrogen carbonate (or sodium carbonate)
- universal indicator paper
- dilute sodium hydroxide solution
- test tubes
- limewater
- thermometer (optional).

1 Take 2 cm depth of ethanoic acid in a test tube. Add a spatula full of sodium hydrogen carbonate. Test the gas evolved with limewater.

2 Take 2 cm depth of ethanoic acid in a test tube. Add a little zinc. Warm if necessary. Test the gas that comes off by bringing it near a flame.

3 Take 2 cm depth of ethanoic acid in a test tube. Add a similar volume of sodium hydroxide solution. Note any signs of a reaction such as a rise in temperature.

4 Take 2 cm depth of ethanoic acid in a test tube. Touch the surface with a little piece of universal indicator paper. Note the pH of the acid.

This investigation shows that ethanoic acid is a typical weak acid. It will react with a carbonate to give carbon dioxide. It will react with a metal high in the reactivity series to give hydrogen. It has a pH below 7 (in fact about pH 3) and will react with an alkali.

The reactions you observed are these:

Ethanoic acid + sodium hydrogen carbonate → sodium ethanoate + carbon dioxide + water

Ethanoic acid + zinc → zinc ethanoate + hydrogen

Ethanoic acid + sodium hydroxide → sodium ethanoate + water

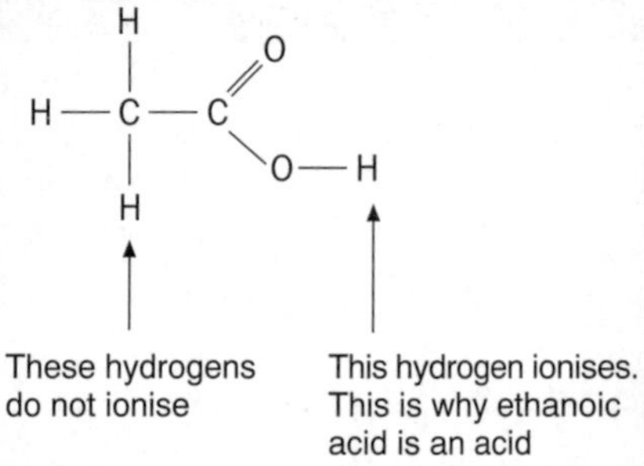

Figure 8.13 Structure of ethanoic acid.

These hydrogens do not ionise

This hydrogen ionises. This is why ethanoic acid is an acid

$$CH_3COOH(aq) + NaHCO_3(s) \rightarrow$$
$$CH_3COONa(aq) + CO_2(g) + H_2O(l)$$
$$2CH_3COOH(aq) + Zn(s) \rightarrow (CH_3COO)_2Zn(aq) + H_2(g)$$
$$CH_3COOH(aq) + NaOH(aq) \rightarrow CH_3COONa(aq) + H_2O(l)$$

The molecule of ethanoic acid contains four hydrogen atoms (Figure 8.13). When it reacts as an acid, only one of these hydrogen atoms takes part in the reaction. You will recall from Chapter 5 that when an acid reacts it donates a hydrogen ion (a proton) to the base or the carbonate. Only one of the four hydrogen atoms in ethanoic acid is donated. You can see from the structure of the acid that one of the hydrogens is joined to an oxygen whereas the others are joined to a carbon atom. It is the one joined to the oxygen that ionises.

The reaction of ethanoic acid with alcohols

The group of atoms in ethanoic acid containing the ionisable hydrogen, -COOH, is called the carboxylic acid group. There are many organic acids containing this group; they are all called carboxylic acids. Some common ones are listed in Table 8.10.

ethanol

concentrated sulphuric acid

*I*nvestigation 8.8

The reaction of ethanoic acid with ethanol

You will need:
- ethanoic acid (concentrated)
- ethanol
- concentrated sulphuric acid (**CARE**)
- test tube
- burner
- boiling chips (bits of broken pot).

1 Add equal quantities of the ethanoic acid and the ethanol in a test tube.

2 Carefully add a few drops of concentrated sulphuric acid. **Safety note** This acid should be handled only by the teacher and any spills washed immediately with plenty of water.

3 Put some boiling chips in the liquid and heat the mixture gently over a small flame. Remove from the flame and smell the vapour. You should detect a sweet smell different from either the alcohol or the acid.

Table 8.10 Carboxylic acids.

Formic acid	The 'sting' of ants
Ethanoic acid	Vinegar
Citric acid	In citrus fruits
Tartaric acid	Used in cooking
Malic acid	In apples
Lactic acid	In sour milk

When ethanoic acid reacts with an alcohol, a substance called an **ester** is formed (Figure 8.14). In this case the ester is called ethyl ethanoate. It has a sweet fruity smell.

Esters are very common in nature. The taste and smell of fruits is often caused by an ester. Fats and vegetable oils, though not sweet smelling, are also esters. The solvent for removing nail varnish is an ester with a particularly sweet smell (called amyl acetate).

We can compare the reaction of ethanoic acid with an alkali and with an alcohol. If we look at the equations, they are very similar but the big difference between them is that the reaction with alkalis is ionic (and irreversible) and the reaction with alcohols is covalent (and reversible).

The general reactions can be written like this:

Ethanoic acid + alkali → salt + water

Ethanoic acid + alcohol ⇌ ester + water

The reactions you did are these:

Ethanoic acid + sodium hydroxide → sodium ethanoate + water

$CH_3COOH(aq) + NaOH(aq) \rightarrow CH_3COONa(aq) + HOH(l)$

Ethanoic acid + ethanol → ethyl ethanoate + water

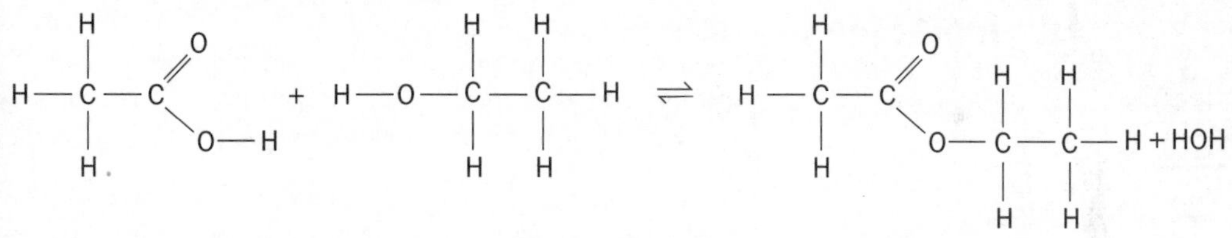

ethanoic acid   ethanol   ethyl ethanoate

■ **Figure 8.14** Esterification.

This kind of reaction, in which the only by-product is water, is called a **condensation** reaction. You will learn more about reactions like this in the next chapter.

Questions

8.16 There are four hydrogen atoms in a molecule of ethanoic acid. Explain why only one of them takes part when ethanoic acid reacts as an acid.

8.17 Carboxylic acids react with alkalis and with alcohols. Show one similarity and one difference between these two reactions.

Review questions on this chapter can be found on pages 242–3.

9 Macromolecules
–Supplement

The last chapter showed that the element carbon forms more compounds than all the other elements put together; millions of compounds in fact. It forms so many because the bonds that join one carbon atom to another are very strong. Some of the compounds that carbon forms have quite small molecules , but most of the others are large molecules; some of them are so large it is not possible to draw their structure on the page. We call them **macromolecules**.

Big molecules

Figure 9.1 shows a number of large molecules that are part of our everyday lives; we eat them, we wear them, we build with them, we use them to keep us clean. We make some of them; others are made naturally by plants and animals.

These molecules all look rather complicated and big. However, if we look carefully at them we find that there are patterns in their structure which make them quite simple to understand. These patterns also allow us to explain some of the interesting and useful properties of these molecules.

Synthetic polymers

Three of the molecules in Figure 9.1, polythene, Terylene and nylon, are synthetic polymers. Synthetic means that they are made by man and do not occur naturally. Polymer means 'many parts'. They are called polymers because the molecules are made up of many small parts joined end-to-end like links in a chain. Each individual small part is called a monomer, which means 'one part'.

Addition polymers

Polythene is a very common material. Its correct name is polyethene because the monomer from which it is made is ethene (see Figures 9.2 and 9.3). In the early days of the manufacture of polythene, there were many explosions in the plant. This was because very high pressures (2000 times atmospheric pressure) were needed to make the ethene molecules polymerise (combine with each other). Modern

■ **Figure 9.1** Everyday large molecules.

Glucose

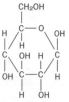

a glucose molecule

Starch

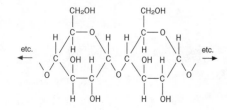

part of a starch molecule

Soap

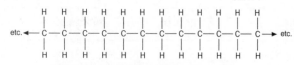

a soap molecule

Polythene

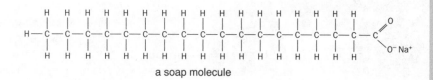

part of a polyethene (polythene) molecule

Terylene

part of a Terylene molecule

Nylon

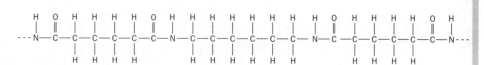

part of a nylon molecule

polythene plants make use of catalysts which allow the reaction to happen at much lower and safer pressures.

The polymerisation of ethene is an addition reaction. In the last chapter you studied how substances reacted with ethene by adding on to the double bond. In this polymerisation, the molecules of ethene add on to each other.

Polythene is the simplest of many polymers made from alkenes. Table 9.1 shows a number of other common polymers which are made from alkenes or from compounds made from alkenes.

■ **Figure 9.3** Karl Ziegler (1898–1973) was a German chemist who discovered a process for making polythene from ethene at atmospheric pressure. He was awarded the Nobel prize for this discovery in 1967. The discovery was made by accident when a chemical he was using with ethene was accidentally contaminated by some nickel.

■ **Table 9.1 Addition polymers made from alkenes.**

| Monomer | | Polymer | | |
Name	Structure	Name	Structure	Use
Propene (propylene)	CH₃, C=C, H, H, H	Polypropylene	CH₃ H CH₃ H CH₃ H chain	water pipes
Chloroethene (vinyl chloride)	Cl, C=C, H, H, H	Polyvinyl chloride (PVC)	Cl H Cl H Cl H chain	electrical insulation
Tetrafluoro-ethene (tetrafluoro-ethylene)	F, C=C, F, F, F	Polytetrafluoro-etheylene "Ptfe" "teflon"	F F F F chain	Non-stick pans

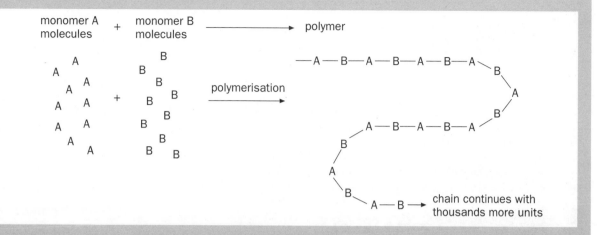

Figure 9.4 Formation of a polymer from two different monomers.

Condensation polymers

Another synthetic polymer in Figure 9.1 is Terylene. This is very different from the addition polymers based on alkenes. One difference is that there are two monomer building blocks and not one. Many polymers have this kind of structure. The two building blocks occur alternately in the polymer (Figure 9.4).

In the last chapter you studied the formation of esters from acids and alcohols. If an organic acid has not one but two carboxylic acid groups, one at each end of the molecule, it can react with two molecules of an alcohol to form a di-ester. If the alcohol also has not one, but two, hydroxyl groups on it then it is possible to obtain a **polyester** from the reaction. A polyester is a long-chain compound consisting alternately of the alcohol part and then the acid part of the ester. Figure 9.5 shows this. We call acids such as these dicarboxylic acids and the alcohols are called diols.

Note that, during this reaction, water is produced. One molecule of water is produced every time a polymer bond is formed between the monomers. A reaction that produces water as the only by-product is called a **condensation reaction** (can you think why?). Polymers like these are called condensation polymers.

Terylene is an example of a polyester made like this. The monomers used to make Terylene are the diol ethane diol (which is also used as antifreeze in car radiators) and a dicarboxylic acid called terephthalic acid (Figure 9.5).

Figure 9.5 The formation of a polyester (such as Terylene).

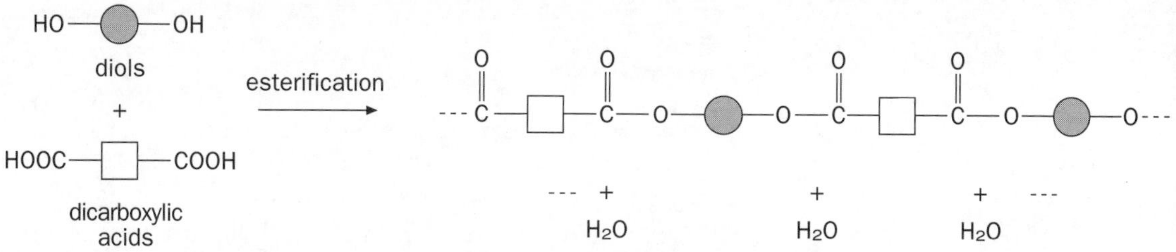

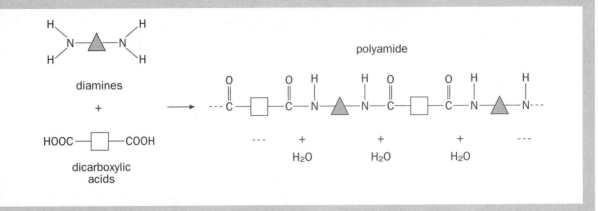

Figure 9.6 The formation of a polymide (such as nylon).

Another well-known condensation polymer is nylon. Nylon is not a polyester but a polyamide. Instead of an alcohol, which contains the -OH group, a substance called an amine, which contains instead the -NH_2 group is used. Otherwise the reaction is the same. The structure of the polymer that is formed is almost the same as a polyester but with an oxygen in the chain replaced by a nitrogen atom (see Figure 9.6).

Both Terylene and nylon are used to make fibres which are then woven into fabrics. They are harder wearing than natural fibres such as cotton and wool and dry more quickly after washing. However, they are less comfortable and not as warm.

Did you know?

The first synthetic plastic was developed by a Belgian chemist, Leo Baekeland (1863–1944), who went to live in the USA. The plastic was first discovered in the nineteenth century but Baekeland was the first to develop it commercially, in 1906, and he called it Bakelite. It still has many uses, particularly as a hard electric insulator. Distributor caps and rotors in cars are made of it. Baekeland also invented the first commercial photographic paper.

uestions

9.1 Explain, with examples, the difference between addition polymers and condensation polymers.

9.2 List six synthetic polymers in a table. Also show in the table the structure of the monomers, the structure of the polymer and its uses.

Natural polymers

All except three of the macromolecules shown in Figure 9.1 occur naturally. These natural polymers are condensation polymers and many have the polyester or polyamide structures like Terylene and nylon.

Polymers in food

You learn in biology that the main constituents of food are proteins, fats and carbohydrates.

Proteins are natural polymers with a polyamide structure (see Figure 9.7). Unlike nylon, which is made out of only two monomers, proteins are made out of up to 20 different monomers (called amino acids). These monomers are arranged in different orders in different proteins and it is the difference in this order that determines the different properties of the protein. Figure 9.7 shows the way in which amino acids are joined together in a protein; the different shapes represent different amino acids. Compare this with the structure of nylon on the opposite page.

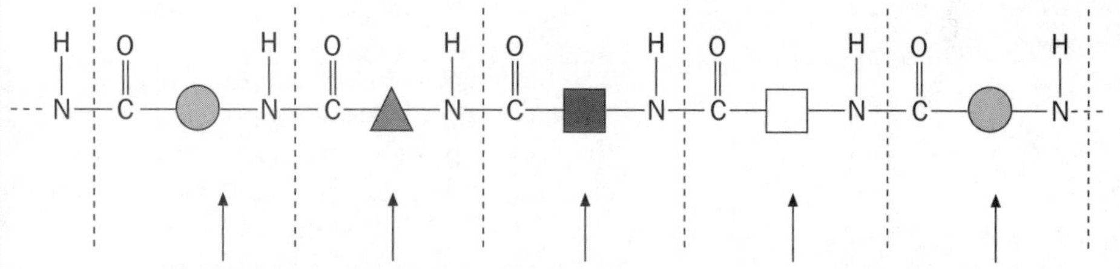

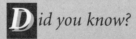

each amino acid has a carboxylic acid group on one end and an amine group on the other

■ **Figure 9.7** Structure of a protein.

Your hair, your red blood cells and the white of an egg are all proteins. The only difference between them is the length of the protein chain and the arrangement of the 20 building blocks, the amino acids, in it. Proteins are large, complex compounds. Some proteins, called enzymes, are very important as they control all the chemical processes that keep our bodies going.

*D*id you know?

The protein insulin helps controls the level of sugar in the blood. Its structure was discovered by Dorothy Hodgkin (page 3, Chapter 1). Even though it is one of the simplest proteins it has the formula $C_{254}H_{377}N_{65}O_{75}S_6$! (Can you calculate its molecular mass?)

Proteins can be broken down into the amino acids from which they are made. This is a process called hydrolysis. Hydrolysis is the reverse of condensation. Condensation is the process in which two compounds join together and water is produced as the only by-product. Hydrolysis is the process in which a substance is broken

amino acids   protein

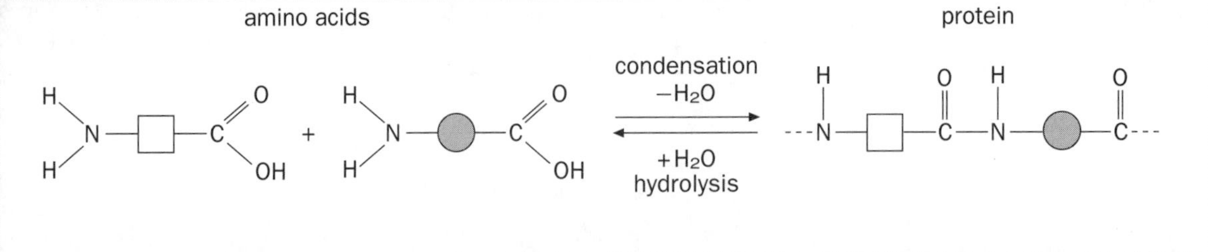

condensation
−H₂O
+H₂O
hydrolysis

Figure 9.8 Condensation and hydrolysis in proteins.

down by heating it with water (see Figure 9.8). The water is usually made either acidic or alkaline which makes the reaction proceed faster.

It is often useful to know which of the 20 amino acids are present in a protein. To find out, the protein is first hydrolysed by boiling it in acidic solution and then the mixture of amino acids is separated by chromatography (see Chapter 1, page 11). The amino acids are not coloured so it is impossible to see them on the chromatography paper. To make them visible, the paper is sprayed with a substance that forms coloured compounds when it reacts with amino acids. We call a substance that is used in this way a **locating agent**. The chemical that is used as a locating agent for proteins is called ninhydrin.

Another way of hydrolysing protein is to use an **enzyme**. Enzymes are themselves proteins and they are complex molecules that catalyse reactions in living cells. There are many different enzymes and each one only catalyses one reaction. An enzyme in the digestive tract, called pepsin, catalyses that hydrolysis of proteins. It does this at normal body temperature; the protein does not have to be boiled in the stomach!

Carbohydrates are substances that are made by plants. The name tells us that they contain the elements carbon (carbo-), hydrogen (-hydr-) and oxygen (-ate). Examples of carbohydrates are sugars, starch and cellulose. All these three substances have a very similar structure. This is not surprising as plants make, first of all, a sugar called glucose, during photosynthesis and then they use the glucose to make the starch and the cellulose. Starch and cellulose are both condensation polymers of glucose.

The structure of glucose is shown in Figure 9.1. You can see that it has a hexagonal ring structure with many hydroxyl groups attached to the ring. (Only two of these are shown in Figure 9.10) The structure of starch is also shown in Figure 9.1 and you can see that it is made of many glucose rings joined together. Cellulose has a very similar structure. The only difference is that in cellulose, every second sugar ring is upside down.

It is interesting to compare the physical properties of starch with those of cellulose. White flour is almost pure starch. It is soluble and anything made of starch (like bread) has no tensile strength at all. Cellulose, on the other hand, is the material that gives all plant matter its strength. Wood is mainly cellulose and is an extremely strong substance. The only difference between the two is that the cellulose

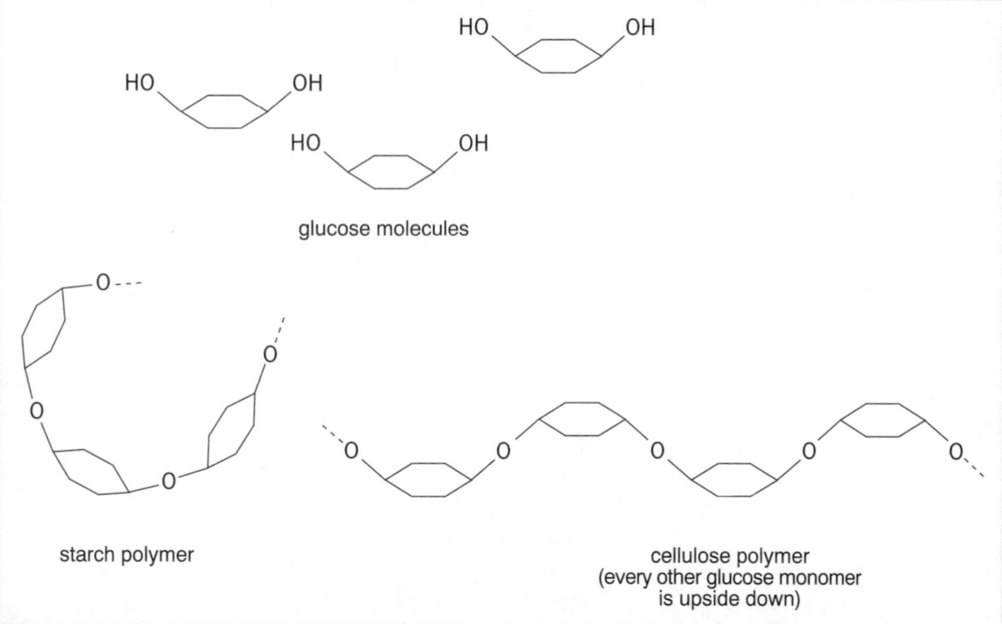

glucose molecules

starch polymer

cellulose polymer
(every other glucose monomer
is upside down)

■ **Figure 9.9** The structures of glucose, starch and cellulose.

chain is straight, because every second monomer is upside down, whereas the starch polymer is curved. This is shown in Figure 9.9.

Like proteins, starch can be hydrolysed with the help of enzymes. Try the next investigation.

*I*nvestigation 9.1

Hydrolysis of starch using saliva

You will need:
- 1% starch solution (boiled maize meal)
- Benedict's reagent (or Fehling's solution)
- iodine solution
- dropper
- test tube
- glass rod
- white tile
- burner.

1 Take about 10 cm^3 of starch solution in a test tube. Carry out two tests on it. The first is a test for starch (which will be positive) and the second is a test for glucose (which will be negative).

Test 1 Take a spot of starch solution and put it onto the tile. Add one drop of iodine solution. The black colour is caused by the presence of starch.

Test 2 Take a drop of the starch solution and add a drop of Benedict's reagent and warm. If a brown precipitate is formed, glucose is present.

Note – diseases such as AIDS can be transmitted in saliva. You should use only your own saliva for this experiment.

2 Add about $1 \, cm^3$ of your saliva to the starch solution. Allow the mixture to stand and repeat the two tests every few minutes.

In your saliva there is an enzyme called ptyalin which catalyses the hydrolysis of starch to glucose. After a few minutes with the ptyalin, the starch test will show that the amount of starch in the solution is decreasing and that glucose is produced. Eventually all the starch will have been hydrolysed and the iodine test will be negative.

It is interesting that we have evolved an enzyme in our mouths that can easily and quickly break down starch but nowhere in our digestive system is there an enzyme that can digest cellulose. Yet cellulose has a very similar structure and would break down, like starch, into glucose.

*D*id you know?

Some animals, such as cattle, horses, antelope and elephant, have evolved ways of breaking down cellulose in their stomachs. Unfortunately it is so complicated and inefficient that, in order to get enough glucose from the cellulose, they have to eat almost all the time. It is a fermentation process which generates a lot of the flammable gas methane, which has to be released from time to time into the air. If the animals do not keep moving all the time, this methane builds up inside them and cannot escape. This is why, if an elephant is stunned with a dart, it must be brought to consciousness after no more than about 20 minutes or the build-up of methane in its stomach will be so great that it could burst like a balloon.

*Q*uestions

9.3 Name three naturally occurring polymers. Name also the building blocks from which the polymers are made.

9.4 Describe one similarity and one difference between starch and cellulose.

9.5 Describe how it is possible to find out which amino acids are present in a protein.

9.6 The two chemical processes hydrolysis and condensation are similar in one way. Explain this similarity.

9.7 Show, with the aid of a diagram, the similarity between proteins and nylon.

Fats and oils

Unlike proteins and starch, fats are not polymers. They are esters. The alcohol that the esters are made from is called glycerol. It is better known by its common name, glycerine. It is a small molecule, only three carbon atoms long and it has three hydroxyl groups, one on each carbon. The acid part of the ester varies according to the fat or oil. These acids usually have 14 to 18 carbon atoms and a carboxylic acid group on one end. Three acid molecules are combined with the glycerol molecule in the fat or oil (see Figure 9.10).

In Chapter 8 you studied the difference between saturated and unsaturated hydrocarbons. The acids in fats are saturated; they have no double bonds in them and the fats themselves are solids. The acids in oils, such as sunflower oil or palm oil, are unsaturated; they have one or more double bonds in them. These esters are all liquids. You will recall from Chapter 8 that margarine is made from vegetable oils by the addition of hydrogen to some, but not all, of the double bonds. The margarine is solid but still is 'unsaturated'. Unsaturated acids are healthier for you than saturated ones and so margarine cartons often advertise that the margarine they contain is unsaturated (see Figure 9.11).

In Chapter 8 you studied how an ester is made from an alcohol and an acid by a condensation reaction. The reverse of condensation is hydrolysis and esters can easily be hydrolysed. The hydrolysis of fats and oils has been an important reaction for hundreds of years. If a fat or an oil is heated with an alkali, it is hydrolysed to glycerol and the acid. The alkali will react with the acid forming a salt. These salts are **soaps**. The manufacture of soaps by hydrolysis of oils and fats is such an important reaction it has been given the special name 'saponification'.

■ **Figure 9.10** A fat is an ester.

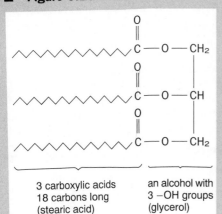

3 carboxylic acids
18 carbons long
(stearic acid)

an alcohol with
3 –OH groups
(glycerol)

The line represents a
hydrocarbon chain,
18 carbons long

■ **Figure 9.11** The label on this margarine pack advertises the fact that the acids in the margarine are unsaturated.

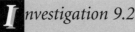

nvestigation 9.2

sodium hydroxide
(concentrated)

methylated
spirits

Saponification of fats and oils

You will need:

- sodium hydroxide solution (concentrated)
- methylated spirits
- animal fat or vegetable oil
- burner
- salt solution (concentrated)
- test tubes
- evaporating basin.

1 Melt a little fat (about 2 cm^3) in a test tube.

2 Turn out the burner and add 4 cm^3 of methylated sprits and mix it with the fat.

3 Add 1 cm^3 of the sodium hydroxide solution and warm the mixture very gently on the burner. The mixture will become stiff like honey.

CARE Concentrated sodium hydroxide solution can burn your skin and damage your clothes. Wash any spills with a lot of hot water.

4 Heat 5 cm^3 of the salt solution in an evaporating basin until it boils and then pour the mixture into it.

5 Heat gently to evaporate the liquid to about half its volume and then leave it to cool. The solid product formed is soap and you can test it by shaking a bit with water in a test tube to see if you can get a lather.

The reaction can be written as an equation (Figure 9.12).

The structure of a soap molecule gives us an idea of how it works. Soaps make grease soluble. The molecule has an ionic 'head' and a covalent 'tail'. The covalent bit is attracted towards the grease particle in a fabric or on your hands. Water readily dissolves ionic compounds and so the ionic end causes the soap molecule to be soluble. A grease particle that is surrounded by soap molecules becomes soluble (Figure 9.13).

■ **Figure 9.12** Saponification of a fat.

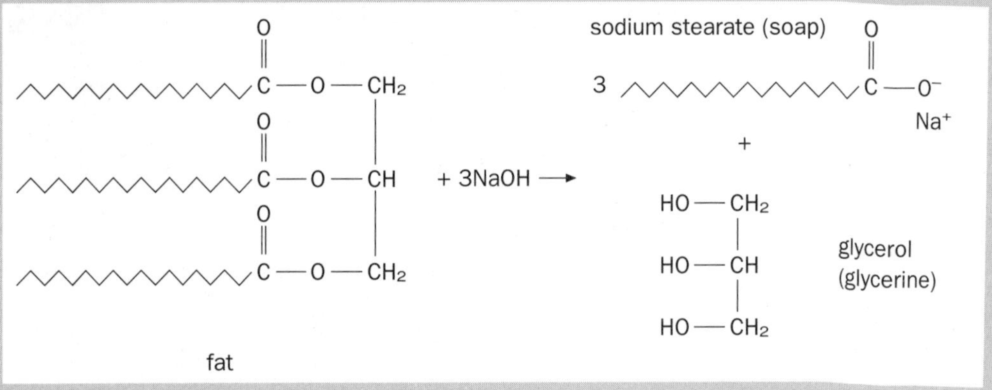

fat + 3NaOH → sodium stearate (soap) + glycerol (glycerine)

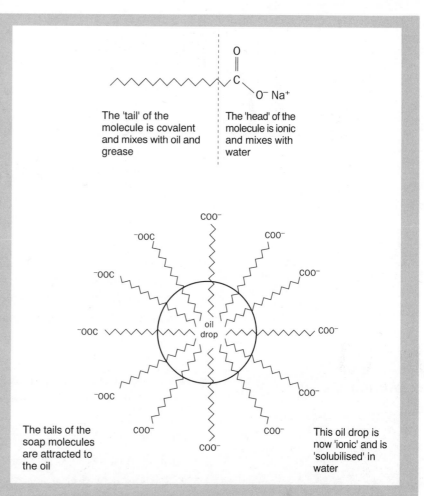

Figure 9.13 How soap molecules can solubilise oil and grease.

The tail' of the molecule is covalent and mixes with oil and grease

The 'head' of the molecule is ionic and mixes with water

The tails of the soap molecules are attracted to the oil

This oil drop is now 'ionic' and is 'solubilised' in water

The process of making soap from fats and oils requires a lot of alkali. It was the demand for soap for cleaning that originally led to the alkali industry being set up and the invention almost 200 years ago of the chemical processes it uses. Now, of course, there are many other useful materials being produced by the industry as you read in Chapter 5.

Questions

9.8 What class of organic compounds are **a** fats and **b** soaps?

9.9 Describe how soap is made from fats and oils. What are the two raw materials that are needed for this process and where do they both come from?

9.10 Explain, with the aid of diagrams, how soap can solubilise a grease spot.

Review questions on this chapter can be found on page 243.

10 How much? –Supplement

When we study any chemical reaction we are interested usually in two things. First we like to know **what** is produced by the reaction. Secondly we like to know **how much** of the product is made. Most of this book is about what. This chapter, however, is about **how much**.

Meaning of an equation

When hydrogen and oxygen are mixed and ignited, there is an explosion as they react and water is formed. The equation for the reaction is this:

$$2H_2(g) + O_2(g) \rightarrow 2H_2O(l)$$

What information can we get from this equation?

• It tells us that hydrogen and oxygen combine to form water.

• It tells us that each molecule of hydrogen consists of two hydrogen atoms.

• It tells us that each molecule of oxygen consists of two oxygen atoms.

• It tells us that a molecule of water is made up of two atoms of hydrogen joined to an atom of oxygen.

• It tells us that two molecules of hydrogen react with one molecule of oxygen to form two molecules of water.

We can also use the equation to tell us something about the masses of the gases that will react together and the mass of the water that is made. To do this, it is necessary to know what is meant by a 'mole'.

The mole

Counting atoms

The relative atomic mass of hydrogen is 1 and that of oxygen is 16. This means that an atom of oxygen is 16 times as heavy as an atom of hydrogen. This means that 1 g of hydrogen contains the same number of atoms as 16 g of oxygen. But how many atoms is this? It was an Italian called Count Amadeo Avogadro, professor of physics at Turin University, who first worked this out as long ago as 1811. The number became known as the Avogadro Number and is around 600 000 000 000 000 000 000 000 (or 6×10^{23}). This number is known as a **mole** (just as 12 is known as a dozen and 144 is known as a gross).

Why is this a useful number? Knowing this number enables us to count atoms and molecules by weighing them, just as bank clerks often count money by weighing it.

1 mole of hydrogen atoms has a mass of 1 g.

1 mole of oxygen atoms has a mass of 16 g.

The relative atomic mass, in grams, of any element contains 1 mole of atoms.

To obtain a sample of an element that contains 1 mole of atoms, we just weigh out its relative atomic mass in grams.

The relative molecular mass of water (H_2O) is $16 + 1 + 1$ which is 18. This means that 18 g of water contains a mole of water molecules.

The relative molecular mass, in grams, of any compound contains 1 mole of molecules.

To go back to the reaction between hydrogen and oxygen on the opposite page:

$$2H_2(g) + O_2(g) \rightarrow 2H_2O(l)$$

This equation now tells us even more about the reaction.

If ...
two molecules of hydrogen react with one molecule of oxygen to form two molecules of water

Then ...
two dozen molecules of hydrogen react with one dozen molecules of oxygen to form two dozen molecules of water.

And so ...
Two moles of hydrogen molecules react with one mole of oxygen molecules to form two moles of water molecules.

How do we convert this number of moles into grams?

The relative atomic mass of hydrogen is 1, therefore the relative molecular mass of the hydrogen molecule (H_2) is $2 \times 1 = 2$

Similarly, the relative molecular mass of oxygen (O_2) is $2 \times 16 = 32$

The relative molecular mass of water (H_2O) is $1 + 1 + 16 = 18$

The mass of 2 moles of hydrogen molecules is therefore $2 \times 2 = 4$ g

The mass of 1 mole of oxygen molecules is therefore 32 g

The mass of 2 moles of water molecules is therefore $2 \times 18 = 36$ g

Thus, the equation also tells us the very useful fact that:

4g of hydrogen will react with 32 g of oxygen to form 36 g of water.

We can summarise the different information the equation can give us like this:

2H$_2$(g)		O$_2$(g)		2H$_2$O(l)
hydrogen		oxygen		water
2 molecules hydrogen	+	1 molecule oxygen	→	2 molecules water
2 moles hydrogen molecules		1 mole oxygen molecules		2 moles water molecules
4 g hydrogen		32 g oxygen		36 g water

The equations below show the relationship between number of moles, mass and relative atomic (or molecular) mass.

$$\text{Number of moles} = \frac{\text{mass}}{\text{relative atomic (molecular) mass}}$$

$$\text{Mass} = \text{number of moles} \times \text{relative atomic (molecular) mass}$$

$$\text{Relative atomic (molecular) mass} = \frac{\text{mass}}{\text{number of moles}}$$

These help us calculate quantitative information about chemicals that we use. The examples below show how.

1 How many moles of calcium carbonate (CaCO$_3$) are used in a reaction if 10 g of the solid are used?

$$\text{Number of moles} = \frac{\text{mass}}{\text{relative molecular mass}}$$

Molecular mass of CaCO$_3$ is $40 + 12 + (3 \times 16) = 100$

$$\text{Number of moles} = \frac{10}{100}$$

$$= \mathbf{0.1\ moles}$$

2 To make 10 moles of water by burning hydrogen, we must burn 10 moles of hydrogen. What mass of hydrogen is this?

$$\text{Mass} = \text{number of moles} \times \text{relative molecular mass}$$

Molecular mass of H$_2$ is $2 \times 1 = 2$

$$\text{Mass} = 10 \times 2$$

$$= \mathbf{20\ g}$$

3 0.2 moles of magnesium oxide are formed when 0.2 moles of magnesium burns. The mass of the oxide formed is 8 g. What is the relative molecular mass of magnesium oxide?

$$\text{Relative molecular mass} = \frac{\text{mass}}{\text{number of moles}}$$

$$\text{Relative molecular mass} = \frac{8}{0.2}$$

$$= \mathbf{40}$$

We are now in a position to answer some of the important 'how much?' questions that chemists might ask, like:

- How much iron will I get from a kilogram of pure iron ore?
- How much sulphur will be needed to make a kilogram of sulphuric acid?
- How much hydrogen will be produced if 10 g magnesium completely reacts with acid?

In order to answer these questions, we need two pieces of information. We need a full knowledge of the reaction, including the formulae of the compounds involved. We also need the relative molecular masses of all the compounds that concern us.

Consider these three questions one by one.

1 How much iron will I get from a kilogram of pure iron ore?

Iron ore is iron oxide, formula Fe_2O_3. From one molecule of this oxide, we should be able to obtain 2 atoms of iron. Therefore from 1 mole of the oxide we should get 2 moles of iron. From tables we can find the relative atomic masses of iron and oxygen (Fe = 56, O = 16) and then we can calculate the relative molecular mass of iron oxide.

Fe_2O_3 Molecular mass $= (2 \times 56) + (3 \times 16)$

$$= 160$$

We can then perform a proportion sum as follows:

From the formula of iron oxide, Fe_2O_3:

1 mole Fe_2O_3 will give 2 moles Fe

In grams this will mean:

160 g Fe_2O_3 will give 2×56 g Fe

$$= 112 \text{ g Fe}$$

Therefore,

1 g Fe_2O_3 will give $\frac{112}{160}$ g Fe

Therefore,

1000 g Fe_2O_3 will give $\frac{112 \times 1000}{160}$ g Fe

$$= \textbf{700 g Fe} \text{ (to 2 significant figures)}$$

2 How much sulphur will be needed to make a kilogram of sulphuric acid?

Sulphuric acid has the formula H_2SO_4. This has in it 1 sulphur atom. We need not know the full details of how sulphur is turned into sulphuric acid. 1 atom of sulphur will make one molecule of sulphuric acid. Therefore 1 mole of sulphur atoms will make 1 mole of sulphuric acid molecules.

Atomic masses, H = 1, S = 32, O = 16.

H_2SO_4 Molecular mass $= (2 \times 1) + 32 + (4 \times 16)$

$$= 98$$

From the formula of sulphuric acid, H_2SO_4:

1 mole sulphuric acid can be made from 1 mole sulphur

In grams this will be:

   98 g   sulphuric acid can be made from   32 g sulphur

Therefore,
   1 g   sulphuric acid can be made from $\frac{32}{98}$ g sulphur

Therefore,
   1000g   sulphuric acid can be made from $\frac{32 \times 1000}{98}$ g sulphur

= **330 g sulphur** (to 2 significant figures)

3 How much hydrogen will be produced if 10 g magnesium completely reacts with acid?

Before this question can be answered, the equation for the reaction must be known. Here are two equations, one with sulphuric acid and one with hydrochloric acid:

$$Mg(s) \quad + \quad H_2SO_4(aq) \quad \rightarrow \quad MgSO_4(aq) \quad + \quad H_2(g)$$
$$Mg(s) \quad + \quad 2HCl(aq) \quad \rightarrow \quad MgCl_2(aq) \quad + \quad H_2(g)$$

In both equations one atom of magnesium liberates one molecule of hydrogen. This does not change if a different acid is used. So, we can use this fact in our calculation.

Atomic masses, $Mg = 24$, $H = 1$, therefore $H_2 = (1 + 1) = 2$

1 mole magnesium can liberate 1 mole hydrogen molecules

In grams: 24 g magnesium can liberate   2 g   hydrogen

Therefore, 1 g magnesium can liberate $\frac{2}{24}$ g   hydrogen

Therefore, 10 g magnesium will liberate $\frac{10 \times 2}{24}$ g hydrogen

= **0.83 g hydrogen** (to 2 significant figures)

uestions

10.1 Calculate the mass of the following:

a 3 moles of aluminium atoms (Al = 27)

b 5 moles of magnesium atoms (Mg = 24)

c 4 moles of sulphur atoms (S = 32)

d 10 moles of carbon atoms (C = 12)

e 0.2 moles of calcium atoms (Ca = 40)

f 0.01 moles of iron atoms (Fe = 56)

g 0.08 moles of sodium atoms (Na = 23)

10.2 Calculate the mass of the following:

a 3 moles of water (H_2O) molecules (H = 1, O = 16)

b 2 moles of sulphur dioxide (SO_2) molecules (S = 32, O = 16)

c 8 moles of carbon dioxide (CO_2) molecules (C = 12, O = 16)

d 10 moles of sodium chloride (NaCl) ions (Na = 23, Cl = 35.5)

e 3 moles of calcium carbonate ($CaCO_3$) ions (Ca = 40, C = 12, O = 16)

f 0.1 moles of ethane (C_2H_6) molecules (C = 12, H = 1)

g 0.02 moles of ammonia (NH_3) molecules (H = 1, N = 14)

h 3 moles of oxygen molecules (O = 16)

10.3 How many moles of atoms (or molecules) are there in the following:

a 14 g silicon (Si = 28)

b 5.6 g iron (Fe = 56)

c 88 g carbon dioxide, CO_2 (C = 12, O = 16)

d 4 kg helium (He = 4)

e 19.6 g sulphuric acid, H_2SO_4 (H = 1, S = 32, O = 16)

f 3.7 g calcium hydroxide, $Ca(OH)_2$ (H = 1, Ca = 40, O = 16)

g 50 g copper sulphate crystals, $CuSO_4.5H_2O$ (H = 1, Cu = 64, S = 32, O = 16)

h 0.32 g methane, CH_4 (H = 1, C = 12)

10.4 Write the equation showing the burning of calcium to give calcium oxide (CaO).

a How many moles of calcium oxide can be made from 1 mole of calcium atoms?

b How many grams of calcium oxide can be obtained from burning 4 g calcium? (Ca = 40, O = 16)

10.5 The equation for the reduction of iron ore by carbon monoxide is:

$$Fe_2O_3 + 3CO \rightarrow 2Fe + 3CO_2$$

a How many moles of iron can be obtained if 1 mole of carbon monoxide is used?

b How many grams of iron can be extracted using 1 mole of carbon monoxide?

c How many grams of iron can be extracted using 1 tonne (1000 kg) of carbon monoxide? (Fe = 56, C = 12, O = 16)

10.6 How much water is produced when 100 g of hydrogen is burnt? (H = 1, O = 16)

10.7 The concentration of sulphur in a sample of coal is 2%.

a How much sulphur dioxide is produced when 1 tonne of coal is burnt?

b If a power station burns 4 tonnes of coal per hour, how much sulphur dioxide is put into the atmosphere in a week? (S = 32, O = 16)

Formulae of compounds

Many formulae are used in this book; some are simple, like water (H_2O), others are more complex, like glucose ($C_6H_{12}O_6$). All of these formulae have been discovered at some time by experiment. These are often not easy experiments to do. For example, scientists have found by experiment that, when 1 g of hydrogen gas is burnt, 9g of water are produced. Hydrogen is a light gas and it is not easy to weigh it. When it burns, it produces water vapour which must all be condensed and weighed.

The results from this experiment on the burning of hydrogen can tell us the formula of water. To find the formula of water, we need to know how many atoms of hydrogen combine with one atom of oxygen. This will be the same as the number of moles of atoms of hydrogen that combine with one mole of atoms of oxygen. The relative atomic mass of oxygen is 16. Therefore, we want to know:

a How many grams of hydrogen combine with 1 mole (16 g) of atoms, and then

b How many moles of atoms of hydrogen this is (relative atomic mass of hydrogen is 1).

Calculating a

From the results we have:

1 g of hydrogen produces 9 g of water

Therefore, 1 g must combine with 8 g of oxygen to give the 9 g of water.

So

$$8 \text{ g} \quad \text{oxygen reacts with} \quad 1 \text{ g} \quad \text{hydrogen to give water}$$

Therefore,

$$1 \text{ g} \quad \text{oxygen reacts with} \quad \frac{1}{8} \text{ g} \quad \text{hydrogen to give water}$$

Therefore,

$$16 \text{ g} \quad \text{oxygen reacts with} \quad \frac{16 \times 1}{8} \text{ g} \quad \text{hydrogen to give water}$$

$$= \textbf{2.0 g hydrogen} \text{ (to 2 significant figures)}$$

Calculating b

If the relative atomic mass of hydrogen is 1, then 2 g hydrogen is 2 moles of hydrogen atoms.

So, from this calculation, we find that 1 mole of oxygen atoms combines with 2 moles of hydrogen atoms. Therefore, 1 atom of oxygen combines with 2 atoms of hydrogen to give water. Therefore, the formula of water must be H_2O.

We are not quite there, however. If the formula of water was H_4O_2 or H_6O_3, we would still find that 1 mole of oxygen atoms would combine with two moles of hydrogen atoms. What we have found is the **simplest** formula for water, H_2O. We call this the **empirical** formula.

In order to find the actual formula for water, we need more information. We need to know the relative molecular mass of water. The relative molecular masses for some of the possible formulae of water are shown in Table 10.1.

■ **Table 10.1 Molecular masses for some possible formulae of water.**

Formula	Relative molecular mass
H_2O	18
H_4O_2	36
H_6O_3	54

To find the relative molecular mass of water, the mass of one mole of water molecules must be found in a separate experiment. Such an experiment gives the mass of one mole of water molecules as 18 and therefore the **molecular** formula of water is H_2O, the same as the empirical formula.

We can use experiments like those that follow to tell us the empirical formula of compounds.

magnesium

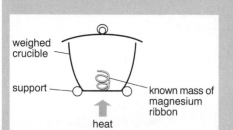

weighed crucible

support

known mass of magnesium ribbon

heat

■ **Figure 10.1** Apparatus for finding the formula of magnesium oxide.

*I*nvestigation 10.1

Finding the formula of magnesium oxide

You will need:
- magnesium ribbon cleaned with iron wool
- crucible with lid
- burner
- balance.

1 Carefully weigh a crucible plus lid empty and with about 5 cm of carefully cleaned magnesium ribbon in it.

2 Heat it strongly to burn the magnesium (see Figure 10.1). Raise the lid from time to time to let in some air. This must be done very carefully because magnesium oxide smoke must not be allowed to escape.

3 When all the magnesium has burnt, allow the crucible to cool and reweigh it.

4 Calculate the mass of the magnesium used and the mass of the magnesium oxide produced.

5 Calculate the mass of oxygen used in the reaction.

6 Given that Mg = 24 and O = 16, calculate the number of moles of oxygen atoms that combine with 1 mole of magnesium atoms.

The reaction that takes place in the crucible is as follows and your results may be something like those in the boxes.

Magnesium   +   oxygen   →   magnesium oxide

| 0.048 g | ? | 0.080 g |

Calculation

To find the mass of oxygen that will combine with one mole (24 g) of magnesium atoms:

Mass of oxygen used is $0.080 - 0.048 = 0.032$ g

Therefore,

    0.048 g   magnesium combines with   0.032 g   oxygen

Therefore

    1 g   magnesium combines with $\dfrac{0.032}{0.048}$ g   oxygen

Therefore

    24 g   magnesium combines with $\dfrac{0.032 \times 24}{0.048}$ g   oxygen

$$= \textbf{16 g oxygen } \text{(to 2 significant figures)}$$

16 g oxygen is 1 mole of oxygen atoms. Therefore, 1 mole of magnesium atoms combine with 1 mole of oxygen atoms. The empirical formula for magnesium oxide is therefore MgO.

Finding the formula of copper oxide

Another experiment that can help us find the formula of a compound is the reduction of copper oxide. In this case, oxygen is removed from a metal oxide to give the metal, the opposite reaction from the one with magnesium above. The apparatus is shown in Figure 10.2.

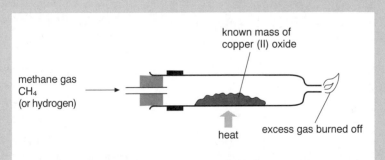

■ **Figure 10.2** Apparatus for reducing copper oxide.

When the copper oxide is heated in a stream of either hydrogen or methane, the oxide is reduced to copper. The reaction that happens is this:

(If hydrogen is used)

Copper oxide + hydrogen → copper + water

(If methane is used)

Copper oxide + methane → copper + carbon dioxide + water

The oxide is weighed before the experiment and the copper that is produced is weighed after it. The difference between these two weighings is the amount of oxygen that was originally combined with the copper.

Examples of results

Mass of copper oxide = 2.0 g

Mass of copper left at the end of the experiment = 1.6 g

Cu = 64, O = 16

Calculation

To find the mass of oxygen originally combined with 1 mole (64 g) of copper:

Mass of oxygen originally combined with the copper, 2.0 − 1.6

$$= 0.40 \text{ g}$$

From the experiment

| 1.6 g | copper combines with | 0.40 g | oxygen |

Therefore

| 1 g | copper combines with | $\dfrac{0.40}{1.6}$ g | oxygen |

Therefore

| 64 g | copper combines with | $\dfrac{0.40 \times 64}{1.6}$ g | oxygen |

$$= \textbf{16 g oxygen} \text{ (to 2 significant figures)}$$

16 g oxygen is 1 mole of oxygen. 1 mole of copper is combined with 1 mole of oxygen and therefore the empirical formula of copper oxide is CuO.

Finding the molecular formula

Sometimes the molecular formula is different from the empirical formula. Think about this example.

10 g of a hydrocarbon is found to contain 8g carbon and 2 g hydrogen. Its relative molecular mass is 30. What is its empirical formula and its molecular formula? C = 12, H = 1.

8 g carbon combines with 2 g hydrogen.

Therefore,

| 1 g | carbon combines with | $\dfrac{12}{8}$ g | hydrogen. |

Therefore,

| 12 g | carbon (1 mole) combines with | $2 \times \dfrac{12}{8}$ g hydrogen |

$$= 3 \text{ g} \qquad \text{hydrogen}$$

$$= 3 \text{ moles hydrogen atoms}$$

A note about the units of volume

We measure volume in cubic centimetres (cm³) or cubic decimetres (dm³). The old name, still in regular use, for a cubic decimetre is the litre (l). Figure 10.3 shows how all these volumes are related (1 dm = 10 cm).

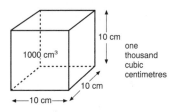

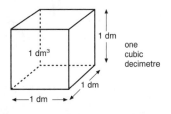

■ **Figure 10.3** Ways of describing one litre.

Therefore, the empirical formula of the hydrocarbon is CH_3.

This cannot be the actual formula because carbon has a valency of four and in CH_3 it is only combined with three other atoms.

The mass given by this empirical formula is $12 + (3 \times 1) = 15$

The actual relative molecular mass is 30 which is twice the empirical formula mass. Therefore the formula must have twice the number of each atom as the empirical formula. **The molecular formula is therefore C_2H_6.**

Questions

10.8 5.6 g iron was found to combine with 2.4 g oxygen. How much oxygen would combine with one mole of iron? What is the simplest formula for the iron oxide? (Fe = 56, O = 16)

10.9 4.6 g sodium combines with chlorine to give 11.7 g of sodium chloride. How much chlorine was used in the reaction? What is the formula of sodium chloride? (Na = 23, Cl = 35.5)

10.10 In an experiment to electrolyse molten lead bromide, 74.6 g lead bromide was weighed and electrolysed. At the end of the experiment a bead of lead weighing 10.4 g was obtained from the bottom of the crucible and the mass of the lead bromide unused was found to be 56.2 g. Calculate **a** how much lead bromide was electrolysed and **b** how much bromine was lost during the electrolysis. Calculate the molecular formula of lead bromide. (Pb = 207, Br = 80)

The volume of a mole of gas

As long as 300 years ago scientists such as Dalton (page 21) were making observations that could only be explained by the rather strange observation that a mole of any gas molecules always occupied the same volume (as long as pressure and temperature were constant). This is so for all gases, no matter how big or small the molecules are. Thus a mole of carbon dioxide molecules (mass 44 g) occupies the same volume as a mole of helium atoms (mass 4 g).

It was Avogadro who finally stated this and he worked out that the volume of a mole of a gas (at 1 atmosphere pressure and 0°C) was 22.4 dm³ (or 22 400 cm³ or 22.4 l). We call this volume the **molar volume**.

A mole of particles is 6.02×10^{23} particles. This means the molar volume of any gas contains this number of molecules. It means also that the gas molecules are *always the same distance apart*, no matter how big the molecules are (see Figure 10.4).

This observation of Avogadro and others is very useful because it is quite difficult to measure the mass of a gas but it is very easy to measure its volume. If we know the volume of a gas (at 1 atm and 0 °C) we can very quickly work out how many moles it contains.

One mole of various gases at 0 °C and 1 atm pressure

1 mole of oxygen molecules	1 mole of ammonia molecules	1 mole of neon atoms

22.4 litres O_2 · 22.4 litres NH_3 · 22.4 litres Ne

$22\,400\ cm^3$ oxygen contains	$22\,400\ cm^3$ ammonia contains	$22\,400\ cm^3$ neon contains
6.02×10^{23} molecules of oxygen	6.02×10^{23} molecules of ammonia	6.02×10^{23} atoms of neon
Mass of this oxygen (O_2) 32 g	Mass of this ammonia (NH_3) 17 g	Mass of this neon (Ne) 20 g

■ **Figure 10.4** Molar volumes of oxygen, ammonia and neon.

Example

The action of some acid on a carbonate produced 5.6 dm³ of carbon dioxide (measured at 1 atm and 0 °C). How many moles of carbon dioxide is this? What is the mass of this gas? (C = 12, O = 16)

Calculating the number of moles of carbon dioxide

Number of moles of carbon dioxide = volume (dm³)/22.4

$$= \frac{5.6}{22.4} \text{ moles}$$

$$= \textbf{0.25 moles} \text{ (correct to 2 significant figures)}$$

Calculating the mass of carbon dioxide

The mass of 1 mole of carbon dioxide (CO_2) is 12 + 16 + 16 = 44 g

Therefore the mass of 0.25 moles of carbon dioxide is 0.25×44 g

$$= \textbf{11 g}$$

> Rules for relating the volume of a gas to the number of moles it contains:
>
> • Volume of gas (dm³) = number of moles × 22.4 dm³
>
> • Number of moles of gas = $\dfrac{\text{volume of gas (dm}^3)}{22.4\ (\text{dm}^3)}$

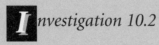

Investigation 10.2

How many moles of magnesium are used to produce hydrogen?
How many grams of magnesium are used to produce hydrogen?

You will need:
• dilute hydrochloric acid
• magnesium ribbon
• burette or graduated tube

magnesium

dilute hydrochloric acid

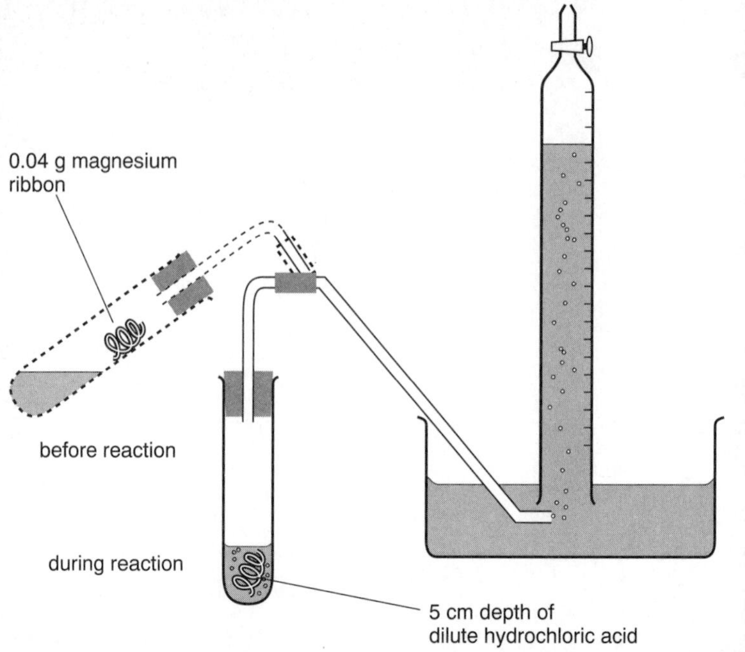

■ **Figure 10.5** Apparatus to collect a measured quantity of hydrogen over water in an inverted burette.

0.04 g magnesium ribbon

before reaction

during reaction

5 cm depth of dilute hydrochloric acid

- test tube and delivery tube
- trough of water.

1 Put about 5 cm depth of dilute hydrochloric acid in a test tube. Put a weighed piece of magnesium (about 0.04 g) higher in the test tube, but do not allow the magnesium to come into contact with the acid yet.

2 Connect the tube to the apparatus. Make sure the burette is full of water. Shake the magnesium down into the acid. Collect the bubbles of hydrogen in the burette (see Figure 10.5).

3 The reaction should stop before the burette is full (if it does not, start again with less magnesium). Equalise the water levels inside and outside the burette; this makes the pressure on the gas inside and outside the same. Read the volume of gas produced and convert it to dm^3 (1 dm^3 = 1000 cm^3).

The equation for the reaction is this:

$$Mg(s) + 2HCl(aq) \rightarrow MgCl_2(aq) + H_2(g)$$

How many moles of hydrogen were produced?

Suppose the volume of hydrogen produced is 40 cm^3 (0.04 dm^3).

$$\text{Number of moles of hydrogen} = \frac{\text{volume of hydrogen}}{22.4 \ dm^3}$$

$$= \frac{0.04}{22.4}$$

= 0.0018 moles (correct to 2 significant figures)

The equation shows that 1 mole of magnesium atoms react with the acid to form 1 mole of hydrogen molecules.

Therefore, number of moles of magnesium atoms used is also 0.0018 moles.

How many grams of magnesium were used?

(Mg = 24)

Mass of magnesium used = number of moles × relative molecular mass

$$= 0.0018 \times 24$$

$$= \textbf{0.043 g} \text{ (correct to 2 significant figures)}$$

So we calculate that 0.043 g of magnesium will make 40 cm^3 of hydrogen (measured at 0° C and 1 atmosphere pressure). How does this calculated mass compare with the mass you used?

Temperature and pressure

The molar volume of a gas is 22.4 dm^3 at 0°C and 1 atmosphere (760 mm mercury) pressure. At any other temperature or pressure the volume will be different. If the pressure is higher, the volume will decrease. If the temperature rises, the volume will increase; for example, the volume of a mole of gas at 100 °C is 30.6 dm^3.

uestions

10.11 How many moles of gas are there in the following (all measured at 0 °C and 1 atm pressure):

a 112 cm^3 chlorine

b 2000 cm^3 hydrogen

c 448 cm^3 carbon dioxide

d 1120 cm^3 methane

10.12 What is the volume (at 0 °C and 1 atm) of the following gases:

a 0.1 moles fluorine molecules

b 10 moles hydrogen molecules

c 0.5 moles argon atoms

d 0.01 moles carbon dioxide molecules

10.13 When acid is added to sodium carbonate, carbon dioxide is evolved. The reaction is as follows:

$$Na_2CO_3(s) + 2HCl(aq) \rightarrow 2NaCl(aq) + H_2O(l) + CO_2(g)$$

a What volume of carbon dioxide (at 0 °C and 1 atm) is produced from one mole of sodium carbonate?

b What volume of carbon dioxide (at 0 °C and 1 atm) is produced from 5.3 g sodium carbonate? (Na = 23, C = 12, O = 16)

10.14 What volume of sulphur dioxide (at 0 °C and 1 atm) is produced from the coal burnt in question 10.7, page 203?

Moles in solutions

Chemists very often use chemicals in solution in water. For example, dilute sulphuric acid is a solution of concentrated sulphuric acid in water and hydrochloric acid is a solution of the gas hydrogen chloride in water. It is often very important to know the **concentration** of the solution. We can measure the concentration of a solute in two different ways. We could measure the number of grams of the solute there are in each dm³, or we could measure the number of molecules (or moles of molecules) there are in each dm³. It is more useful to know the concentration in moles per dm³. We call this the **molarity** of the solution.

So:

A **molar** (1 M) solution is a solution which contains 1 mole of solute per dm³ (1 mol/dm³).

A 2 molar (2 M) solution contains two moles per dm³ (2 mol/dm³).

A 0.1 M solution contains 0.1 moles per dm³ (0.1 mol/dm³).

1 dm³ of a 1 M solution contains 1 mole of solute.

0.5 dm³ of a 2 M solution contains 1 mole of solute.

10 dm³ of a 0.1 M solution contains 1 mole of solute.

Rules for relating the number of moles in a solution to the volume of a solution and the molarity:

Number of moles in solution = volume of solution (in dm³) × molarity

$$\text{Molarity} = \frac{\text{number of moles}}{\text{volume of solution in dm}^3}$$

$$\text{Volume of solution in dm}^3 = \frac{\text{number of moles}}{\text{molarity}}$$

Problems

We can use the equations above to solve a number of problems like these:

a What is the molarity of a solution of sodium chloride which contains 0.5 moles in 200 cm³?

b What volume of a 1 M solution of hydrochloric acid will contain 10 moles?

c How much sodium hydrogencarbonate ($NaHCO_3$) will be needed to make up 500 cm^3 of a 4 M solution? (Na = 23, H = 1, C = 12, O = 16).

Solutions to problems

a Molarity = number of moles/volume of solution in dm^3

$$= \frac{0.5}{0.2}$$

$$= \textbf{2.5 M}$$

b Volume of solution in dm^3 = number of moles/molarity

$$= \frac{10}{1}$$

$$= \textbf{10 dm}^3$$

c Number of moles in solution

$$= \text{volume of solution (in dm}^3) \times \text{molarity}$$

$$= 0.5 \times 4$$

$$= 2.0 \text{ moles}$$

The relative molecular mass of $NaHCO_3$ is 23 + 1 + 12 + (3×16)
$$= 84$$

One mole of sodium hydrogencarbonate has a mass of 84 g

Therefore mass of sodium hydrogencarbonate

$$= 2 \times 84$$

$$= \textbf{168 g}$$

Reacting volumes

When hydrochloric acid is neutralised by sodium hydroxide, the reaction that occurs is shown by this equation.

$$HCl(aq) + NaOH(aq) \rightarrow NaCl(aq) + H_2O(l)$$

From the equation we can see that one mole of the acid is neutralised exactly by one mole of the alkali. We know therefore that 1 dm^3 of 1 M alkali will neutralise...

- 1 dm^3 of 1 M acid or ...
- 500 cm^3 of 2 M acid or ...
- 10 dm^3 of 0.1 M acid

because all these volumes contain 1 mole of the acid.

The reaction between sulphuric acid and sodium hydroxide is a little different:

$$H_2SO_4(aq) + 2NaOH(aq) \rightarrow Na_2SO_4(aq) + H_2O(l)$$

In this case 2 moles of the alkali are needed to neutralise 1 mole of the acid. Can you work out what volumes of 1 M acid, 2 M acid and 0.1 M acid will be needed to neutralise 1 dm^3 of 1 M alkali in this case?

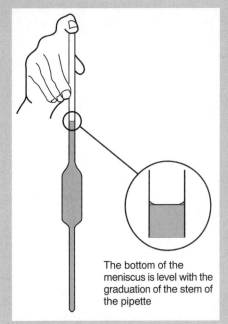

The bottom of the meniscus is level with the graduation of the stem of the pipette

■ **Figure 10.6** Pipette with inset showing meniscus when pipette is full.

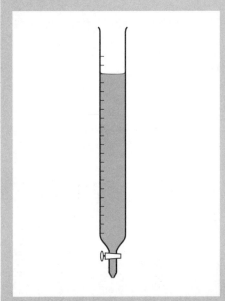

■ **Figure 10.7** Burette.

dilute
sulpuric acid

sodium
hydroxide

Titrations

When reactions in solution like these neutralisations are being investigated, we need to have ways of measuring volumes accurately. This requires special apparatus for measuring the volumes.

A pipette is used for measuring out accurately a known volume of solution (Figure 10.6). The liquid is sucked up into the pipette using a pipette filler until the bottom of the meniscus is level with the line on the stem of the pipette. (The meniscus is the name given to the top of the liquid; it is not horizontal but raised slightly at the edges where the liquid is attracted to the glass.) Your eye should be on the same level as the meniscus.

A burette is used for measuring accurately a volume that we do not know in advance (Figure 10.7). The volume is read at the beginning. We can then run out as much of the solution as we want and then read the burette again. The difference between the two readings tells us how much we have run out. Again to read it, we look at the graduation at the bottom of the meniscus.

The volumetric flask is used to make a solution of accurately known concentration. How this is done is shown in Figure 10.8.

The next investigation shows how this apparatus is used and the kind of work it is used for. You will try to find out how pure a sample of sodium hydroxide is. This kind of work is called **quantitative analysis**.

Sodium hydroxide reacts with the carbon dioxide in the air and so it is never 100% pure. In this experiment you will weigh out a sample of sodium hydroxide accurately and make it into a solution in a volumetric flask so that the solution is around 0.1 M. You will then neutralise this with sulphuric acid that you know is exactly 0.1 M. This acid is called a **standard solution** and it is made up for you by the manufacturer. When you add the acid you will need to know when the point has been reached when the solution has been neutralised exactly (to the nearest drop!). To find this, litmus solution is added to the alkali, and when the neutralisation point is reached, it will be neither blue nor red but a purple colour. This point in the titration is called the **end-point**. The whole process is called a **titration**; you are **titrating** the alkali with acid.

I *nvestigation 10.3*

Finding the percentage purity of a sample of sodium hydroxide

You will need:
- sodium hydroxide
- 0.1 M sulphuric acid
- 1 dm³ volumetric flask

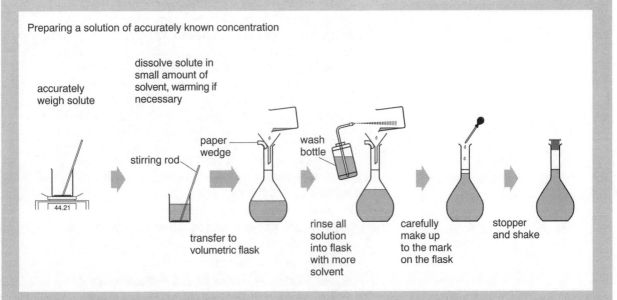

accurately weigh solute

dissolve solute in small amount of solvent, warming if necessary

stirring rod

paper wedge

transfer to volumetric flask

wash bottle

rinse all solution into flask with more solvent

carefully make up to the mark on the flask

stopper and shake

■ **Figure 10.8** Use of volumetric flask.

- balance accurate to 1 mg
- distilled water
- wash bottle
- watch glass
- 25 cm^3 pipette
- pipette filler
- 50 cm^3 burette
- litmus solution in dropping bottle
- white tile
- several conical flasks.

All glassware must be very clean.

1 Weigh out accurately (to the nearest milligram) about 4 g of sodium hydroxide.

2 Dissolve the sodium hydroxide in distilled water in a volumetric flask and make the volume up to 1 dm^3. This procedure is shown in Figure 10.8. Stopper the flask and invert it several times to mix it thoroughly.

3 Wash the burette with the acid and then fill it.

4 Wash a conical flask with distilled water.

5 Wash the pipette with the alkali and fill it to the mark using a pipette filler. Empty it into the conical flask.

6 Add one or two drops (only) of litmus solution to the flask. Note that the solution turns blue.

7 Carry out an approximate titration (Figure 10.9). Read the initial level of the acid in the burette. Run 1 cm^3 of acid into the flask. Swirl it to ensure mixing. Note the indicator colour. Repeat this process until the indicator colour changes permanently. You now

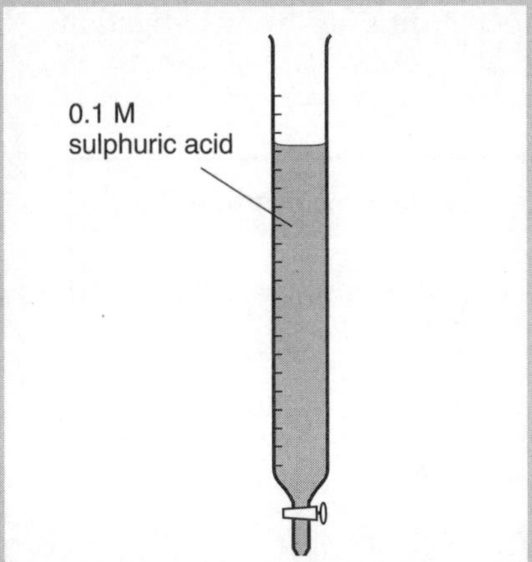

0.1 M sulphuric acid

white tile

25 cm^3 of the solution of sodium hydroxide + a few drops of litmus indicator

■ **Figure 10.9** Carrying out titration

know, to the nearest 1 cm³, how much acid you must add to reach the end-point.

8 Carry out an accurate titration by repeating Steps 5 and 6 and then adding acid until you are within 1 cm³ of the end-point. Swirl the flask to make sure it is mixed. Then add the acid a drop at a time, swirling the flask after each drop. Note the volume in the burette after each drop. Eventually the litmus will change to purple. After the next drop it will change to red. Record the level of the acid after the drop that made the colour change to purple. This is the exact end-point.

9 Repeat step 8 until you have two values for the amount of acid added which agree to within 0.1 cm³.

10 Calculate:

• the number of moles of sulphuric acid used

• the number of moles of sodium hydroxide in the pipette

• the number of moles of sodium hydroxide in the sample weighed

• the number of grams of pure sodium hydroxide in the sample weighed

• the percentage purity of the sodium hydroxide.

Table 10.2 shows some specimen results for this investigation.

■ **Table 10.2 Results of titration.**

	Rough titration	Titration 1	Titration 2
Initial reading	0.0	12.9	25.4
Final reading	12.9	25.4	38.0
Vol. of acid used	12.9	12.5	12.6

Average of the two readings = 12.55 cm³ acid used

The equation for the reaction is:

$$H_2SO_4(aq) \quad + \quad 2NaOH(aq) \quad \rightarrow \quad Na_2SO_4(aq) \quad + \quad H_2O(l)$$
1 mole   2 moles   1 mole   1 mole

Calculating the number of moles of sulphuric acid used

Volume of sulphuric acid used (see Table 10.2) is 12.55 cm³ (0.012 55 dm³)

$$\text{Number of moles} = \text{volume (in dm}^3) \times \text{molarity}$$
$$= 0.012\,55 \times 0.1$$
$$= \textbf{0.001\,255 moles}$$

Calculating the number of moles of sodium hydroxide in the pipette

From the equation, one mole of the acid reacted with two moles of the alkali. Therefore, the number of moles in the pipette sample is $2 \times 0.001\,255 = \textbf{0.002\,51 moles}$.

Calculating the number of moles of sodium hydroxide in the sample weighed

The pipette holds 25 cm^3 of solution. The flask holds 1000 cm^3.

$$25 \text{ cm}^3 \text{ of solution contains } 0.002\,51 \text{ moles}$$

$$\text{Therefore,} \quad 1 \text{ cm}^3 \text{ of solution contains } \frac{0.002\,51}{25} \text{ moles}$$

Therefore,

$$1000 \text{ cm}^3 \text{ of solution contains } \frac{0.002\,51 \times 1000}{25} \text{ moles}$$

$$= \textbf{0.1004 moles}$$

Calculating the number of grams of pure sodium hydroxide in the sample weighed

Calculating the relative molecular mass of sodium hydroxide:

Na = 23, O = 16, H = 1. Therefore, NaOH = 23 + 16 + 1 = 40

$$\text{The number of grams in the flask} = \text{number of moles} \times \text{relative molecular mass}$$
$$= 0.1004 \times 40$$
$$= \textbf{4.016 g}$$

Calculating the percentage purity of the sodium hydroxide

The number of grams weighed out originally was 4.12 g. The number of grams of pure sodium hydroxide that this contains was found by the titration to be 4.016 g.

The percentage purity of a substance can be calculated using the formula:

$$\text{Percentage purity} =$$

$$\frac{\text{mass of pure material}}{\text{total mass of material}} \times 100$$

$$= \frac{4.016}{4.12} \times 100$$

$$= \textbf{97\%} \text{ (correct to 2 significant figures)}$$

A note on accuracy

It is possible to carry out very accurate titrations but only with accurately made apparatus and with very pure chemicals. If you work carefully you can get two results for the acid added which agree with each other to within 0.1 cm^3. The total amount added is around 12 cm^3 so your error is ± 0.1 in 12 which is a little less than 1%. This means that any answer you give at the end of your calculations should be corrected to 2 significant figures.

If you give it to 3 significant figures, it would be 97.5% which means anything between 97.45 and 97.54%. This variation is 0.09 parts in 97 which means an error of almost 0.1%. This is less than the error involved in the experiment itself.

 uestions

10.15 What is the molarity of the following solutions?

a 1000 cm^3 sodium chloride solution containing 2 moles

b 500 cm^3 hydrochloric acid containing 2 moles

c 100 cm^3 copper sulphate solution containing 0.1 moles

d 10 dm^3 sodium carbonate solution containing 1 mole

e 10 dm^3 sodium chloride solution containing 0.1 moles

f 2 dm^3 sulphuric acid containing 0.5 mole

g 50 cm^3 ammonia solution containing 0.01 moles

h 1 cm^3 sodium chloride solution containing 0.003 moles

10.16 How many moles are there in each of the following solutions?

a 1000 cm^3 of 0.5 M copper sulphate solution

b 2000 cm^3 of 2 M sulphuric acid

c 100 cm^3 of 0.2 M sodium sulphate solution

d 1 cm^3 of 0.5 M hydrochloric acid

e 10 dm^3 of 0.5 M copper sulphate solution

f 5 dm^3 of 0.01 M sodium sulphate solution

g 10 cm^3 of 0.05 M ammonia solution

h 5 dm^3 of 2 M nitric acid

10.17 What is the molarity of the following solutions?

a 1 dm^3 of solution containing 73 g hydrogen chloride, HCl (H = 1, Cl = 35.5)

b 1 dm^3 of solution containing 4 g sodium hydroxide, NaOH (H = 1, O = 16, Na = 23)

c 100 cm^3 of solution containing 19 g magnesium chloride, MgCl$_2$ (Mg = 24, Cl = 35.5)

d 10 dm^3 of solution containing 9.8 g sulphuric acid, H$_2$SO$_4$ (H = 1, S = 32, O = 16)

e 10 cm^3 of solution containing 0.8 g copper sulphate, CuSO$_4$ (Cu = 64, S = 32, O = 16)

f 1 dm^3 of solution containing 0.4 g copper sulphate, CuSO$_4$ (Cu = 64, S = 32, O = 16)

g 5 dm^3 of solution containing 34 g ammonia (H = 1, N = 14), NH$_3$

h 200 cm^3 of solution containing 2.1 g nitric acid (H = 1, N = 14, O = 16), HNO$_3$

10.18 Excess of calcium carbonate was added to 200 cm^3 of 2 M hydrochloric acid.

a Write an equation for the reaction.

b How many moles of carbon dioxide were produced?

c What volume of carbon dioxide was produced (measured at 0 °C and 1 atm pressure)?

d What mass of calcium carbonate was used in the reaction? (Ca = 40, C = 12, O = 16)

10.19 a What volume of 2 M copper sulphate would be needed to react with 13 g zinc according to the equation:

$$Zn(s) + CuSO_4(aq, 2 M) \rightarrow Zn\,SO_4(aq) + Cu(s)$$

b What mass of copper is produced in the reaction? (Cu = 64, Zn = 65)

10.20 In an experiment to determine the concentration of a solution of potassium hydroxide, 25 cm^3 of it was titrated with 0.1 M hydrochloric acid. 16.2 cm^3 of the acid was required. What is the molarity of the potassium hydroxide?

10.21 Baking powder is a mixture of sodium hydrogen carbonate and flour. In an experiment to work out the proportion of sodium hydrogen carbonate in the mixture, 10.20 g of the powder was mixed with water and made up to 1 dm^3 in a volumetric flask. 25 cm^3 of this was then titrated against exactly 0.10 M hydrochloric acid. It was found that 22.2 cm^3 of acid was needed to neutralise the baking powder. What percentage of the baking powder was sodium hydrogen carbonate? (Na = 23, H = 1, C = 12, O = 16)

Review questions on this chapter can be found on pages 243–4.

11

How fast?

Chemical reactions go on around us (and inside us) all the time. Some are slow reactions, such as the reactions in cooking and in our stomachs. Other reactions, such as a bush fire, are fast. In this chapter you will study some reactions and try to find out why some reactions are faster than others. You will also look at some reactions that can go both ways. These reactions can be made to go one way or the other just by changing the reaction conditions. How fast a chemical reaction proceeds, and in which direction, depends on a number of factors and these will be studied in this chapter.

Making reactions go faster

Figure 11.1 shows three different reactions that occur at very different rates.

For a reaction to take place two things have to happen.

- First the two reacting molecules or ions have to hit each other.
- Second, the collision has to result in a reaction.

In this chapter you will be studying ways of making reactions go faster by causing more collisions and by causing harder collisions. First, however, it is necessary to think up some ways of measuring how fast a reaction is going. The following investigations show two ways. The second is the better one but it needs a balance that will permit quick accurate weighing.

The reaction in the investigations that follow is the well-known one between an acid and a carbonate in which carbon dioxide is produced.

■ **Figure 11.1** The explosion takes a fraction of a second. The change in white of egg protein on boiling takes 4 minutes. The formation of the sugars in a ripe apple takes several months.

Calcium carbonate + hydrochloric acid → calcium chloride
+ water + carbon dioxide

$$CaCO_3(s) + HCl(aq) \rightarrow CaCl_2(aq) + H_2O(l) + CO_2(g)$$

*I*nvestigation 11.1

Measuring a reaction rate by counting bubbles

You will need:

- marble chips
- dilute hydrochloric acid (2 M)
- large measuring cylinder or similar tall tube
- test tube and long rubber delivery tube
- timer.

1 Put 10 cm^3 of dilute hydrochloric acid into the test tube.

2 Add some lumps of calcium carbonate (marble chips) and quickly put in the bung with the tube (Figure 11.2). Watch the bubbles rising in the cylinder. Count the number of bubbles rising each minute. Carry on until the reaction has finished.

3 Calculate the total number of bubbles that have been produced after the end of each minute. (Add the bubbles produced in a particular minute to the total of all the bubbles produced in the previous minutes).

4 Plot a graph of the number of bubbles produced in the reaction against time (*x*-axis).

dilute hydrochloric
acid

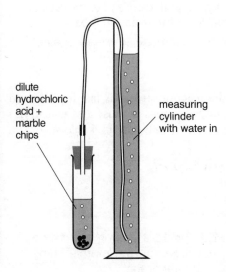

dilute
hydrochloric
acid +
marble
chips

measuring
cylinder
with water in

■ **Figure 11.2** Apparatus for bubble counting.

dilute hydrochloric
acid

*I*nvestigation 11.2

Measuring reaction rate by mass loss

You will need:

- marble chips (lumps of calcium carbonate)
- conical flask
- cotton wool
- dilute hydrochloric acid (2 M)
- top pan electronic balance.

1 Put 40 cm^3 dilute hydrochloric acid in the flask. Put it on the balance. Place about 20 g of marble chips in a piece of folded paper on the balance. Note the mass reading (Figure 11.3a).

2 Add the marble chips to the acid in the flask and quickly put in the cotton wool plug. Put the empty piece of paper back on the balance pan (Figure 11.3b).

a

cotton wool plug

b

40 cm³ of
2.0 M
hydrochloric acid

about 20 g
marble chips

folded
paper

top pan
balance

150.5

149.5

■ **Figure 11.3** Rate measuring apparatus using top pan balance.

3 Read the mass again after every minute until the reaction stops. The mass will decrease because carbon dioxide gas is lost from the reaction mixture.

4 Plot a graph showing the decrease in mass against time (*x*-axis).

Both graphs will show that the reaction proceeds fast initially and then slows down and finally stops. It stops because all the acid has been used up. A typical result is shown in Figure 11.4 below.

What is the effect of particle size?

*I*nvestigation 11.3

Repeat Investigation 11.2 (or 11.1) using the same quantities of materials, but break up the marble chips into smaller pieces. Plot a similar graph.

Figure 11.4 shows typical results for both these experiments plotted on the same axes.

The *y*-axis of your graph shows the loss of carbon dioxide from the reaction. If you used the bubble counting method, this will be calibrated in number of bubbles of carbon dioxide lost. If you used the top pan

diute hydrochloric
acid

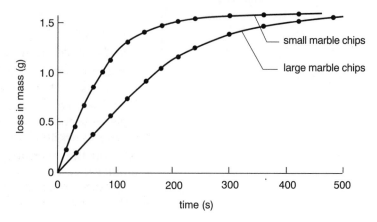

small marble chips

large marble chips

loss in mass (g)

time (s)

■ **Figure 11.4** Graphs of loss of mass against time for different particle sizes.

balance method the graphs will be calibrated in loss of mass of the mixture. The shape of the graphs in both cases will be the same as the two methods are ways of measuring the same thing, the loss of carbon dioxide.

There are a number of important points to note about the graphs:

• The overall amount of carbon dioxide lost in both experiments is the same. This is because the reaction stopped when all the acid had been used and the amount of acid used in each experiment was the same.

• In both cases the reaction started rapidly and gradually slowed down as the acid was used up.

• The rate of reaction with the small chips was faster than with the larger chips and the reaction was over sooner.

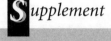

Supplement

We can easily explain these observations. As the acid was used up, there were fewer and fewer acid particles around to collide with the marble. If the number of collisions decreases, the reaction will slow down. When the marble chips are crushed to make smaller ones, we increase the total surface area of the marble. If we increase the area, more acid particles will collide with it and therefore there will be more particles reacting. The reaction is therefore faster with smaller-sized marble chips.

What is the effect of varying the acid concentration?

diute hydrochloric acid

Investigation 11.4

Repeat Investigation 11.2 (or 11.1) a number of times using different concentrations of acid (such as 0.5 M, 1.0 M, 3.0 M, 4.0 M, etc).
In this experiment the number of moles of acid should always be the same. If you used 40 cm³ of 2 M acid, you should use 20 cm³ of 4 M acid, 80 cm³ of 1 M acid, and so on.
Use always the same sized sample of marble. Finely divided marble is recommended; if the lumps are too large, the time taken for the bubbles to cease is rather long for the more dilute acids.

This time the graphs will look something like Figure 11.5. Look carefully at them. Some important points should be noted.

• Again, the overall amount of carbon dioxide lost in all experiments is the same because the amount of acid used in each experiment was the same.

• Again, the reaction started rapidly and gradually slowed down as the acid was used up.

• The reaction went fastest when the concentration of acid was greatest. This is because when there are more acid particles around in a given volume, there will be more collisions with the calcium carbonate and therefore more particles will react.

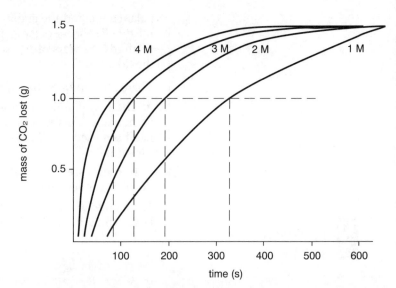

■ **Figure 11.5** Graphs of loss of mass against time for different acid concentrations.

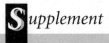

Looking further at the results of Investigation 11.4

The graph can be analysed further. For each concentration, read from the graph the time taken for a particular mass (or number of bubbles) of carbon dioxide to be lost. In the graph above the mass of 1 g of carbon dioxide has been chosen. Note that this time is shortest for the highest concentration. Make a table of the results from the graph like Table 11.1.

■ **Table 11.1 Results from Figure 11.5.**

Concentration (molarity)	Time to lose 1 g CO_2 (s)	$\dfrac{1}{\text{time}}$
4 M	80	0.0125
3 M	120	0.0083
2 M	190	0.0060
1 M	325	0.0030

Plot a graph of this time, t against concentration of the acid. This should give a curve like the one in Figure 11.6 (a). This is not a particularly useful shape to draw any conclusions from. However, we are really interested in finding out how the **rate** of the reaction varies with concentration, not the **time** taken to produce 1 g of carbon dioxide.

The rate of reaction is the amount of carbon dioxide produced **per second**. To calculate this, we simply divide the mass of carbon dioxide (1 g) by the time taken to produce it. These values are shown in column 3 of Table 11.1.

The second graph is a plot of this rate, $1/t$ against concentration (Figure 11.6 (b)). This graph is a straight line and you will know from your mathematics that this means that the rate of the reaction is directly proportional to the concentration of the acid. This means that, if the concentration of the acid doubles, the reaction goes twice as fast. If you think of what is happening to the particles, you would

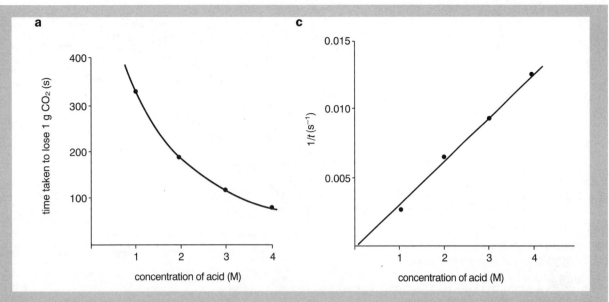

Figure 11.6 Two graphs for acid/marble experiment.

expect this result. If we double the number of particles per cm^3, we will double the number hitting the marble in any given time. This will double the number of collisions that result in a reaction and so double the rate of reaction.

What is the effect on the rate of changing the temperature of the reaction?

*I*nvestigation 11.5

Repeat Investigation 11.2 (or 11.1) a number of times using different temperatures. Before mixing the reagents, heat the acid. Take the temperature of the acid during the reaction. Plot curves of the reaction at different temperatures on the same axes.

The graph in Figure 11.7 clearly shows that the reaction at the higher temperature is faster than the reaction at the lower temperature.

*D*id you know?

A chemical reaction happens when you boil an egg. The white part of the egg changes from one kind of protein to another as it turns white. This reaction takes 4 minutes at 100 °C. At 90 °C, just 10 °C lower, this reaction would take thousands of years to complete. This means that, on top of Mount Kilimanjaro, say, where the boiling

diute hydrochloric acid

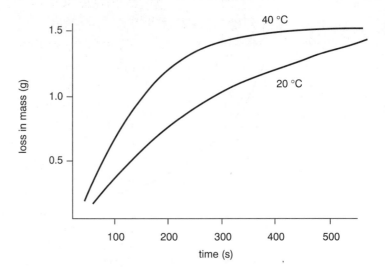

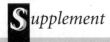
Figure 11.7 Graph of rates of reaction at different temperatures.

point of water is only 92 °C, it would not be possible to have a freshly hard-boiled egg for breakfast, should you feel like one.

*S*upplement

Particle theory can explain the observation that a reaction gets faster if the temperature is increased. If the temperature of the acid is higher, the particles will be moving faster. If they move faster, they will hit the particles of marble more frequently and they will also hit the marble harder. There would therefore be more collisions and the collisions would be more likely to result in a reaction. The rate of the reaction would therefore be expected to increase.

If you look at the time taken to produce 1 g of carbon dioxide at several different temperatures, it is possible to obtain a graph of rate of reaction against temperature in the same way as it was done for concentration of acid. In this case, however, the result will probably not be a straight line but a curve.

How does a catalyst affect the rate of reaction?

There have been many references to catalysts throughout this book. The use of transition metals as catalysts is discussed in Chapter 4. The use of catalysts in the manufacture of ammonia and of sulphuric acid has been mentioned. In Chapter 9 you met the use of catalysts in the manufacture of margarine and of polythene. Not all catalysts are good for us, however; you have also read in Chapter 7 about how chlorine atoms can catalyse the destruction of the protective ozone layer.

Catalysts are very important because they speed up chemical reactions and allow us to carry them out using much less energy. An important property of catalysts is that they are not themselves used up during the reaction.

Here are two simple examples of the use of a catalyst that will show how they work.

hydrogen

diute sulphuric acid

Investigation 11.6

Making hydrogen

You will need:

- test tube
- granulated zinc
- dilute sulphuric acid
- copper sulphate crystals.

1 Put some dilute acid in a test tube to a depth of about 3 cm. Add a piece of granulated zinc and note that hydrogen bubbles appear.

2 Add a few small crystals of copper sulphate to the mixture. Note that the zinc becomes coated in a layer of copper. When this happens, note carefully what happens to the rate of the reaction producing hydrogen.

In this reaction, the rate of reaction of zinc with the acid is increased by the presence of copper in contact with the zinc. The copper itself is not used up.

The copper catalyst first has to be made by the reaction between the zinc and copper sulphate:

Zinc + copper sulphate → zinc sulphate + copper

You could have used pieces of copper instead of the copper sulphate. All that is needed to cause the reaction to get faster is some copper in contact with the zinc. Using copper sulphate to make the copper is, however, an easy way to make a small quantity of copper with a good contact with the zinc.

hydrogen

Investigation 11.7

Burning hydrogen

You will need:

- gas jar of hydrogen
- platinum on mineral wool (platinised mineral wool)
- tongs
- burner.

1 Heat the platinised mineral wool to white heat in a flame to clean it. It should not give any colour to the flame when it is clean. Allow the wool to cool to room temperature.

2 Hold the wool in tongs near the top of the jar of hydrogen and remove the lid. Note what happens.

This is a spectacular demonstration of the effect of a catalyst. Hydrogen is a very flammable gas but normally it needs energy in the form of a flame to ignite it. However, the metal platinum will catalyse the burning of hydrogen so well that the energy in the air at room temperature is then sufficient to ignite it. Just putting the platinum in the gas will cause it to burst into flame.

Supplement

How does a catalyst work? A catalyst works by helping the reactants get close enough to each other for long enough for a reaction to occur. The hydrogen gas in Investigation 11.7 is held close to the oxygen of the air on the surface of the platinum metal (Figure 11.8).

In this case, once the catalyst has started the reaction, so much heat is given out by the reaction that it is able to carry on without the catalyst, and the hydrogen all burns.

Light and chemical reactions

Heat speeds up chemical reactions. Heat is just one form of energy and there are many other forms. One other form is light and so it

■ **Figure 11.8** Action of surface action catalyst.

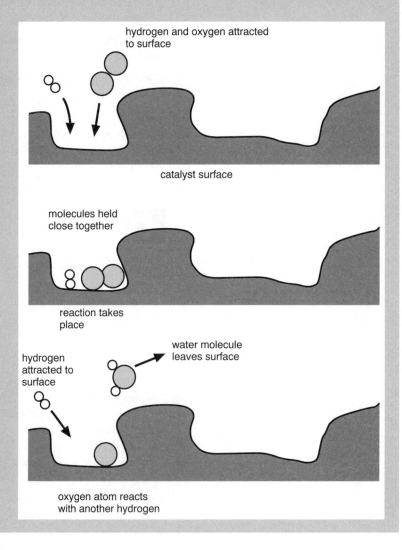

hydrogen and oxygen attracted to surface

catalyst surface

molecules held close together

reaction takes place

hydrogen attracted to surface

water molecule leaves surface

oxygen atom reacts with another hydrogen

should not be surprising that light can also affect some chemical reactions. One example is shown in the next investigation.

silver nitrate
dilute hydrochloric acid

*I*nvestigation 11.8

Light causing a chemical reaction

You will need:

- filter paper
- silver nitrate solution
- dilute hydrochloric acid.

1 Dip a small piece of filter paper in a dilute solution of silver nitrate. Silver nitrate is very expensive but the solution can be very dilute. Allow the paper to dry. The paper is now coated in silver nitrate.

2 Dip the paper quickly in and out of a solution of hydrochloric acid.

3 Place the paper in the light with some objects such as coins covering part of it. After a few minutes look carefully at the paper.

You will be able to see the outline of the coins as light patches on the paper, which has gone rather dark in the parts that were exposed to the light.

The reaction is the basis of photography. The chemical on the filter paper is silver chloride. This is formed as a white insoluble solid when the paper that is coated in silver nitrate is dipped in the hydrochloric acid:

Silver nitrate + hydrochloric acid → silver chloride + nitric acid

$$AgNO_3(s) + HCl(aq) \rightarrow AgCl(s) + HNO_3(aq)$$

Silver chloride slowly decomposes into silver and chlorine. This reaction is very slow in the dark but goes much faster in light.

Silver chloride → silver + chlorine

$$2AgCl(s) \rightarrow 2Ag(s) + Cl_2(g)$$

What you see on the filter paper is a fine coating of silver metal on the parts of it that were exposed to light. This makes the filter paper look greyish in colour.

Another chemical reaction that requires light energy is a very important one. Without this reaction we could not exist. The reaction is **photosynthesis** and it takes place during the day in the leaves of green plants. The leaves take in carbon dioxide from the air and water from the ground. In the reaction these are converted into glucose. As you read in Chapter 9, the glucose can then be converted by plants into either starch or cellulose.

Carbon dioxide + water → glucose + oxygen

$$6CO_2(g) + 6H_2O(l) \rightarrow C_6H_{12}O_6(aq) + 6O_2(g)$$

Questions

11.1 Explain the following observations.

a A car engine does not work very efficiently just after it has started on a cold day.

b When you throw some iron filings into a flame they spark immediately but when you put an iron rod into a flame for the same time nothing happens.

c A piece of paper that has been crushed into a ball burns more slowly on a fire than a flat piece of paper.

d Magnesium burns more brightly in pure oxygen than in air.

e Vegetables cook faster in a pressure cooker than in an open pan.

f If you want potatoes to cook faster you slice them up.

g Plants grow faster in warm wet climates than in cool dry ones.

11.2 Name three industrial processes that use catalysts. In each case name the catalyst. Explain how the catalysts speed up the reactions.

■ **Table 11.2 Table of results.**

Time (s)	0	10	20	30	40	50	60	70	80	90	100	110	120	130	140	150
Vol. of hydrogen (cm^3)	0	5	15	26	40	55	75	90	100	115	128	133	136	137	137	137

11.3 Table 11.2 shows the results for the formation of hydrogen from a sample of magnesium placed in excess dilute acid.

a Plot a graph showing the production of hydrogen.

b What was the total amount of hydrogen produced in the reaction?

c Why was the rate of production of hydrogen greatest at the beginning of the reaction?

d Why did hydrogen eventually stop being produced?

e Draw on the same axes another line showing how the hydrogen would have been produced if the concentration of the acid was halved. Label this curve 'c'.

f Draw on the same axes another line showing how the hydrogen would have been produced if the temperature of the acid was increased. Label this curve 't'.

g Sketch the apparatus suitable for carrying out this investigation.

h Assume that a mole of hydrogen at the temperature of the reaction occupies 22.5 dm^3.
How many moles of hydrogen were produced in the experiment? What mass of magnesium was used? (Mg = 24)

Reactions that go both ways

Look at the pictures at the beginning of this chapter. Are these reactions reversible or irreversible? Is it possible to unboil a boiled egg? Most reactions are irreversible but in Chapter 9 you saw some reactions that can go both ways.

Starch is a large molecule that can be changed to glucose in your mouth by the enzyme ptyalin in your saliva. You can show this easily by chewing a piece of bread or some flour for several minutes. You will notice that it gradually becomes sweet. This process is called the hydrolysis of starch and you studied it in Investigation 9.1.

Plants make glucose by photosynthesis. They then convert most of it into starch in their leaves.

We can summarise this:

- you can convert starch into glucose in your mouth
- plants can convert glucose into starch in their leaves.

■ **Table 11.3 Conditions for starch and glucose reaction.**

Starch → glucose	Glucose → starch
37 °C	10–40 °C (approx)
Ptyalin catalyst	Several enzymes and chlorophyll
Alkaline solution	Light

This reaction can be made to go both ways under different conditions. These conditions are summarised in Table 11.3. There are many reactions like this. They are called reversible reactions. The next investigation shows another example of a reversible reaction.

Investigation 11.9

copper sulpate

Heating copper sulphate

You will need:

- blue copper sulphate crystals
- tin lid or gauze
- burner
- dropper.

1 Heat the blue copper sulphate crystals gently on a tin lid or gauze. Watch carefully the changes that take place.

2 Allow the copper sulphate to cool and add a drop of water. Again note the changes.

Blue copper sulphate crystals contain water. These water molecules are part of the crystalline structure of the blue form of copper sulphate and, without them, blue copper sulphate crystals cannot form. We call the blue crystals **hydrated** copper sulphate. When the blue crystals are heated, the water is driven off leaving white copper sulphate. We call this form of copper sulphate **anhydrous** copper sulphate; anhydrous means 'without water'. The anhydrous form can be converted back to the hydrated form by adding water .

Hydrated copper sulphate $\rightleftharpoons$ anhydrous copper sulphate + water

$$CuSO_4 \cdot 5H_2O \rightleftharpoons CuSO_4 + 5H_2O$$

The equations for reversible reactions are written with a special double arrow sign to indicate that they go both ways.

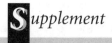

Supplement

How changing the reaction conditions affects the products of a reversible reaction

If we warm a blue hydrated copper sulphate crystal, it will gradually decompose giving off water and leaving the white crystals behind. As soon as some water is produced, however, the reverse reaction can happen. The water can react with the white crystals to form the blue ones. We can prevent the reverse reaction happening by driving off the water by evaporating it. If we do this, we will convert all the blue crystals to the white ones. But if we do not take all the water vapour away – if we heat it in a sealed container, for example – the reverse reaction will always be happening and we will never get the pure white form.

You can show this just by leaving a crystal of blue copper sulphate around in the air. If you look at it in dry weather, you will see a coating of white copper sulphate on the outside of it. In dry weather, the water is removed from the reaction and the white form is left. In wet weather, there is a lot of water around in the air and this will react with the white coating on the crystal to form the blue copper sulphate again. (You can make 'wet weather' by putting the crystal in a sealed flask which also contains some cotton wool soaked in water.)

So, we can control a reversible reaction by altering the reaction conditions. This is a general equation for a reversible reaction in which the materials A and B react to form the products C and D. These products will also react to give back A and B.

$$A + B \rightleftharpoons C + D$$

We can make the reaction go to the right by removing either C or D as soon as it is formed. On the other hand, we could make the reaction go to the left by adding C or D or by removing A or B. Many important industrial reactions are reversible and these ideas are used to make sure that the reaction goes the way we want it to.

Another reversible reaction

Another example of a reversible reaction that can easily be investigated is the reaction between ammonia and hydrogen chloride. Both these compounds are gases. Ammonia gas is given off all the time from concentrated ammonia solution and hydrogen chloride is the gas

Figure 11.9 Formation of ammonium chloride.

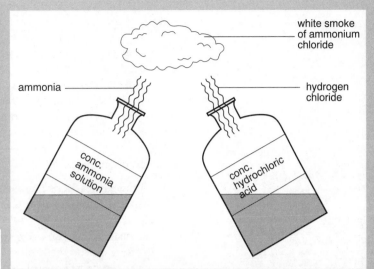

white smoke of ammonium chloride

ammonia

hydrogen chloride

conc. ammonia solution

conc. hydrochloric acid

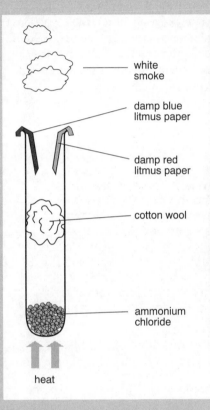

white smoke

damp blue litmus paper

damp red litmus paper

cotton wool

ammonium chloride

heat

Figure 11.10 Thermal decomposition of ammonium chloride.

Gas phase reactions

that can be smelt when the concentrated hydrochloric acid bottle is opened. If these two bottles are brought near each other and unstoppered, white fumes of ammonium chloride can be seen (Figure 11.9).

The reaction is this:

Ammonia + hydrogen chloride $\rightleftharpoons$ ammonium chloride

$NH_3(g) + HCl(g) \rightleftharpoons NH_4Cl(g)$

If ammonium chloride is heated, the reaction is reversed and hydrogen chloride and ammonia are formed. The apparatus in Figure 11.10 shows how these can be detected. The ammonium chloride is heated in the tube and forms the two gases ammonia and hydrogen chloride.

Ammonia gas dissolves in water to form an alkaline solution. Hydrogen chloride, on the other hand, forms an acid, hydrochloric acid, when it dissolves. The gases formed rise up the tube but the ammonia rises faster because it is much less dense than the hydrogen chloride. When the gases first reach the moist litmus papers on the side of the tube, the red one turns blue indicating the presence of ammonia. A little later, the hydrogen chloride turns both of the papers red.

When the mixture of gases cools above the tube, the decomposition reaction reverses and the gases recombine to form white clouds of ammonium chloride.

Think back to all the really important industrial reactions you have met in this book; Haber's process for making ammonia (page 157), the making of nitric acid from ammonia (page 157), the Contact Process for making sulphur trioxide (page 116), the cracking of alkanes (page 176), the manufacture of polythene (page 188). All these reactions take place in the gas phase. Chemical engineers like gases; they flow easily along pipes, they mix easily and the conditions of the reactions are easily controlled because they heat up uniformly and quickly. (You can explain why all these happen if you think back to Chapter 1 on how gas particles behave.) Gases can also easily be brought into contact with catalysts, such as gauzes made out of transition metals.

Another reason why chemical engineers like gas phase reactions is that it is easy to make a gas reaction *continuous*. This means that the starting materials flow in one end of the process and the product flows out of the other end continuously, 24 hours a day, seven days a week. The opposite of a continuous process is a *batch* process and reactions involving solids – like the electric arc furnace – are often of this type. Batch processes are always more expensive than continuous processes.

All the gas reactions mentioned above are reversible. This gives the chemical engineers a problem. They want to make something and they do not want to see it decompose as soon as they have made it. Fortunately they can use their knowledge about reversible reactions to create exactly the right conditions to give them the best yield of the product they want. The conditions they can vary are the temperature, the pressure, the rate of flow of the gases and the length of time the gases are in contact with the catalysts.

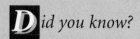

id you know?

> It was Fritz Haber who invented the process for making ammonia from the nitrogen in the air, but it was a chemical engineer called Carl Bosch who was responsible for developing the chemical plant at Ludwigshaven in Germany that turned Haber's discovery into a manufacturing process. Haber was awarded the Nobel prize for Chemistry in 1918 for his discovery. Bosch was awarded the Nobel prize for Chemistry in 1931, not for building the Ludwigshaven plant, but for his work on high pressure gas reactions.

The equations for the Haber and the Contact processes are these:

$$N_2(g) + 3H_2(g) \rightleftharpoons 2NH_3 + energy$$

$$2SO_2(g) + O_2(g) \rightleftharpoons 2SO_3(g) + energy$$

When these reactions take place, as soon as any product is formed, the backward reaction can start. As more product is formed, more of the product will change back into the starting gases. Eventually the product will decompose as fast as it is produced. There will then be a mixture of starting materials and products and the amount of each will be constant, even though both the backward and forward reactions are happening all the time. This point is called the *equilibrium* mixture. It is called a *dynamic equilibrium* because dynamic means moving and in this equilibrium the product is continuously being formed and continually decomposing.

The job of the chemical engineers is to try and create the right conditions for two things to happen:

- get to the position of equilibrium quickly
- ensure that at the position of equilibrium there is a lot of product and not much starting material.

Figure 11.11 The reactor vessel in this Haber ammonia plant needs large bolts to ensure the vessel does not leak at high pressure.

If you look at the Haber and Contact reactions you will see in the first case, four molecules of starting materials give two molecules of product. In the second case there is also a decrease in the number of molecules. If the number of molecules decreases in a gas reaction, then the volume of the gases will also decrease (a mole of any gas molecules, remember, occupies 22.4 litres at room temperature and pressure). This means that if pressure is applied to the gases in these reactions, more of the product will be present in the equilibrium mixture as the product occupies a smaller volume than the starting gases.

Both of these forward reactions are exothermic. This means that the reverse reactions are endothermic and take in heat when they take place. If heat is taken away as the gases react, by cooling the reaction mixture, this will make the reverse reaction more difficult and the forward reaction easier. So if the reaction is cooled the equilibrium mixture will contain a higher concentration of the product. Unfortunately, as you have discovered earlier in this chapter, reactions go slower in the cold than they do when they are warm. Because of this, even though cooling these reactions would increase the amount of product at equilibrium, it would also take much longer to get to the position of equilibrium.

All catalysts used in reversible reactions catalyse the reverse reaction just as well as they catalyse the forward reaction. They speed up both reactions equally. The catalyst therefore does not affect *how much* product is present in the equilibrium mixture but *how fast* the mixture gets to equilibrium.

So you can see that the chemical engineers can do quite a lot to try and make the gases react faster and to ensure that at equilibrium there is as much product as possible. They can vary the temperature and the pressure and also the time the mixture is in contact with the catalyst.

In the Haber process, high pressures will give a greater yield of ammonia and so the reaction takes place at pressures between 250 and 1000 times the pressure of the atmosphere. Cooling the reaction would also increase the amount of ammonia present at equilibrium. However, cooling it will also slow the reaction down and so it would take a long time to reach equilibrium. So a temperature of between 300 °C and 600 °C is usually used.

The Contact process produces sulphur trioxide which is an extremely corrosive gas and this can be very dangerous at high pressures. So, although the yield would be greatly improved by carrying out the reaction at a high pressure, this is not done for safety reasons.

Questions

11.4 What is meant by a reversible reaction? Give an example.

11.5 Cobalt chloride forms pink crystals. When they are heated water is evolved and they turn blue. Explain how you could use cobalt chloride as a test for water.

11.6 Nitrogen dioxide exists naturally in equilibrium with dinitrogen tetroxide (N_2O_4).

$$N_2O_4(g) \rightleftharpoons 2NO_2(g) - heat$$

a In which direction is the reaction endothermic?

b What conditions of temperature and pressure (high or low) will increase the concentration of dinitrogen tetroxide at equilibrium? Explain your answer.

Review questions on this chapter can be found on page 244.

Chapter 1

1 Some copper filings have been mixed accidentally with some copper sulphate crystals. Describe how you would attempt to get both of these substances from the mixture in a pure form.

2 A food scientist investigating the coloured substance in some jam used paper chromatography. The results below show a chromatogram (**A**) produced from the jam and another (**B**) produced by coloured substances that are permitted for use in foods.

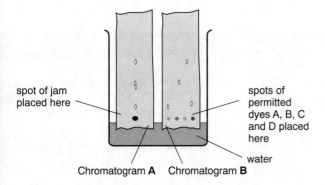

spot of jam placed here

spots of permitted dyes A, B, C and D placed here

water

Chromatogram **A**   Chromatogram **B**

(a) What permitted dyes are present in the jam?

(b) What other information could the food scientist write in her report?

3 The table shows some properties of four materials.

Material	Melting point (°C)	Electrical conductivity
A	−39	good
B	−10	poor
C	280	poor
D	1083	good

(a) Which material would be most suitable for the pins of an electric plug?

(b) Which material will be most suitable for the case of the plug?

In each case, give the reason for your choice.

4 (a) From the list of changes below, select those that are physical changes.

(b) From the same list, select the chemical changes.

In each case, give the reason for your choice.

- melting sulpur
- dissolving copper sulphate in water
- burning sulphur
- drying clothes
- the digestion of food
- running down a battery
- burning petrol in an engine
- respiration

5 Study Table 1.2 (page 15), and answer the following questions.

(a) List the solid elements that do not sink in water.

(b) Give one difference between the metals that have been known since ancient times such as iron, gold, silver and copper and those that have been discovered only in the last 200 years or so such as aluminium, sodium and calcium.

(c) Silicon and carbon are two non-metallic elements. In what way do they differ from most of the other non-metallic elements in the table?

6 Study Table 1.3 (pages 16–17), and answer the following questions.

(a) Give one difference between compounds formed from hydrogen and non-metals and compounds formed from metals and non-metals.

(b) Give a difference between compounds of copper and compounds of sodium.

(c) Give a difference between most sodium compounds and most calcium compounds.

(d) Sulphur is present in a number of compounds listed in the table. It is present in sulphates and in oxides of sulphur. Give one difference between the oxides of sulphur and the sulphates.

Chapter 2

1 Copy and complete the following table showing the electronic structure of four elements.

Element	Proton number	Number of electrons in:		
		Shell 1	Shell 2	Shell 3
Hydrogen	1			
Helium		2	0	0
Carbon			4	
Sodium	11			

2 Use Table 1.3 (pages 16–17) to answer the following questions. In each case give a reason explaining your answer.

(a) Which of the following compounds are covalent? Magnesium oxide, phosphorus trichloride, calcium chloride, hydrogen iodide, potassium iodide.

(b) Predict whether the following compounds, in their liquid state, will be good or bad conductors of electricity. Phosphorus trichloride, copper oxide, calcium chloride, hydrogen sulphide.

3 The relative atomic mass of potassium is 39.

(a) Explain what is meant by 'relative atomic mass'.

(b) The relative atomic mass of chlorine is 35.5. Explain why it is not a whole number.

(c) Write down the formula of carbon dioxide. Calculate the relative molecular mass of carbon dioxide.

4 The table below shows the electron arrangement of six elements, A, B, C, D, E and F.

Element	Electron arrangement
A	2.4
B	2.8.1
C	2.8.2
D	2.8.7
E	2.8.8
F	2.8.8.2

(a) Which element is an inert gas?

(b) Which element belongs to Group IV?

(c) Two elements have very similar properties. Which two?

(d) Which of the elements are likely to be metals? Give a reason for your answer?

(e) Which element readily forms a negative ion?

5 The following diagram shows the electron arrangement in three atomic particles A, B and C.

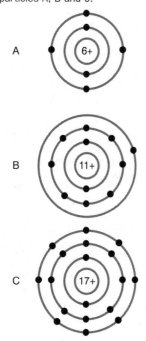

(a) Which one could readily form a positive ion?

(b) Which one is a negative ion?

(c) Which one is an atom of a non-metal?

In each case give a reason for your answer.

Chapter 3

1 The figure below shows an outline of the Periodic Table. Some of the elements are indicated by numbers.

(a) Give the number of the element which has properties similar to those of carbon.

(b) Give the number of the element which forms an ion with two negative charges.

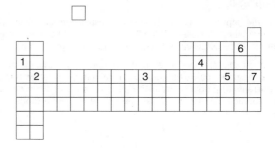

(c) Give the number of the element which is an inert gas.

(d) Give the number of the element which forms coloured compounds.

(e) Give the numbers of two elements which together will form an ionic compound.

(f) Give the number of the element which will form a covalent oxide.

2 In which parts of the Periodic Table are you likely to find the following elements:

(a) A metal which floats on water

(b) A gas used for filling light bulbs

(c) The metal used for light bulb filaments

(d) Metals used to make jewellery

(e) Gaseous elements

(f) Metals which form colourless compounds

3 Using the Periodic Table on page 46, answer the following questions.

(a) Predict the formula of hydrogen selenide (a compound of selenium).

(b) Draw the complete electronic structure of the compound silane (SiH_4).

(c) Predict the formula of the compound formed between strontium and iodine.

(d) What are the states at room temperature of the elements xenon and osmium? Predict two other properties of osmium.

(e) Which of the following chlorides are coloured solids and which are likely to be liquids?

Lithium chloride, magnesium chloride, manganese chloride, phosphorus trichloride, potassium chloride, vanadium chloride

4 (a) Using the Periodic Table on page 46, draw the electronic structures of **(i)** a lithium ion and **(ii)** a chloride ion.

(b) Predict the formula of lithium chloride, giving reasons for your prediction.

(c) Draw the electronic structure of the compound hydrogen chloride.

(d) Explain why you would expect lithium chloride to have a higher melting point than hydrogen chloride.

5 This question uses information given in Tables 1.2 and 1.3 (pages 15–17).

(a) Metallic elements are more dense than non-metallic elements. Comment on this statement.

(b) From the table, give another difference between metallic and non-metallic elements.

(c) Predict the melting point of the fourth element in Group I, rubidium.

(d) Plot a graph of atomic number (x-axis) against the melting point of the chloride of the elements up to calcium (not all are shown in the table). Comment on the shape of the curve. Predict the melting point of lithium chloride.

Chapter 4

1 The element titanium is found on the reactivity series between magnesium and zinc. Describe the effect the following chemicals will have on titanium. **(a)** water **(b)** dilute hydrochloric acid **(c)** steam **(d)** concentrated nitric acid

2 The table below shows some reactions of four metals. Place the metals in order of reactivity giving reasons for your order.

Metal	Reaction with water	Reaction with dilute hydrochloric acid
Cadmium	Slow reaction	Slow reaction
Nickel	No reaction	Very slow reaction
Silver	No reaction	No reaction
Strontium	Reacts rapidly	Reacts rapidly

3 Table 4.4 (page 71) shows the reactivity series for metals.

(a) Explain why only those metals at the bottom were known in Roman times 2000 years ago.

(b) Some of the metals can only be extracted by electrolysis. Which metals are these? Explain why it is not possible to extract them by any other means.

(c) You are given a sample of an unknown metal X. Describe how you would find out where to place X in the reactivity series.

4 Iron is manufactured in a blast furnace. The flow chart illustrates this process.

(a) Give the name of one of the ores that might be used.

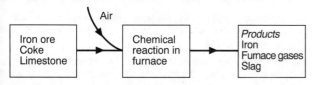

(b) In some countries other fuels such as lignite or natural gas are used instead of coke. Give a reason for this.

(c) The reaction in the blast furnace that converts the ore into iron is as follows:

$$Fe_2O_3 + 3CO \rightarrow 2Fe + 3CO_2$$

(i) Name the reducing agent in this reaction.

(ii) How was the reducing agent produced in the furnace?

(d) The iron produced by the furnace contains around 4% carbon. Describe how this affects the properties of the iron.

(e) Limestone is added to the furnace. Describe, with the aid of an equation, the reason for this.

5 Pure aluminium was first obtained by the French chemist, Deville, in 1854. He reduced aluminium chloride by heating it with sodium. The aluminium produced in this way was more expensive than silver. This method is used today to produce the metal titanium.

(a) Write an equation showing the reaction of sodium with aluminium chloride ($AlCl_3$).

(b) Why is titanium an expensive metal when the ore is quite common?

(c) Aluminium is close to magnesium on the reactivity series and yet it is used to make products such as pans for cooking. Explain why aluminium can be used to make such items.

(d) Titanium is used to build high-speed aircraft. What properties would you expect titanium to have for it to be used in this way?

Chapter 5

1 Starting from an acid, explain how you would prepare the following gases:

(a) hydrogen

(b) carbon dioxide.

Describe the test for each of these gases.

2 In an experiment to neutralise some hydrochloric acid, magnesium oxide was added to it 10 mg at a time. After each addition, the pH of the solution was measured. The results are shown in the table.

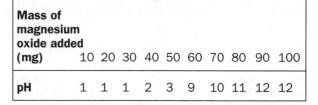

Mass of magnesium oxide added (mg)	10	20	30	40	50	60	70	80	90	100
pH	1	1	1	2	3	9	10	11	12	12

(a) Plot a graph showing how the pH changes as magnesium oxide is added (pH on the y-axis).

(b) How much magnesium oxide was needed to neutralise the acid exactly?

(c) Explain why the curve is almost horizontal at the extreme left and at the extreme right.

3 Copper(II) oxide was added to a colourless liquid. The two were warmed and allowed to react and the liquid turned blue. More copper(II) oxide was added until no further reaction took place and some of the oxide was left at the bottom of the flask. The mixture was filtered. Blue crystals were eventually obtained from the solution.

(a) The colourless liquid used turned blue litmus red. What does this tell you about the liquid?

(b) If blue litmus paper was put into the filtrate at the end, what would you expect to see? Explain your answer.

(c) How would you obtain the blue crystals from the solution?

(d) Some of the blue crystals were dissolved in water and some barium chloride solution was added. A white precipitate was formed. Name the colourless liquid used in the experiment. Explain your answer.

4 The flow chart shows some commercial reactions involving limestone.

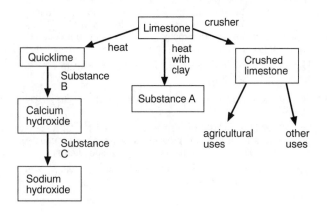

(a) Write an equation showing the action of heat on limestone.

(b) Give two uses for limestone in addition to agricultural uses.

(c) (i) What is substance A?

(ii) What happens to substance A when water is added and it is left for several hours?

(d) What is substance B?

(e) What is the substance C that is added to calcium hydroxide to make sodium hydroxide?

5 (a) The non-metal sulphur forms both ionic and covalent compounds.

(i) Give an example of a covalent compound of sulphur.

(ii) Draw the electronic structure of the sulphide ion.

(iii) What is the formula of the compound that contains the ions V^{3+} and S^{2-}?

(b) Large quantities of sulphur dioxide are thrown up into the upper atmosphere when volcanoes erupt. This sulphur dioxide can affect the earth's climate by dissolving in rain droplets.

(i) What is the name of the liquid formed when this happens?

(ii) Explain why this liquid can cause damage to plants and to buildings.

(c) Sulphur dioxide is converted into sulphuric acid by the Contact Process.

(i) Write an equation for the main reaction in this process.

(ii) Name a major source of sulphur dioxide used in the Contact Process.

(iii) Give two uses for sulphuric acid.

(d) Sulphur dioxide is produced as an unwanted waste product in some power stations, particularly in some coal-fired ones.

(i) Explain how this happens

(ii) In some power stations the sulphur dioxide is removed from the waste gases. Explain how this is done.

Chapter 6

1 Potasssium hydrogen carbonate powder was added slowly to some dilute hydrochloric acid in a test tube. After each addition of 10 mg the solution was stirred until there was no further sign of reaction and the temperature was taken. The table shows the results.

Mass of potassium hydrogencarbonate added (mg)	Temperature of solution (°C) (to the nearest °C)
10	25
20	24
30	23
40	22
50	21
60	21
70	20
80	20
90	21
100	21
110	22
120	22
130	23
140	24
150	24

(a) Plot a graph showing how the temperature of the reaction mixture changes as the potassium hydrogencarbonate is added. The temperature should be on the *y*-axis.

(b) Is the reaction exothermic or endothermic? Explain your answer.

(c) How much potassium hydrogencarbonate was required to react with all the acid? Explain your answer.

(d) Why did the temperature gradually rise at the end of the experiment?

(e) Write a word equation showing what happens when potassium hydrogencarbonate reacts with dilute hydrochloric acid.

2 Figure 6.7 on page 130 shows the world consumption of fuels since 1950.

(a) Coal is the most abundant fuel and is found all over the world. Yet the graph shows that the consumption of coal has not increased since 1950 as much as the consumption of oil or gas. Suggest reasons for this.

(b) Over the next 40 years oil will become more scarce and more expensive to extract. How is this likely to affect our consumption of the different fuels shown?

(c) Explain the difference between a renewable fuel and a non-renewable one. Give examples of each. What do we mean by a 'sustainable supply of energy'?

(d) The three main fuels in Figure 6.7, coal, oil and natural gas, all have one element in common. What is the element? Write an equation showing the exothermic reaction that occurs when the element is burnt.

(e) Explain why these three fuels are known as 'fossil fuels'.

(f) It is often said that hydrogen is the ideal fuel because it is non-polluting. Explain why it is a non-polluting fuel. Hydrogen is not yet widely used as a fuel. Explain why this is so.

3 The figure shows the apparatus for electroplating a copper ring with a coating of nickel.

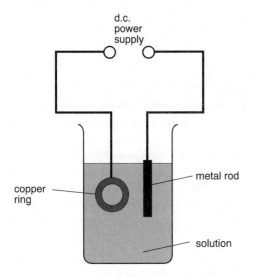

d.c. power supply

copper ring

metal rod

solution

(a) Which of the two poles is the anode and which the cathode?

(b) What metal ions are present in the solution?

(c) What is the metal rod made of?

(d) Explain what happens at each of the electrodes and in the solution when the current is switched on.

4 (supplement) The following figure shows a cell. Metal A is more reactive than copper.

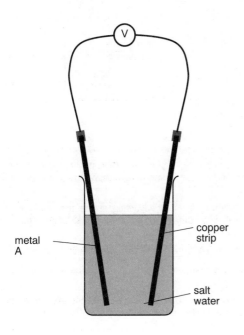

V

metal A

copper strip

salt water

(a) Which of the metals is the positive pole of the cell? Explain your answer.

(b) Which cell would give the higher voltage, a cell where metal A is magnesium or a cell where metal A is zinc? Give reasons for your answer.

5 (supplement) **(a)** Oxidation was originally used to describe a reaction in which oxygen combined with another element. An example is the burning of magnesium in air.

(i) Write an equation for this reaction.

(ii) When magnesium is added to a solution of copper sulphate, copper is produced. Write an equation for this reaction.

(iii) Show how the reaction of magnesium in (i) and (ii) is the same.

(b) For each of the following reactions, write the equation, state what you would see (if anything) when you observe the reaction, and state whether the reaction is a redox reaction or an acid–base reaction, or neither of these.

(i) Chlorine is bubbled through a solution of potassium bromide.

(ii) Solutions of ammonia and sulphuric acid are mixed.

(iii) A solution of barium chloride is added to a solution of potassium sulphate.

(iv) Chlorine is passed over heated iron wool.

Chapter 7

1(a) Using information on page 150, calculate approximately what volume of argon you breathe in and out each day.

(b) Argon is used for filling tungsten filament light bulbs. Explain why it is particularly suitable for this.

2 Petrol is a mixture of hydrocarbons.

(a) What are the two products when it burns in a plentiful supply of air?

(b) When a car burns petrol, other gases are also produced. The following table shows some of these.

Harmful gases	Percentage
Carbon monoxide	6.5
Hydrocarbons	0.2
Oxides of nitrogen	0.25
Sulphur dioxide	0.005

(i) Explain why carbon monoxide is present in the exhaust fumes.

(ii) How can carbon monoxide affect the health of people.

(iii) How are the oxides of nitrogen formed in the car engine?

(iv) What are the effects of nitrogen oxides and sulphur dioxide on the environment?

(c) How are the amounts of these gases produced being reduced in modern cars?

3 We all need water to survive. Harmful bacteria can live in water and these have to be removed before we drink it.

(a) What are the two processes which help to remove the bacteria when water is purified?

(b) Bacteria in water feed on organic matter. Explain how water that contains a lot of organic matter can lose its dissolved oxygen and become seriously polluted.

4 (supplement) The upper atmosphere contains a gas called ozone that is a form of oxygen. In the upper atmosphere radiation from the sun is able to split up normal oxygen molecules into individual atoms and these react with more oxygen molecules to form ozone.

(a) (i) What is the formula for ozone?

(ii) Write an equation showing how ozone is formed.

(b) Is the formation of ozone endothermic or exothermic? Give a reason for your answer.

(c) Explain why the ozone layer is important to life on the surface of the earth.

(d) Scientists are worried that some chemicals in the atmosphere can destroy ozone. Name one chemical, or a class of chemicals, that do this and describe where they come from.

5 (supplement) Some gases that escape into the atmosphere can trap energy from the sun. This can cause the Earth to retain more of the sun's energy and cause the temperature of the atmosphere to rise. This process is called the 'greenhouse effect'. Carbon dioxide and methane are two gases which can do this.

(a) Mankind's activities produce much carbon dioxide. Explain how.

(b) How could we reduce the amount of carbon dioxide we put into the atmosphere?

(c) Give two ways in which the burning of forests (such as the rain forests) can lead to an increase in carbon dioxide in the atmosphere.

Chapter 8

1 The table gives information about the first six alkanes.

Name	Formula	Relative molecular mass	Boiling point (°C)
Methane	CH_4	16	−161
Ethane	C_2H_6	30	−89
Propane	C_3H_8	44	−42
Butane	C_4H_{10}		0
Pentane		72	37
Hexane	C_6H_{14}	86	70

(a) What is the formula of pentane?

(b) What is the relative molecular mass of butane?

(c) Plot a graph showing how the boiling point (y-axis) changes as the number of carbon atoms in the molecule changes. Predict the boiling point of octane which has eight carbon atoms.

(d) Describe the reaction between alkanes and chlorine.

(e) A sample of hexane is boiled and the vapour is passed over some pieces of broken pot that are strongly heated. The resulting gas is collected over water.

(i) What would you see if you added a small quantity of bromine water to the product?

(ii) Another sample of the product is ignited and a few drops of limewater are put into the tube. The limewater turns milky.

Explain both these observations.

2 The table shows data about three organic compounds.

Name	Formula	Boiling point (°C)
Methanol	CH_3OH	65
Ethanol	C_2H_5OH	
Propanol		97

(a) Suggest a formula for propanol.

(b) Suggest a boiling point for ethanol.

(c) These compounds are members of the same homologous series.

(i) What is meant by 'homologous series'?

(ii) What do members of this series have in common and what is the series called?

(iii) How do the members of this series differ from each other?

(iv) Suggest a general formula for the members of this series.

(d) Describe two ways in which ethanol is made commercially.

(e) Ethanol is used in some countries as a fuel. It is classified as a 'renewable' fuel.

(i) Explain why it can be used as a fuel.

(ii) Explain why it is classified as a renewable fuel.

3 The figure shows wood chippings being heated in a closed test tube.

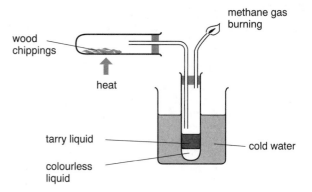

(a) The gas burning is methane. Give the formula of methane and write an equation to show the reaction that takes place when it burns.

(b) The colourless liquid collecting in the test tube is mainly water but it also contains other compounds. One of these compounds is methanol.

(i) Which class of organic compounds does methanol belong to?

(ii) What characteristic group of atoms does this class of compounds contain?

(iii) Describe how you might obtain pure methanol from the mixture in the test tube.

(iv) (supplement) Methanol can be converted to methanoic acid. How could this be done?

(c) What substance do you think is likely to be left in the wood chipping tube after the experiment? Give reasons for your answer.

4 The flow chart shows how ethene can be made into other compounds.

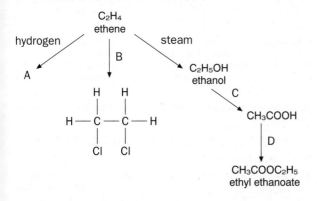

(a) What is the product A?

(b) What is reagent B?

(c) (supplement) What are reagents C and D?

(d) (supplement) What is the name of the product CH_3COOH?

(e) What are the conditions needed for the reaction with hydrogen? What important industrial reaction uses this process?

(f) (supplement) Why is the reaction of ethanol with reagent C described as an oxidation?

(g) (supplement) What are the reaction conditions necessary for the preparation of ethyl ethanoate using reagent D?

Chapter 9 (supplement)

1 Draw the structures of the polymers made from the following monomers. Indicate which are addition polymers and which are condensation polymers.

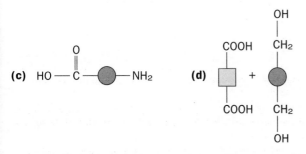

2 The diagram shows part of a molecule of Terylene. Draw the structure of the monomers obtained when Terylene is hydrolysed.

3 Fatty acids are important foodstuffs.

(a) How does the body make use of them?

(b) Explain the difference between unsaturated and saturated fatty acids.

Chapter 10 (supplement)

1 The element phosphorus has a covalent structure in which four atoms of phosphorus join together to form a molecule (P_4). Phosphorus will react with chlorine (Cl_2) to form the liquid phosphorus trichloride (PCl_3).

(a) Write a balanced equation for the reaction between phosphorus and chlorine.

(b) Draw the electronic structure of the covalent phosphorus trichloride molecule.

(c) Phosphorus trichloride is hyrolysed rapidly by water to form phosphoric(III) acid. The equation is as follows:

$$PCl_3(l) + 3H_2O(l) \rightarrow H_3PO_3(aq) + 3HCl(aq)$$

(i) Calculate the mass of phosphoric(III) acid needed to make a litre of 1 M solution.

(ii) Calculate the mass of phorphorus trichloride needed to make this amount of phosphoric(III) acid.

(iii) How many litres of 1 M phosphoric(III) acid could be made from one mole of phosphorus molecules?

($P = 31$, $Cl = 35.5$, $O = 16$, $H = 1$)

2 Titanium is an important element used in making aircraft. It is extracted from an ore called ilmenite which has a formula $FeTiO_3$ which is converted to titanium dioxide (TiO_4). The titanium dioxide is then converted into titanium chloride ($TiCl_4$) by heating in a stream of chlorine. Finally the titanium chloride is heated with a reactive metal such as sodium to obtain the titanium. ($Fe = 56$, $Na = 23$, $O = 16$, $Ti = 48$)

(a) Calculate the relative molecular mass of ilmenite, $FeTiO_3$.

(b) How much ilmenite will contain 1 tonne of titanium?

(c) Write a balanced equation for the reaction between titanium chloride and sodium.

(d) What is the minimum mass of sodium needed to obtain one tonne of titanium from titanium chloride?

(e) Why will the actual mass of sodium used always be more than the amount calculated in (d)?

3 In an experiment to make carbon dioxide, 2.0 g of impure magnesium carbonate ($MgCO_3$) is added to an excess of 1 M hydrochloric acid. The volume of carbon dioxide obtained was 448 cm^3 (measured at STP). ($C = 12$, $Mg = 24$, $O = 16$)

(a) Write a balanced equation for the reaction.

(b) How many moles of carbon dioxide were produced in the reaction?

(c) What mass of pure magnesium carbonate would produce this amount of carbon dioxide?

(d) Calculate the percentage purity of the magnesium carbonate used.

4 Baking powder is often a mixture of sodium hydrogencarbonate ($NaHCO_3$) and starch. It is possible to calculate the percentage of sodium hydrogencarbonate in a sample of baking powder by titrating a filtered solution of the powder with 0.1 M hydrochloric acid. ($C = 12$, $H = 1$, $Na = 23$, $O = 16$)

(a) Why do you think it is necessary to filter the solution?

(b) Write a balanced equation for the reaction between sodium hydrogencarbonate and hydrochloric acid.

(c) 20 g of baking powder was mixed with water and the solution made up to 1 dm³. 25.0 cm³ of the filtered solution was titrated with acid and it was found that 22.5 cm³ of acid was used. Calculate the molarity of the sodium hydrogencarbonate solution.

(d) Calculate the mass of sodium hydrogencarbonate in the baking powder sample.

(e) Calculate the percentage of sodium hydrogencarbonate in the baking powder.

Chapter 11

1 In modern coal-fired power stations, the coal is crushed to a powder before it is burnt. One reason for this is that powdered coal can be blown along pipes into the furnace. Give another reason why powdered coal is preferred to lump coal.

2 Equal masses of magnesium in three different forms were allowed to react with excess dilute hydrochloric acid. The three forms were A, magnesium ribbon, B, magnesium ribbon broken into small pieces and C, magnesium powder. The hydrogen produced was measured every 15 seconds and the results plotted on a graph.

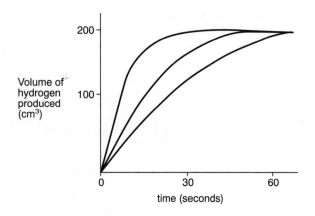

(a) Sketch the graph and label the three lines correctly with A, B or C to show the curve produced by each form of magnesium.

(b) Explain why each line reaches the same maximum.

(c) Draw a fourth line on the graph to show the reaction of the magnesium ribbon with excess acid of a lower concentration than the one used in the experiment.

3 (supplement) A piece of filter paper soaked in silver nitrate solution is then dipped in potassium bromide solution. It is then left in the laboratory with a coin on top of it. After some time the colour of the paper had changed from white to dark grey except for the part covered by the coin.

(a) Explain why the paper had darkened except for the part covered by the coin.

(b) How could the rate of darkening of the paper be increased?

(c) Write an equation for the reaction that was happening.

4 (supplement) Hydrogen is made industrially from methane by reacting it at high temperatures in the gas phase with steam. The reaction is endothermic and is shown by the equation below.

$$CH_4(g) + H_2O(g) \rightleftharpoons CO(g) + 3H_2(g)$$

(a) How will the composition of the equilibrium mixture of gases be affected by:

(i) increasing the pressure

(ii) increasing the temperature

(iii) using a catalyst?

(b) How will the rate at which the equilibrium mixture is reached be affected by:

(i) increasing the pressure

(ii) increasing the temperature

(iii) using a catalyst?

(c) If you were the chemical engineer designing the plant for this reaction, what kind of conditions would you try to achieve in order to maximise the rate of production of hydrogen?

Index

Note: references to the Periodic Table are shown in **bold** page numbers